ELEMENTARY THEORY OF NUMBERS

INTERNATIONAL SERIES IN PURE AND
APPLIED MATHEMATICS

WILLIAM TED MARTIN, *Consulting Editor*

ELEMENTARY
THEORY OF NUMBERS

HARRIET GRIFFIN

Associate Professor of Mathematics
Brooklyn College

McGRAW-HILL BOOK COMPANY, INC.

NEW YORK   TORONTO   LONDON

1954

ELEMENTARY THEORY OF NUMBERS

Library of Congress Catalog Card Number 53-12046

v

24785

PREFACE

The arithmetic theory of numbers is ever a fascinating subject, the fundamentals of which can be presented with ease and profit to the average undergraduate student of mathematics and to those who are preparing to teach mathematics provided that these students are stimulated by a clear and logical treatment of carefully selected topics. It is the aim of this textbook to offer such a development of the subject. The facts and methods of proof are old, indeed, but the author believes that her experience of teaching the theory of numbers for over fifteen years has enabled her to choose the topics that not only develop the student's insight into the problems of this field but also furnish an ample basis for more advanced work. The simplicity and lucidity of the presentation have been tested time and again in the classroom. Experiment has shown that the student appreciates knowing on exactly what foundation the reasoning is to be constructed. Consequently, care has been taken to orient him at a level and in language he can readily understand. Definitions are precise, but in elementary form. Each new concept is illustrated. Theorems are proved in detail. Brief historical comments elucidate the material and provide a setting for it. The exercises are graded. They include a sufficiently large number of numerical problems to develop the student's power of inspection, some to test his understanding of simple theoretical questions, and others to challenge his originality.

It is to be emphasized that this book is just a text. It is written for the student rather than the teacher. It is neither erudite nor exhaustive. The reader with a good grasp of algebra and the ability to concentrate will be able to understand it. It is hoped, moreover, that it will interest him and induce him to pursue his inquiries further.

The author is indebted to her students in both the graduate and undergraduate divisions of Brooklyn College for their help in accomplishing this work. They have patiently perused mimeographed and lithoprinted material, indicating by their lively reactions the parts to be retained, improved, or deleted. One of them, Miss Alice Osterberg, has given expert assistance in reading the proof. Their contributions are gratefully acknowledged.

v

It is apparent that there is more material in the text than can be covered by the average class of undergraduates in only one semester. Owing either to the importance of the information or to the method of proof involved, however, with the exception of Theorem 3-20, on the number of primes not exceeding the positive integer n, it is suggested that no theorem be omitted until Chap. 4 has been completed.   Then, for the ordinary course, Theorems 5-7, 5-8, 5-9, and 5-11, Theorems 6-3 through 6-6 and 6-9 through 6-12, Theorems 7-11 through 7-16, as well as all of Chap. 8 may be omitted.   For the convenience of the reader the theorems just mentioned have been marked with an asterisk.   Most instructors will wish to include as much of Chap. 9, on quadratic residues, as time permits.   Theorems from Chap. 10 may be selected at pleasure provided that Theorem 10-4, on the Pythagorean triangle, is included. The last two chapters will, doubtless, have to be omitted in a 45-hour course.

HARRIET GRIFFIN

CONTENTS

CHAPTER 11. POLYNOMIALS

CHAPTER 12. PARTITIONS

CHAPTER 1

THE FUNDAMENTAL LAWS

1-1. The Development of the Integers. The rational integers are the result of many centuries of development of the concept of number. Doubtless man learned first to distinguish oneness and otherness without abstracting the idea of number itself. The basic notion in the concept of number is that of one-to-one correspondence. If there are two sets of elements, A and B, and if to each element of A there is assigned exactly one element of B, while each element of B is thereby related to a single element of A, the relationship is called a *one-to-one reciprocal correspondence*. By means of such a relation a man could determine that he had exactly as many rings as he had fingers even though he had not learned to count. Any two sets that can be put into one-to-one correspondence are said to have the same number. Thus the concept of number implies the abstraction of that property which is common to sets that are so related. However imperfect these concepts may have been, man did eventually learn to count and to represent by marks the ideas now represented by the symbols 1, 2, 3, ... These numbers have the single property of denoting quantity. They answer the question, How many units? They are the natural numbers, and they were the only numbers known to the Greeks until Diophantus (c. 275) extended the concept of number to include fractions. To be sure the Ahmes papyrus, which was written before 1700 B.C., indicates that in their calculations the Egyptians employed symbols that are equivalent to fractions with numerator one, but such symbols, even to the Greeks of Euclid's time, referred to the notion of magnitude rather than number. The art of calculating was thus distinguished from the science of number. It is to be noted that zero is not among the natural numbers. The Greeks had no symbol for zero. It was probably not until the fifth century that the Hindus introduced a symbol for zero and the principle of position in writing numbers. These were, indeed, great accomplishments in the field of arithmetic. By the twelfth century the advancement of the Hindus in algebra almost matched their achievements in arithmetic, for they were the first to recognize the existence of negative quantities even though they did not admit them as solutions of their problems. It was not until the sixteenth century that European mathematicians reached this stage of development

1

of the idea of number, and it remained for Descartes (1596–1650) to grasp completely the concept of signed numbers.*

The signed numbers have two basic properties. They compound the idea of quantity with that of quality. Thus, although each of the symbols $+1$, -1, $+5$, and -5 represents but one number, that number has two fundamental attributes. It is evident, moreover, that a one-to-one correspondence can be set up between the positive integers and the natural numbers in the following manner: $+1 \leftrightarrow 1$, $+2 \leftrightarrow 2$, $+3 \leftrightarrow 3$, ...

1-2. The System of Rational Integers. The classical theory of numbers, arithmetica, is properly concerned with the study of only the natural numbers $1, 2, 3, ...$ Nevertheless, we shall make use of the system of rational integers $0, \pm 1, \pm 2, . . .$ because, besides being of interest in itself, this set has properties not possessed by the natural numbers that enable us to develop many theorems expounding the qualities of the natural numbers through methods that have the facility characteristic of an algebraic presentation. Throughout this text, therefore, the word "integer," unless otherwise stated, will refer to a rational integer, and the letters $a, b, c, . . . , x, y, z$, will represent these integers. Moreover, we shall, as a rule, observe the usual convention of omitting the positive signs in writing $+1, +2, +3, ...$

What shall we study about these integers? Just consider the integers from 1 through 10, and they will serve to illustrate some salient facts. It is apparent that the product of three consecutive integers is divisible by 6, that when two consecutive even integers are chosen, one is divisible by 4. You will claim you have known all your life that we need only the 10 digits $0, 1, . . . , 9$ to write any integer, but can this be accomplished in another way? Have you ever noticed the remarkable fact that, of the consecutive integers 8 and 9, one is a perfect cube and the other a perfect square? Surely you have not overlooked the familiar right triangle whose sides have the lengths 3, 4, and 5. Again, the sum of the positive divisors of 6 is double itself. Can you find another integer having this property? Although for its size 6 has many divisors, you notice that 5 has but ± 1 and ± 5. Observe how close the first few integers of the latter type are. Would you be interested in examining the law indicated by the following equations?

$$
\begin{array}{ll}
3 = 1 + 1 + 1 & 4 = 1 + 3 \\
5 = 1 + 1 + 3 & 6 = 1 + 5 = 3 + 3 \\
7 = 1 + 1 + 5 = 1 + 3 + 3 & 8 = 1 + 7 = 3 + 5 \\
9 = 1 + 1 + 7 = 1 + 3 + 5 & 10 = 3 + 7 = 5 + 5
\end{array}
$$

Perhaps these few examples will stimulate the reader to look for some other significant facts. Having made a discovery, he certainly will want

* F. Cajori, "A History of Mathematics."

to determine why it is so. That, indeed, is the attitude we wish to foster, and so, starting with elementary notions, we shall set up a basis for showing that certain laws do hold.

We shall assume that the reader is familiar with the concepts of number, uniqueness, relation, sum, difference, product, equality, greater than, absolute value, etc. We shall assume that he understands the fundamentals of algebra and the derivative with respect to x of a rational integral algebraic function of the real variable x. We shall also suppose that he is familiar with the content of the following system of postulates which the integers obey:

1. The set of rational integers contains $+1$ (positive real one) and at least one other integer.

2. The law of closure for addition: For each pair of integers a and b, in that order, the sum of a and b exists and is a unique integer c. Thus $a + b = c$.

3. The commutative law for addition: $a + b = b + a$.

4. The associative law for addition: $(a + b) + c = a + (b + c)$.

5. The equation $a + x = c$ has a solution for x that is an integer.

The second postulate tells us that the operation of addition exists for the rational integers. Moreover, since $+1$ is in the set, we can generate a subset of integers by merely adding $+1$ to itself and to each result so obtained. Thus we have $1 + 1 = 2$, $2 + 1 = 3$, ... We call all these numbers *positive integers*, and 1, 2, 3, . . . are distinct.

Furthermore, if $a + c = b$ and c is positive, we say that $a < b$ (a is less than b) or that $b > a$ (b is greater than a). The set of rational integers is ordered by this relation "less than."

The fifth postulate says that subtraction exists, and we therefore write the statement $a + x = c$ in the form $c - a = x$. We shall show later that we can derive the fact that there is a single integer 0 such that $a + 0 = a$ for any integer a.

6. The law of closure for multiplication: For each pair of integers a and b, in that order, the product of a and b exists and is a uniquely determined integer c. Thus $a \cdot b = c$, or $ab = c$.

7. $a(+1) = a$ for any integer a.

8. The commutative law for multiplication: $ab = ba$.

9. The associative law for multiplication: $(ab)c = a(bc)$.

10. The distributive law: $a(b + c) = ab + ac$.

11. The cancellation law for multiplication: If $ab = ac$ and $a \neq 0$, then $b = c$.

12. There is no integer x such that $a < x < a + 1$.

The last statement means that there is no integer between a and $a + 1$. Hence, a and $a + 1$ are called *consecutive integers*. We say, then, that the rational integers form a discrete set, for when they are arranged according to the relation "less than" and then separated into any two parts without disturbing the array, there is a first integer in one part and a last integer in the other.

13. Any sequence of integers n_i, where $i = 1, 2, 3, \ldots$, such that $n_1 > n_2 > \cdots > 0$ has a least positive integer.

14. If $a = b$ and $c = d$, then $a + c = b + d$ and $ac = bd$.

15. If $a = b$, then either one may be substituted for the other in any relation.

16. If $+1$ has a property and if $n + 1$ has this property whenever the positive integer n has it, then every positive integer has the property.

This last postulate is the one on which the method of mathematical induction, sometimes called "finite induction," is based. We shall use this method for both definition and proof. For example, we can define the sum of a finite number of integers inductively on the basis of the second postulate. Thus $a + b + c = (a + b) + c$, $a + b + c + d = (a + b + c) + d$, and, in the general case, $a + b + \cdots + m + n = (a + b + \cdots + m) + n$.

It is worth while recalling that the relation "equals" which we have used so frequently in stating these postulates has the following properties:

1. Equals is reflexive; that is, $a = a$.
2. Equals is symmetric; that is, if $a = b$, then $b = a$.
3. Equals is transitive; that is, if $a = b$ and $b = c$, then $a = c$.

The system of postulates which we have stated above is certainly not the most concise one that might have been chosen. To be sure, some of the statements can be derived from others. But the set is sufficiently elementary for our purposes and permits us to develop the ideas we need on a basis that will be readily understood by the student.

We shall prove first that there is a unique integer 0 such that, for any integer b, $b + 0 = b$. The fifth postulate tells us that corresponding to a particular integer a there is an x such that $a + x = a$. We shall call this integer 0_1 and shall show that $b + 0_1 = b$ for any b. We have $a + 0_1 = a$. But c exists such that $b = c + a$. Hence,

$$b + 0_1 = (c + a) + 0_1$$
$$= c + (a + 0_1)$$
$$= c + a$$
$$= b$$

This integer 0_1 is unique, for if there were a second integer 0_2 such that $b + 0_2 = b$ for any b, then $0_2 + 0_1 = 0_2$ and $0_1 + 0_2 = 0_1$. But $0_1 + 0_2 = 0_2 + 0_1$, and therefore $0_1 = 0_2$. There is, then, but a single integer, zero, designated by 0, such that $b + 0 = b$ for any b. We may also write this statement in the form $b - b = 0$.

Since $0 + b = b$, it follows immediately that if b is positive, b is greater than zero, and conversely.   Moreover, $0 + 1 = 1$ shows that 0 and $+1$ are consecutive integers.

Furthermore, for each integer a there exists an integer x such that $a + x = 0$.   This integer x is called the *negative of a*.   It is the inverse of a with respect to addition, and it is designated by $-a$.   Thus $a + (-a) = 0$.   This inverse is unique because the following argument shows that subtraction is always unique.

Suppose that subtraction is not unique and that when a and c are given, both b_1 and b_2 are such that

$$a + b_1 = c = a + b_2$$

Since

$$a + (-a) = (-a) + a = 0$$

and since

$$(-a) + (a + b_1) = (-a) + (a + b_2)$$

it follows that

$$[(-a) + a] + b_1 = [(-a) + a] + b_2$$

and that

$$0 + b_1 = 0 + b_2$$

Hence,

$$b_1 = b_2$$

Consequently, subtraction is unique.

The inverse of a positive integer is said to be a *negative integer*.   Accordingly, we write $-(+2) = -2$; that is, the negative of positive two is negative two.   Moreover, each of these negative integers is less than zero, for $(-a) + a = 0$, where a is positive.   For the same reason, $-(-a) = a$. This means that a is the inverse with respect to addition of $-a$; that is, a is the negative of negative a.   This statement implies that the positive integers are the negatives of the negative integers.   To summarize, we have proved that:

Theorem 1-1.   There is a unique integer 0 such that, for any integer b, $b + 0 = b$.

Theorem 1-2.   Subtraction is unique, and each integer has a unique inverse with respect to addition.

Has it ever occurred to you that $b \cdot 0 = 0$ for any b because of the basic principles we have stated?   We know that $a + 0 = a$, and so when $a \neq 0$, consider the equation $b \cdot a + b \cdot 0 = b \cdot a$.   But $b \cdot a = c$ and uniquely so.   Hence, $c + b \cdot 0 = c$.   However, $c + 0 = c$, and subtraction is unique.   Therefore, $b \cdot 0 = 0$.   Notice that when $b = 0$, this statement includes $0 \cdot 0 = 0$.   Thus we have:

Theorem 1-3.   For any integer b, $b \cdot 0 = 0$.

We have seen that $c + (-c) = 0$.   Hence, $ac + a(-c) = a \cdot 0 = 0$.

But $ac + (-ac) = 0$, and this inverse is unique. Consequently, $a(-c) = -ac$. When $c = 1$, this equation includes $a(-1) = -(a(+1)) = -a$.

Furthermore, subtraction can be accomplished by addition, for we can prove:

Theorem 1-4. $a - b = a + (-b)$.

According to the definition of subtraction, $a - b = x$, where the integer x is such that $b + x = a$. We wish to prove that $a + (-b)$ is the proper value of x. Substituting $a + (-b)$ for x in the last equation, we have

$$\begin{aligned} b + [a + (-b)] &= b + [(-b) + a] \\ &= [b + (-b)] + a \\ &= 0 + a \\ &= a \end{aligned}$$

Theorem 1-5. If $a > b$, then $-b > -a$, and conversely.

If $a > b$, then $a = b + c$ with c positive, and, by multiplying each member of the equation by -1, we find that $-a = (-b) + (-c)$. Hence, $(-a) + c = [(-b) + (-c)] + c$, and finally $(-a) + c = -b$, so that $-b > -a$. The converse is now evident.

Theorem 1-6. $-(a - 1) = -a + 1$.

We know that

$$\begin{aligned} -(a - 1) &= (a - 1)(-1) \\ &= [a + (-1)](-1) \\ &= -a + 1 \end{aligned}$$

As a result there is no integer between $-a$ and $-(a - 1)$; that is, if two integers are consecutive, as are $a - 1$ and a, so are their negatives. We must conclude, therefore, that the integers are positive, zero, or negative.

EXERCISES

1. Show that if $a = b$, then the negative of a equals the negative of b.
2. Show that if $a = b$, it cannot also be true that $a > b$.
3. Show that $a < b$ and $a > b$ cannot both be true.
4. Show that if $a < b$ and $a = b + c$, then c is a negative integer.
5. If $a = b + c$ and c is negative, prove that $a < b$.
6. Prove that $a(b - c) = ab - ac$.
7. On the basis of postulate 11, prove that if $ab = 0$ and $a \neq 0$, then $b = 0$.
8. Show that the theorem of Exercise 7 is a sufficient condition for the cancellation law for multiplication.
9. Prove the law of signs for addition.
10. Prove the law of signs for multiplication.

1-3. Definitions. The law of closure with respect to addition together with the principle of finite induction shows that when we apply the operation of addition to a finite number of integers of our set, the result is necessarily in the set. We know also that subtraction can be converted into addition and that the result is unique. When we restrict ourselves to the use of integers, it is also evident that our laws provide that the product of a finite number of them always exists. But it is not always possible to find an integer that will satisfy the equation $ax = b$ when a and b are any integers, and therefore it is necessary to define what we mean by division.

An integer b is said to divide an integer a if there exists an integer c such that $a = bc$. Under these conditions it is also said that a is divisible by b. The operation is written in the form $b \mid a$ and is read, "*b divides a.*" If no integer c exists, we write $b \nmid a$ and read it, "*b does not divide a.*" When $b \neq 0$ and c exists, c is unique, for if $a = bc_1$ and $a = bc_2$, then $bc_1 = bc_2$ and $c_1 = c_2$ by the cancellation law for multiplication. When $b = 0$, c does not exist unless $a = 0$, in which case c is not unique.

When $a = bc$, b is said to be a *factor* of a, or a *divisor* of a; a is a *multiple* of b; and when $b \neq 0$, c is the *quotient* of a by b. The integer c is often referred to as the factor of a that is *complementary* to b.

We recall that $|a| = a$ if a is positive or zero and $|a| = -a$ if a is negative. It is clear, therefore, that when $a \neq 0$ and $a = bc$, then $|a| \geq |b|$, for $a = bc$ implies that neither b nor c is zero and that $|a| = |b| |c|$. But $|c|$ being positive, it is at least $+1$. Hence, $|c| = 1 + r$, where $r \geq 0$, and $|a| = |b|(1 + r) = |b| + |b|r$. When $r = 0$, it is thus evident that $|a| = |b|$, and when $r > 0$, $|a| > |b|$.

Theorem 1-7. If b divides a, and if c divides b, then c divides a.

Since $b \mid a$ and $c \mid b$, integers d and e exist such that $a = bd$ and $b = ce$. Hence, $a = (ce)d = c(ed)$, and therefore $c \mid a$.

Theorem 1-8. If b divides a, and b divides c, then b divides $a + c$.

Theorem 1-9. If b divides a, and b does not divide c, then b does not divide $a + c$.

Since $b \mid a$, then $a = bd$ and $a + c = bd + c$. If b did divide $a + c$, we should have $a + c = be$ and $be = bd + c$. Hence, $b(e - d) = c$, and b would divide c.

Theorem 1-10. If $b \neq 0$, the difference between two of the nonnegative integers $0, 1, 2, \ldots, |b| - 1$ is not divisible by b unless the two integers are equal.

Choose r_1 and r_2 so that $0 \leq r_1 < |b|$ and $0 \leq r_2 < |b|$. (These statements are often combined by writing $0 \leq r_1, r_2 < |b|$.) Suppose that $r_1 > r_2$. If $r_1 - r_2 = mb$, then $r_1 = mb + r_2$. Therefore, $r_1 \geq |b|$, for $mb > 0$. But this result is contrary to the hypothesis, and consequently $b \nmid (r_1 - r_2)$.

A *common factor*, or *common divisor*, of two or more integers is an integer that divides each of the given integers.

A *greatest common divisor* of a set of two or more integers, not all **zero,** is, if it exists, a common divisor of the set that is divisible by every common divisor of the set.* We notice then that if $+d$ is a greatest common divisor of a set of integers, so is $-d$. It is conventional, however, to refer to the one of the two integers $+d$ and $-d$ that is positive as the greatest common divisor. It is evident, too, that the greatest common divisor of a set of integers is unchanged if any a_i of the set is replaced by $-a_i$. The symbol $d = (a_1, a_2, \ldots, a_r)$ is used to denote that d is the greatest common divisor of the set $a_1, a_2, \ldots, a_r$; for example, $3 = (6, 12, -15)$, and $12 = (36, 48)$.

A *common multiple* of two or more integers is an integer that is divisible by each of the given integers.

A *least common multiple* of two or more integers is, if it exists, a common multiple that is a divisor of every common multiple of the given integers. It is evident that if $a \neq 0$ is a least common multiple of a set of integers, then $-a$ is also. Again, it is usual in this case to refer to the positive integer that fits the definition as the least common multiple. The least common multiple is unchanged if any of the given integers a_i is replaced by $-a_i$. The least common multiple of 6, -15, and 9 is 90.

A *unit* is an integer that divides every integer. Since $+1$ and -1 divide every integer, they are both units.

Theorem 1-11. The rational integers have but two units, $+1$ and -1.

If there is a third unit, let it be denoted by x. Then x divides $+1$, and therefore $|x| \leq +1$. But because $+1$ is a unit and x is an integer, $+1$ divides x and thus $+1 \leq |x|$ since $x \neq 0$. Consequently, $|x| = +1$, and x is $+1$ or -1.

The *null element* is an integer that divides only itself. We know from the definition of division that zero divides only itself. For any a, however, $a \cdot 0 = 0$, and consequently any integer divides zero. Therefore, no integer different from zero is a null element. Hence, we have:

Theorem 1-12. Zero is the null element of the rational integers.

The *associates of an integer* are the results of multiplying it by the units. Thus $+6$ and -6 are a set of associates. When an integer is divisible by some integer, it is obviously divisible by each of the associates of that integer and consequently in any problem it is necessary to show only the division by one of the associates.

A *prime* is an integer, not a unit, that is divisible by only its associates and the units. This definition implies that the greatest common divisor of a prime p and an integer a is 1, or the positive associate of p.

---

* This definition and that of a least common multiple are so worded that they will apply equally well in a domain of algebraic integers where we cannot say of two distinct integers that one must be less than the other. For instance, the set of algebraic integers of the form $a + bi$ with a and b rational integers is not ordered by the relation "less than."

An integer that is not the null element, a unit, or a prime is a *composite*.

Two or more integers are *prime to each other*, or *relatively prime*, if their greatest common divisor is $+1$. The integers 6, -9, and 14 are relatively prime.

Two or more integers are said to be *prime each to each*, or *relatively prime in pairs*, if the greatest common divisor of all possible pairs is $+1$. The integers 3, 4, and 35 are relatively prime in pairs.

Theorem 1-13. If d is the greatest common divisor of a and b, the quotients obtained by dividing them by d are relatively prime.

If $d = (a, b)$, let $a = a_0 d$ and $b = b_0 d$. Let e be any common divisor of a_0 and b_0. Then $a_0 = ek$, $b_0 = em$, and $a = dek$, $b = dem$. Hence, de is a common divisor of a and b and must divide d; that is, $d = des$. Therefore, $es = 1$. But this is impossible unless $e = \pm 1$. Consequently, $(a_0, b_0) = 1$.

1-4. The Principle of Archimedes. Among the early mathematicians who contributed to the theory of numbers were Euclid (c. 300 B.C.), and Archimedes (c. 225 B.C.). Euclid was very much interested in the theory of numbers. He collected and organized many propositions concerning the integers in his "Elements." On the other hand, although Archimedes is considered one of the greatest mathematicians of all time, he did little with this branch of the subject and but one theorem in the theory of numbers bears his name. This theorem is, however, a basic one.

We shall assume the *principle of Archimedes* extended to include the rational integers. This principle states that any integer a either is a multiple of an integer $b \neq 0$ or lies between two consecutive multiples of b; that is, corresponding to each pair of integers a and $b \neq 0$, there exists an integer m such that, for $b > 0$,

$$mb \leq a < (m + 1)b$$

and, for $b < 0$,

$$mb \leq a < (m - 1)b$$

Theorem 1-14. The theorem of Euclid. Corresponding to two integers a and $b \neq 0$, there exist two integers m and r such that

$$a = bm + r \qquad 0 \leq r < |b|$$

and m and r are unique.

Except for the unicity of m and r the theorem follows immediately from the principle of Archimedes, for when $b > 0$, it is evident that the inequalities yield $0 \leq a - mb$ and $a - mb < b$, and when $b < 0$, $0 \leq a - mb$ and $a - mb < -b$. Thus $r = a - mb$ exists and fulfills the required conditions. Suppose then that $a = bm_1 + r_1$ and $a = bm_2 + r_2$, where $0 \leq r_1, r_2 < |b|$. Hence, $b(m_1 - m_2) = r_2 - r_1$, and b divides

$r_2 - r_1$. Therefore, $r_1 = r_2$, and $b(m_1 - m_2) = 0$. Since $b \neq 0$, this equation shows that $m_1 - m_2 = 0$ and that $m_1 = m_2$.

We shall call r the *remainder* and m the *quotient in the division of a by b*.

Theorem 1-15. An integer a is or is not prime to an integer $b \neq 0$ according as the remainder in the division of a by b is or is not prime to b.

The theorem of Euclid shows that

$$a = bm + r \qquad 0 \leq r < |b|$$

and hence an integer d divides a and b if and only if d divides both r and b. For example, to find out whether or not 152 is prime to 21, just divide 152 by 21, getting the remainder 5. Since $(5, 21) = 1$, then $(152, 21) = 1$.

Theorem 1-16. All integers take the form $2n$ or $2n + 1$.

According to the theorem of Euclid, any integer a can be expressed in the form

$$a = 2n + r \qquad 0 \leq r < 2$$

so that r is either 0 or 1.

An *even integer* is one that is a multiple of 2. An integer that is not even is *odd*. The classification of the integers into odd and even integers was made by the Pythagoreans.

EXERCISES

1. Prove that the product of any two consecutive integers is divisible by 2.

The product of any two consecutive integers can be written in the form $n(n + 1)$. But then, according to the theorem of Euclid, n has the form $2k$ or $2k + 1$, whence the product has the form $2k(2k + 1)$ or $(2k + 1)(2k + 2) = 2(2k + 1)(k + 1)$. In either case the product has the factor 2.

2. Show that the sum of an integer and its square is even.

3. Show that all integers take the form $3n$, $3n + 1$, or $3n - 1$.

4. Prove that the product of any three consecutive integers is divisible by 3.

5. Prove that the square of an odd integer has the form $8n + 1$.

6. Prove by induction: $1 + 3 + 6 + \cdots + n(n + 1)/2 = n(n + 1)(n + 2)/6$ for $n > 0$.

When $n = 1$, the left-hand member is 1 and the right-hand member is $1(2)(3)/6 = 1$. The statement is thus true in the first case. Now assume that the statement is true for $n = k$. The first term of this series is 1, and the kth term, given by the term formula $n(n + 1)/2$, is $k(k + 1)/2$. Hence,

$$1 + 3 + \cdots + \frac{k(k + 1)}{2} = \frac{k(k + 1)(k + 2)}{6} \tag{1}$$

where the right-hand member of the equation is the sum of the first k terms of the series obtained from the formula for the sum of n terms.

We must now show by a general method that the sum of the first $k + 1$ terms of the series can be correctly obtained from the sum formula. To accomplish this end, we shall build up the series of $k + 1$ terms by adding the $(k + 1)$st term to the indicated sum of the first k terms. The $(k + 1)$st term is obtained from the term formula by substituting $k + 1$ for n and is $(k + 1)(k + 2)/2$. But if we add this number to one member of Eq. (1), we must add it to the other member also to maintain an equality. Thus we have

$$1 + 3 + \cdots + \frac{k(k + 1)}{2} + \frac{(k + 1)(k + 2)}{2} = \frac{k(k + 1)(k + 2)}{6} + \frac{(k + 1)(k + 2)}{2} \quad (2)$$

But the right-hand member of Eq. (2) can be factored and simplified, giving

$$\frac{k(k + 1)(k + 2)}{6} + \frac{(k + 1)(k + 2)}{2} = (k + 1)(k + 2)\left(\frac{k}{6} + \frac{1}{2}\right) = \frac{(k + 1)(k + 2)(k + 3)}{6}$$

Assuming that the law is correct in the kth case, $(k + 1)(k + 2)(k + 3)/6$ is the correct sum of the first $k + 1$ terms. Consequently, unless the sum formula gives this result for the sum of $k + 1$ terms, the sum formula is in error. Substituting $k + 1$ for n in the formula $n(n + 1)(n + 2)/6$, we find that it also gives $(k + 1)(k + 2)(k + 3)/6$. We must conclude that this formula is correct, for it gave the correct result for $n = 1$, and, upon the assumption of its truth for $n = k$, we found it gave the correct result for $n = k + 1$. Hence, being true for $n = 1$, it is true for $n = 2, 3, \ldots$.

7. Prove by induction: $1 + 2 + \cdots + n = n(n + 1)/2$ for $n > 0$.

8. Prove by induction: $1^2 + 2^2 + \cdots + n^2 = n(n + 1)(2n + 1)/6$ for $n > 0$.

9. Prove by induction: $1^3 + 2^3 + \cdots + n^3 = n^2(n + 1)^2/4$ for $n > 0$.

10. Prove by induction that $a^n - b^n$ is divisible by $a - b$ if n is a positive integer. If $n = 1$, $a - b$ is divisible by $a - b$.

Assume that $a^k - b^k = (a - b)F(a, b)$. Now divide $a^{k+1} - b^{k+1}$ by $a - b$, getting the quotient a^k and the remainder $a^k b - b^{k+1}$. Thus

$$a^{k+1} - b^{k+1} = (a - b)a^k + a^k b - b^{k+1}$$
$$= (a - b)a^k + b(a^k - b^k)$$

But since $a - b$ is a factor of $a^k - b^k$, the distributive law shows that $a - b$ is a factor of $a^{k+1} - b^{k+1}$. Then according to postulate 16, $a^n - b^n$ is divisible by $a - b$ for $n > 0$.

11. Prove that if n is a positive odd integer, $a^n + b^n$ is divisible by $a + b$.

12. Prove that if n is a positive even integer, $a + b$ is a factor of $a^n - b^n$.

13. Prove by induction that $10^n + 3 \cdot 4^{n+2} + 5$ is divisible by 9 if n is zero or a positive integer.

If $n = 0$, then $1 + 3(16) + 5 = 54$ and this integer is divisible by 9. Now form the difference between the $(n + 1)$st and the nth case and simplify by factoring, getting the result

$$10^{n+1} + 3 \cdot 4^{n+3} + 5 - (10^n + 3 \cdot 4^{n+2} + 5) = 10^n(9) + 3 \cdot 4^{n+2}(3)$$

The right-hand member is clearly divisible by 9. Substituting $n = 0$ and applying the distributive law, the above equation implies that $10 + 3 \cdot 4^3 + 5$ is a multiple of 9, and hence the theorem is true for $n = 1$. But, being true for $n = 1$, it is likewise true for all the positive integers.

14. Prove that:

a. $7^{2n} + 16n - 1$ is divisible by 64 for $n > 0$.

b. $2 \cdot 7^n + 3 \cdot 5^n - 5$ is divisible by 24 for $n > 0$.

c. $3^{4n+2} + 5^{2n+1}$ is divisible by 14 for $n \geq 0$.

15. Prove that the cube of any integer is equal to the difference of the squares of two integers.

To solve a problem of this type, we often set up a few examples with the purpose of discovering the law by inspection. Thus

$$1^3 = 1^2 - 0^2$$
$$2^3 = 3^2 - 1^2$$
$$3^3 = 6^2 - 3^2$$
$$4^3 = 10^2 - 6^2$$

The sequence of integers 1, 3, 6, 10, . . . reminds us of the sum of the series $1 + 2 + \cdots + n = n(n + 1)/2$. Hence, we should like to show that n^3 is the difference of $[n(n + 1)/2]^2$ and $[(n - 1)n/2]^2$. This statement is correct, for

$$\left[\frac{n(n + 1)}{2} \right]^2 - \left[\frac{(n - 1)n}{2} \right]^2 = \frac{n^2(n^2 + 2n + 1 - n^2 + 2n - 1)}{4}$$
$$= n^3$$

16. Show that if $7x - 5$ is a multiple of 3, then $28x^2 - 13x - 5$ is a multiple of 9.

17. Show that if $2x + 1$ is a multiple of 5, then $14x^2 + 19x - 19$ is a multiple of 25.

18. Show that if an integer is both a square and a cube, it is of the form $5n$, $5n + 1$, or $5n + 4$.

19. Show that the square of an integer that is not a multiple of 2 or 3 is of the form $24k + 1$.

20. Prove that the sum of the odd integers from 1 through $2n - 1$ is a perfect square, n^2.

21. Prove that every odd cube, n^3, is the sum of n consecutive odd integers. **Find** a corresponding law for an even cube.

22. We have assumed the principle of Archimedes, but just as some of our other postulates are not independent, it is possible to prove the principle of Archimedes on the basis of the assumptions already made.

Case 1. Let $a \geq 0$ and $b > 0$. If $a < b$, then $0 \leq a < b$ and $m = 0$. If $a = b$, then $b = a < 2b$ and $m = 1$. If $a > b$, there is a positive multiple of b that is less than a. But

$$a < a + 1 \leq (a + 1)b$$

Thus in the sequence of multiples of b,

$$(a + 1)b > ab > \cdots > 0$$

there is a least positive multiple of b that is greater than a. Let this multiple of b be $(m + 1)b$. Then

$$mb \leq a < (m + 1)b$$

Case 2. Let $a < 0$ and $b > 0$. Then nonnegative c exists so that

$$cb \leq |a| < (c + 1)b$$

and

$$-cb \geq a > (-c - 1)b$$

If $a < -cb$, let $m = -c - 1$, but if $a = -cb$, then $a < (-c + 1)b$ and $m = -c$. Let the student complete the proof.

23. If $a \neq 0$ and $|b| > |a|$, then b does not divide a.

24. What values can you assign to r in order that $4n + r$ include all odd primes?

25. Using the idea of Exercise 24, write another set of expressions whose values include all odd primes.

26. If n is a positive integer, the triangular numbers are given by the formula $n(n + 1)/2$. Find by trial some integers that are both square and triangular.

27. Is the set of even integers closed under the operation of addition? Do the odd integers have this property? Is the set of even integers closed under multiplication? What important property that pertains to multiplication does the set of even integers lack?

28. Peano stated the following postulates, together with the principle of finite induction, to define the natural numbers:

a. There is a number 1.

b. Every number n has a unique successor n^+.

c. The number 1 is not the successor of any number.

d. If $n^+ = m^+$, then $n = m$.

Define addition and multiplication, and derive the commutative, associative, and distributive laws for the natural numbers on the basis of these postulates.

CHAPTER 2

THE LINEAR DIOPHANTINE EQUATION

2-1. The Form $ax + by$. A *polynomial* in the variables x_1, x_2, . . . , x_r is a rational integral algebraic expression in these variables. Thus $a_0 x^n + a_1 x^{n-1} + \cdots + a_n$, where the exponents of the variable x are positive integers or zero, is a polynomial in x. The expression $b_1 x^2 + b_2 xy + b_3 xy^3$ is a polynomial in x and y. The *degree* of a polynomial is the degree in all its variables of its term or terms of highest degree. The first polynomial is of degree n, and the second is of the fourth degree. The second, however, is of only the second degree in x, but it is of the third degree in y. If all the coefficients of a polynomial are integers, it is said to be an *integral polynomial*.

A *form** in the variables x_1, x_2, . . . , x_r is a homogeneous polynomial in these variables; that is, each term of the polynomial is of the same degree. The *degree* of a form is the degree in all its variables of any term of the form. The polynomial $3x^2 y + 5xy^2 - y^3$ is a form of the third degree. All the forms with which we shall be concerned will have integers as coefficients. We shall make use of the form $ax + by$ to show that the greatest common divisor of two rational integers (not both zero) exists and is a rational integer.

Theorem 2-1. The least positive integer in the set of integers defined by $ax + by$, where a and b are not both zero, is the greatest common divisor of the set.

Consider the set of integers defined by the linear form $ax + by$ when a and b are constants and x and y are variables whose values are all the integers. Since there is but a finite number of integers between zero and any positive integer, and since the set $ax + by$ contains a positive integer, this set has a least positive integer. Let it be represented by

$$L = ax_0 + by_0$$

This integer L divides every integer of the set because, according to the

---

* This technical use of the word "form" is not to be confused with the ordinary sense in which we have made use of the term. When we say, for instance, that an integer has the form $6k + 1$, the word is synonymous with "mold" or "structure" and in this case designates that the given integer is always a multiple of six, plus one. Whenever "form" is used to mean a homogeneous polynomial, the implication will be clear from the text.

14

theorem of Euclid, corresponding to the integers $n = ax_1 + by_1$ and L there exist integers m and r such that

$$n = mL + r \qquad 0 \leq r < L$$

Hence,

$$ax_1 + by_1 = m(ax_0 + by_0) + r$$

and

$$a(x_1 - mx_0) + b(y_1 - my_0) = r$$

Therefore, r is an integer of the set, but, being less than L, r must be 0. The least positive integer of the set thus divides every integer of the set and is necessarily a common divisor of the set. But L is in the set, and therefore any common divisor of the set divides L. Hence, L is the greatest common divisor of the set $ax + by$, for it satisfies the stated definition by being a positive integer which is a common divisor of the set and which is divisible by every common divisor of the set.

Theorem 2-2. The greatest common divisor of a and b, where not both are zero, exists and is the least positive integer in the set defined by $ax + by$.

The integers a and b are determined by the form $ax + by$, when $x = 1$, $y = 0$, and when $x = 0$, $y = 1$, respectively. Hence, Theorem 2-1 shows that L is a common divisor of a and b. But $L = ax_0 + by_0$, and thus any common divisor of a and b divides L. Therefore, the greatest common divisor of a and b exists and is L.

Theorem 2-3. If d is the greatest common divisor of a and b, then d is the greatest common divisor of the set of integers $ax + by$.

If $d = (a, b)$, so that $a = a_0 d$, $b = b_0 d$, we see that d is a common divisor of the set, for $ax + by = d(a_0 x + b_0 y)$. On the other hand, any common divisor of the set divides a and b, for both a and b are in the set. But any common divisor of a and b is a divisor of d. Thus a common divisor of the set $ax + by$ necessarily divides d. The integer d is, therefore, the greatest common divisor of the set.

Theorem 2-4. The greatest common divisor of the set of integers $ax + by$ is unique.

Suppose that both d_1 and d_2 are greatest common divisors of the set $ax + by$ and that they are positive. Then, according to the definition, $d_1 \mid d_2$ and $d_2 \mid d_1$. Consequently, $d_1 \leq d_2$, and $d_2 \leq d_1$, so that $d_1 = d_2$.

It follows, then, that the greatest common divisor of a and b is the least positive integer in the set $ax + by$ and that $d = (a, b)$ can be expressed as a linear function of a and b with integral coefficients. Thus $4 = (12, 20)$ can be written $4 = 12(2) + 20(-1) = 12(-18) + 20(11)$.

The fact that the greatest common divisor of any two rational integers a and b, where not both are zero, can be written in the form $ax + by$ with x and y rational integers is an important characteristic of the set of rational integers.   Not all sets of integers have this property.   Consider, for instance, the set of even rational integers.   Although the integers 4 and 6 have the greatest common divisor 2 which is in this particular set, 2 cannot be written in the form $2 = 4x + 6y$, where x and y are selected from the set of even integers.

Theorem 2-5.   The set of integers $ax + by$ consists of all the multiples of $d = (a, b)$.

It has been shown that every integer of the set $ax + by$ is a multiple of d.   Moreover, every multiple of $d = ax_0 + by_0$ is in the set, for $k(ax_0 + by_0) = a(kx_0) + b(ky_0)$.   Therefore, all and only multiples of d are members of the set defined by $ax + by$.

It is interesting to notice that because d is not zero, the set $ax + by$ never consists of just one integer.   Furthermore, the sum and difference of any two integers defined by $ax + by$ are also in this set.

Any set of at least two elements is called a *modul* if its elements obey the associative and commutative laws for addition and if the equation $a + b = c$ is satisfied by an element of the set whenever two of the three elements a, b, c are chosen from the set.   It is now apparent that the integers $ax + by$ form a modul.

EXERCISES

1. Describe the set of integers $3x + 6y$.

2. Use the form $ax + by$ to define a set of integers all of which are even.

3. Use the form $ax + by$ to define a set of integers that are multiples of 5.   Are all multiples of 5 included?

4. Use the linear form in two variables to determine a set of even integers that are multiples of 5.

5. When will the set $ax + by$ include all the integers?

2-2. The Diophantine Equation $ax + by = n$.   Diophantus (c. 275) was the one Greek mathematician of note who devoted himself to algebra. He solved quadratic equations in a single variable, but he found only one answer and discarded all but positive rational numbers as solutions.   He even considered types of quadratics in two unknowns and two simultaneous equations of this kind.   He is credited with enlarging the concept of number to include the fractions.   Because he sometimes restricted his solutions to integers, his name is now attached to the kind of equation defined below.   Diophantus developed no general method for the solution of these equations, however. It was not until the Hindus attacked the problem that such general methods were devised.

A *Diophantine equation* is a rational integral algebraic equation in which the coefficients of the variables and the absolute term are integers and of which the *solutions*, or values of the variable or variables that satisfy the equation, must be integers. Such an equation would be used to solve the problem: In how many ways can \$25 be paid in five-dollar bills and two-dollar bills?

Theorem 2-6. The linear Diophantine equation $ax + by = n$ has a solution if and only if the greatest common divisor of a and b divides n.

Since we have shown that $d = (a, b)$ divides $ax + by$ for all integral values of x and y, if $ax + by = n$ has a solution, d divides n.

If d divides n, let $n = n_0 d$. Because d has been proved to be an integer of the set $ax + by$, it follows that $n = n_0(ax_0 + by_0) = a(n_0x_0) + b(n_0y_0)$. This result shows that $x = n_0x_0$, $y = n_0y_0$ is a solution of the equation.

Corollary. A necessary and sufficient condition that a and b be relatively prime is that there be a solution of the linear Diophantine equation $ax + by = 1$.

The preceding proof also implies that if $(a, b) = d$ and $ax + by = n$ has a solution $x = x_0$, $y = y_0$, then this very pair satisfies $a_0x + b_0y = n'$, where $a = a_0d$, $b = b_0d$, $n = n'd$. Again, if $(a, b) = 1$, the equation $ax + by = n$ has a solution and that same solution holds for $kax + kby = kn$. The problem of solving the equation $ax + by = n$ is, therefore, reduced to finding a general method for solving the equation in the case where the coefficients of the variables are relatively prime.

Theorem 2-7. If m divides ab, and m and a are relatively prime, then m divides b.

Since $(m, a) = 1$, the equation $mx + ay = 1$ has a solution $x = x_1$, $y = y_1$. Then

$$b(mx_1 + ay_1) = b$$

and

$$mbx_1 + aby_1 = b$$

But $m \mid mb$, and $m \mid ab$. Therefore, $m \mid b$.

Observe that Theorem 2-7 holds even when $m = 0$, for then if $(m, a) = 1$, it is necessary that $a = \pm 1$. But $m \mid ab$ implies that $ab = 0$. Consequently, $b = 0$, and $m \mid b$.

Notice also that if $m \neq \pm 1$ is prime to an integer n, then m does not divide n. On the other hand, if m does not divide n, the integers m and n need not be relatively prime; for example, $6 \nmid 15$, but $(6, 15) = 3$.

Corollary 1. If m is prime to both a and b, then m is prime to ab.

Corollary 2. If m is prime to $a_1, a_2, \ldots, a_n$, then m is prime to their product.

EXERCISES

1. Prove that the product of three consecutive integers is divisible by 6.

Let $P = n(n + 1)(n + 2)$. Then P is divisible by both 2 and 3. Hence, $P = 2k = 3m$. But $(2, 3) = 1$, and $2 \mid 3m$. Therefore, $2 \mid m$. Thus $m = 2s$, and $P = 3(2s) = 6s$.

2. Show that $n(n^2 - 1)$ is a multiple of 24 if n is odd.

3. Show that $n^5 - n$ is a multiple of 30.

4. If n^2 is divisible by 3 but not by 4, then $n^2 - 1$ is divisible by 4.

5. Prove that $\sqrt{2}$ is irrational.

A number is rational if and only if it can be expressed as a quotient a/b of two rational integers with the denominator b different from zero. Hence, assume that $\sqrt{2} = a/b$ with $(a, b) = 1$. From $2b^2 = a^2$ we see that $b \mid a^2$. Now apply Theorem 2-7, and show a contradiction.

6. Prove that $\sqrt{3}$ and $\sqrt[3]{2}$ are irrational.

7. When m is a positive integer, prove that if $\sqrt[n]{m}$ is not an integer, it is irrational.

8. If the sum of two fractions $a/b + c/d$ in their lowest terms is an integer, $b = +d$ or $-d$.

9. If $(a, b) = 1$ and $c > 0$, then $(ac, bc) = c$.

10. If $(a, b) = 1$, the greatest common divisor of $a + b$ and $a - b$ is either 1 or 2. Notice that $(a + b) - (a - b) = 2b$ and $(a + b) + (a - b) = 2a$. Furthermore, $(2a, 2b) = 2$. Thus $d = (a + b, a - b)$ is a divisor of 2.

11. If $(a, b) = 1$, the greatest common divisor of $a^2 + b^2$ and $a + b$ is either 1 or 2.

12. Show that if $(a, b) = 1$, the greatest common divisor of $a^3 + b^3$ and $a^2 + b^2$ is a divisor of $a - b$.

Theorem 2-8. The greatest common divisor d of a finite set of integers $a_1, a_2, \ldots, a_n$ can be expressed in the form

$$a_1x_1 + a_2x_2 + \cdots + a_nx_n = d$$

where the x_i, for $i = 1, 2, \ldots, n$, are integers.

Let us start with the integers $a_1, a_2,$ and a_3, and let $d_1 = (a_1, a_2)$. Then y_1 and y_2 exist so that

$$a_1y_1 + a_2y_2 = d_1$$

Any common divisor of $a_1, a_2,$ and a_3 must be a common divisor of d_1 and a_3, and hence a divisor of $d_2 = (d_1, a_3)$. But d_2 is itself a common divisor of $a_1, a_2,$ and a_3, and therefore d_2 is the greatest common divisor of these three integers. Since integers z_1 and z_2 exist so that

$$d_1z_1 + a_3z_2 = d_2$$

we have

$$(a_1y_1 + a_2y_2)z_1 + a_3z_2 = d_2$$

and finally

$$a_1x_1 + a_2x_2 + a_3x_3 = d_2$$

Using induction, we can similarly raise the number of the integers in the set to n.

Furthermore, as in Theorem 2-6, we can now show that when $d = (a_1, a_2, \ldots, a_n)$ and $d \mid m$, there exist integers x'_i, where $i = 1, 2, \ldots, n$, that satisfy the equation $a_1x_1 + a_2x_2 + \cdots + a_nx_n = m$ and that if such an equation has a solution in integers, $d \mid m$.

Corollary. If d_1 is the greatest common divisor of $a_1, a_2, \ldots, a_k$, then the greatest common divisor of $a_1, a_2, \ldots, a_k, a_{k+1}$ is the greatest common divisor of d_1 and a_{k+1}.

Theorem 2-9. If a and b are relatively prime and $x = x_0$, $y = y_0$ is a solution of the equation $ax + by = n$, all solutions are given by the equations $x = x_0 + kb$, $y = y_0 - ka$ for all integral values of k.

Supposing that both pairs of integers x_0, y_0 and x', y' satisfy $ax + by = n$, we have

$$ax_0 + by_0 = n$$

and

$$ax' + by' = n$$

so that

$$a(x' - x_0) + b(y' - y_0) = 0$$

and

$$a(x' - x_0) = -b(y' - y_0)$$

Since $(a, b) = 1$, provided that $b \neq 0$, it follows that $b \mid (x' - x_0)$ and therefore that $x' - x_0 = kb$, or $x' = x_0 + kb$. Substituting kb for $x' - x_0$, we obtain

$$akb = -b(y' - y_0)$$

After applying the cancellation law, we find that $y' = y_0 - ka$. If $b = 0$, the original equation is clearly trivial.

That the integers $x = x_0 + kb$, $y = y_0 - ka$ satisfy $ax + by = n$ for all integral values of the parameter k can be determined by substituting them in the given equation.

2-3. A Method for Finding a Solution of $ax + by = n$. If $(a, b) = d$ and $d \mid n$, we have shown that, by dividing each term of the equation $ax + by = n$ by d, we obtain an equivalent equation, that is, one which is satisfied by all and only the solutions of the original equation. Consequently, it will be sufficient to solve the equation $ax + by = n$ when $(a, b) = 1$.

If $a \mid n$, so that $n = n_0 a$, let $y = 0$ and $x = n_0$, and the equation is satisfied.

If $a \nmid n$, then $a \neq \pm 1$ and we may suppose that $1 < |a| < |b|$. Then

$$b = q_1 a + r_1 \qquad 0 < r_1 < |a|$$

and

$$n = q_2 a + r_2 \qquad 0 < r_2 < |a|$$

Therefore,

$$ax + (q_1 a + r_1)y = q_2 a + r_2$$

Since a solution of $ax + by = n$ exists, $r_1 y - r_2$ is a multiple of a; that is, $r_1 y + az = r_2$. If $r_1 \mid r_2$, choose $z = 0$, and y is thus determined. Then by substituting in the original equation, a value for x is found. But if $r_1 \nmid r_2$, proceed as before, using y and z as the variables and r_1 as the divisor since $r_1 < |a|$. Therefore, where

$$a = q_3 r_1 + r_3 \qquad 0 < r_3 < r_1$$

and

$$r_2 = q_4 r_1 + r_4 \qquad 0 < r_4 < r_1$$

we have

$$r_1 y = q_4 r_1 + r_4 - (q_3 r_1 + r_3)z$$

and, as above,

$$r_3 z + r_1 w = r_4$$

If we continue in this manner, we find that $|a| > r_1 > r_3 > \cdots >$ $r_{2s-1} > 0$. Each of the remainders r_{2k+1} and r_{2k+2} determined when r_{2k-3} and r_{2k}, respectively, are divided by r_{2k-1} is less than r_{2k-1}. We see, therefore, that each new set of two nonnegative remainders has an upper bound r_{2k-1} which is smaller than the upper bound of the preceding set of two. Within a finite number of steps the process will necessarily end, for some r_{2k-1} will divide r_{2k}. Supposing that this happens when $k = s$, the equation $r_{2s-1}u + r_{2s-3}v = r_{2s}$ will be solved by letting $v = 0$ and $u = m$, where $r_{2s} = m r_{2s-1}$. The original variables can then be determined by substitution.

Example. Solve the Diophantine equation $69x + 111y = 9000$.

Solution. Since $(69, 111) = 3$, we solve the equivalent equation $23x + 37y = 3000$. Thus

$$23x + (23 + 14)y = (130)(23) + 10$$

Hence,

$$14y + 23z = 10$$

and

$$14y + (14 + 9)z = 10$$

so that

$$9z + 14w = 10$$

Again,

$$9z + (9 + 5)w = 9 + 1$$

and

$$5w + 9v = 1$$

Therefore,

$$5w + (5 + 4)v = 1$$

and

$$4v + 5s = 1$$

Finally,

$$4v + (4 + 1)s = 1$$

so that

$$s = 1$$

Therefore, $v = -1$, $w = 2$, $z = -2$, $y = 4$, and $x = 124$. Consequently, all the solutions of the original equation are of the form

$$x = 124 + 37k$$
$$y = 4 - 23k$$

If we wish only the positive integers that satisfy the given equation, we take

$$124 + 37k > 0$$

and

$$4 - 23k > 0$$

so that

$$\tfrac{4}{23} > k > -\tfrac{124}{37}$$

Hence, k can have only the values -3, -2, -1, and 0.

EXERCISES

Solve the equations and determine the number of solutions for which both x and y are positive.

1. $16x + 7y = 601$.   **2.** $14x - 45y = 11$.
3. $75x + 91y = 320$.   **4.** $56x - 50y = 74$.
5. $40x - 63y = 135$.   **6.** $123x + 57y = 393$.
7. $77x + 165y = 3553$.

8. Separate 1591 into two parts such that one part is a multiple of 23 and the other a multiple of 34.

2-4. The Solution of the Linear Diophantine Equation in More than Two Variables. A single linear Diophantine equation in more than two variables or a simultaneous set of such equations can be solved very expeditiously, when there is a solution, by the reduction of the augmented matrix of the equation or system of equations to a canonical form.* This method enables us to determine a linear transformation the application of which substitutes for the original equation or equations a set of one or more equations which is easily solved. We shall not develop any of this theory, but we shall show in the case of a single equation in three variables how a linear transformation can be used to facilitate the finding of the solutions.

Consider the equation

$$a_1x + a_2y + a_3z = m \qquad (1)$$

If $(a_1, a_2, a_3) = d$, there is no solution unless $d \mid m$. Supposing that $d \mid m$, to find the solutions we should first divide each member of the equation by d. Therefore, let us assume that $(a_1, a_2, a_3) = 1$. Then if $d_1 = (a_1, a_2)$, it is necessary and sufficient that d_1 divide $a_3z - m$ in order that there be a solution of the given equation. But $(a_3, d_1) = 1$, and therefore

$$a_3z + d_1t = m$$

has the solutions $z = z_0 - d_1w$, $t = t_0 + a_3w$, where $z = z_0$, $t = t_0$ is one

* H. J. S. Smith, "Collected Mathematics Papers," Vol. 1, Oxford University Press, New York, 1894.

solution.   Hence, $z_0 - d_1w$, for all integral values of the parameter w, gives all and only values of z for which $a_3z - m$ is a multiple of d_1.

Now consider the linear transformation

$$x = b_1u + b_2v$$
$$y = c_1u + c_2v$$

(2)

We, of course, wish u and v to be integers, and we know that

$$u = \frac{c_2x - b_2y}{b_1c_2 - b_2c_1}$$
$$v = \frac{b_1y - c_1x}{b_1c_2 - b_2c_1}$$

Therefore, any choice of integral values for b_1, b_2, c_1, c_2 that makes

$$b_1c_2 - b_2c_1 = 1$$

will force u and v to be integers since x and y have only integral values. Applying this transformation (2) to the original equation (1), and substituting $z = z_0 - d_1w$, the resulting equation is

$$a_1(b_1u + b_2v) + a_2(c_1u + c_2v) + a_3(z_0 - d_1w) = m$$

or

$$(a_1b_1 + a_2c_1)u + (a_1b_2 + a_2c_2)v - a_3d_1w = d_1t_0$$

(3)

since

$$a_3z_0 + d_1t_0 = m$$

Because we introduced two independent variables u and v, we are permitted to impose a second condition upon the coefficients of the transformation.   We, therefore, set

$$a_1b_2 + a_2c_2 = 0$$

Since $(a_1, a_2) = d_1$, let $a_1 = a_{01}d_1$, $a_2 = a_{02}d_1$, and then

$$a_{01}d_1b_2 = -a_{02}d_1c_2$$

or

$$a_{01}b_2 = -a_{02}c_2$$

Let us, therefore, choose $b_2 = -a_{02}$ and $c_2 = a_{01}$.   Then the condition $b_1c_2 - b_2c_1 = 1$ becomes

$$a_{01}b_1 + a_{02}c_1 = 1$$

and this equation determines b_1 and c_1 since $(a_{01}, a_{02}) = 1$.   Choose a set of values so determined for b_1 and c_1 in which neither b_1 nor c_1 is zero. Now if we multiply each member of the last equation by d_1, we have

$$a_1b_1 + a_2c_1 = d_1$$

and therefore the transformed equation (3) takes the form

$$d_1 u - a_3 d_1 w = d_1 t_0$$

and

$$u = t_0 + a_3 w$$

which is the same as the value found for t. Then by eliminating u from Eqs. (2) for x and y, we find that the solutions of the original equation are of the form

$$x = b_1 t_0 - a_{02} v + a_3 b_1 w$$
$$y = c_1 t_0 + a_{01} v + a_3 c_1 w$$
$$z = z_0 - d_1 w$$

where v and w are the parameters. That all these values of x, y, and z determined by integral values of the parameters satisfy the equation is easily verified.

It is evident that the solution of a Diophantine equation in four variables can now be made to depend upon the solution of one with three variables in the same manner as we have used equations in two variables in the above development to solve an equation in three variables.

Example. Solve: $6x + 24y - 41z = 91$.

Solution. $(6, 24) = 6$, and $-41z + 6t = 91$ has the solutions $z = 1 - 6w$, $t = 22 - 41w$. The equations $a_1 b_2 + a_2 c_2 = 0$ and $b_1 c_2 - b_2 c_1 = 1$ become $6b_2 + 24c_2 = 0$ and $b_1 + 4c_1 = 1$, so that $b_2 = -4$, $c_2 = 1$; $b_1 = -3$, $c_1 = 1$. Since $u = t$, it is easy to compute the answer in the form $x = -3(22 - 41w) - 4v = -66 + 123w - 4v$, $y = 22 - 41w + v$, $z = 1 - 6w$.

2-5. Simultaneous Linear Diophantine Equations. A set of two equations in three variables may or may not have a solution in integers. Consider the set

$$a_1 x + a_2 y + a_3 z = m_1$$
$$b_1 x + b_2 y + b_3 z = m_2 \tag{4}$$

If $(a_1, a_2, a_3) = d_1$ does not divide m_1 or if $(b_1, b_2, b_3) = d_2$ fails to divide m_2, there is, of course, no solution for the set. But even when these conditions are fulfilled, there need not be a common solution. Take, for instance, the set

$$2x + 3y + z = 7$$
$$2x - y + 3z = 8$$

If the second equation is subtracted from the first, the result is

$$4y - 2z = -1$$

Any y and z that, together with an x, satisfy the given set must satisfy this equation, but because $(4, 2) = 2$, the equation has no solution whatever.

When each individual equation has a solution, we can always determine the common solutions, if they exist, by solving one equation and substituting these values in the second. Thus, when the solutions of the equation

$$a_1x + a_2y + a_3z = m_1 \tag{5}$$

are

$$
\begin{aligned}
x &= r_1 + s_1v + t_1w \\
y &= r_2 + s_2v + t_2w \\
z &= r_3 + s_3v
\end{aligned}
\tag{6}
$$

with parameters v and w, upon substituting these expressions in $b_1x + b_2y + b_3z = m_2$, we obtain an equation of the form

$$Aw + Bv = C$$

The given equations have a common solution if and only if this last equation is solvable. Suppose the solutions exist and are of the form

$$
\begin{aligned}
w &= w_0 + B_1t \\
v &= v_0 + A_1t
\end{aligned}
$$

When these values are substituted in the solutions (6) of the first equation (5), the common solutions of (4) take the form

$$
\begin{aligned}
x &= X_0 + K_1t \\
y &= Y_0 + K_2t \\
z &= Z_0 + K_3t
\end{aligned}
$$

where there is but one parameter t.

Example. Solve the set of equations: $6x + 24y - 41z = 91$,
$2x - 3y + 7z = 2$.

Solution. Substituting in the second equation the solutions of the first one arrived at in the preceding example, we have $2(-66 + 123w - 4v) - 3(22 - 41w + v) + 7(1 - 6w) = 2$, or $327w - 11v = 193$. Hence $w = -2 + 11k$, and $v = -77 + 327k$. Therefore $x = -66 + 123(-2 + 11k) - 4(-77 + 327k) = -4 + 45k$; $y = 22 - 41(-2 + 11k) + (-77 + 327k) = 27 - 124k$; $z = 1 - 6(-2 + 11k) = 13 - 66k$.

EXERCISES

1. Solve: $2x - 5y + 3z = 17$.

2. Solve: $3x - 6y + 2z = 11$.

3. Solve: $10x + 16y - 4z = 48$.

4. Solve: $127x + 319y - 43z = 521$.

5. Solve the set: $2x + 2y + 7z = 22$,
$7x - 4y - 5z = 29$.

6. Solve the set: $x + 3y - z = 11$,
$5x - 5y - 3z = 33$.

7. A room has 100 seats. How many men, women, and children should be admitted to realize exactly $10 if the men will pay 50 cents each; the women, 20 cents each; and the children, 1 cent each?

8. If 100 pieces of money in denominations of 50 cents, $5, and $10 are to amount to $100, how many of each denomination must there be?

CHAPTER 3

PROPERTIES OF INTEGERS

3-1. The Composite. Perhaps one of the facts with which you are most familiar is that a composite has a prime factor, but have you ever proved it?

Theorem 3-1. Every composite has a prime factor.

Because any negative integer can be expressed as the product of its positive associate and the unit -1, we shall assume that the composite m is positive. Since m is neither a unit nor a prime, it has a factor that is not a unit or an associate of m. Therefore, let $m = f_1 f_2$, where both factors are positive. Then $f_1 < m$, and f_1 is either a prime or another composite. If f_1 is a prime, the theorem is complete, but if f_1 is a composite, it, in turn, has a factor other than an associate or a unit. Then $f_1 = f_3 f_4$, where $0 < f_3 < f_1$. If f_3 is not a prime, the line of reasoning continues in the above manner, but only for a finite number of steps, for since

$$m > f_1 > f_3 > \cdots > 0$$

we must arrive at a positive factor f_{2n-1} that is divisible only by its associates and the units. The integer f_{2n-1} is, therefore, a prime, and by substitution it is obviously shown to be a factor of m.

3-2. The Sieve of Eratosthenes (c. 230 B.C.). It is evident that one way to test whether or not a positive integer m is a prime would be to write all the integers from 1 through m; then to leave 2, and strike out every second integer thereafter; next to leave 3, and strike out every third integer thereafter; generally, to leave the next unstruck integer p, and strike out every pth integer thereafter. Each integer except 1 that is not crossed off by this process is obviously a prime. For how long must this process be continued before we know that m is a prime? Eratosthenes answered this question by means of the following theorem and thus presented a useful test for a prime:

Theorem 3-2. A positive integer m is prime if it has no positive prime factor less than or equal to I, where I is the greatest integer such that I^2 is less than or equal to m.

Suppose that m is not a prime but is a composite. Then m has a prime factor. This prime factor p must be greater than I according to the

25

hypothesis of the theorem. But when $m = pf$, the complementary factor f must also be greater than I, for if it were not, a prime factor of it, which would necessarily be a prime factor of m, would be less than or equal to I. Therefore, both p and f are at least equal to $I + 1$, and $m = pf$ shows that

$$m \geq (I + 1)^2$$

This statement is contrary to the hypothesis which says that $(I + 1)^2 > m$, and hence m is a prime.

Example. To test 2503 to see whether or not it is a prime, we try to divide 2503 by the primes 2, 3, 5, through 47, since in this case I is 50. Because none of these primes is a divisor of 2503, this integer is a prime.

3-3. The Number of Primes. Euclid included the following theorem in his "Elements."

Theorem 3-3. The number of primes is infinite.

So that we may understand the method of this proof, let us recall that a set of elements is said to be infinite if it has a proper subset, that is, a subset different from the whole set, which can be put into one-to-one correspondence with the whole set. Otherwise, a set is said to be finite. Consequently, if it can be shown that, in addition to a finite subset of a set, there is always another element that belongs to the set, the set is infinite.

Suppose that the number of primes is finite. Then there is a largest prime p. Form the integer N by taking the product of all the primes from 2 through p and adding the integer 1; thus

$$N = (2 \cdot 3 \cdot 5 \cdot \ \cdots \ \cdot p) + 1$$

N is either a prime or a composite. But if N is a prime, it is greater than p, which is contrary to the assumption. If N is a composite, it has a positive prime factor. This factor is not one of the primes in the set 2, 3, 5, . . . , p, or according to the distributive law it would divide 1, which is impossible. Consequently, it is a prime larger than p. Because we have shown that when we assume the number of primes is finite, we can always find a positive prime that was not previously counted, the number of primes is infinite.

It is evident, moreover, that Euclid's proof shows that if $p_1, p_2, \ldots, p_r$ are the first r primes, the next prime lies in the interval from $p_r + 1$ through $p_1 p_2 \cdots p_r + 1$.* This interval provided one of the first answers to the question, Where is the next prime larger than a given prime?

* D. N. Lehmer has compiled a "List of Prime Numbers from 1 to 10,006,721," Carnegie Institution of Washington, Washington, D.C., 1914.

Theorem 3-4.   The number of primes of the form $4n - 1$ is infinite.

Suppose the number of positive primes of the form $4n - 1$ is finite, and let p be the largest one of them.   Determine all such primes from 1 through p, and form their product.   Then construct the integer N by multiplying this product by 4 and subtracting 1 from the result.   Thus

$$N = (4 \cdot 3 \cdot 7 \cdot \ \cdots \ \cdot p) - 1$$

If N is a prime, it is one of the form $4n - 1$ that was not previously counted, for it is larger than p.   But if N is a composite, it has an odd prime factor.   Consequently, this factor has the form $4n - 1$ or $4n + 1$. If it is of the form $4n - 1$, it is not one of the primes from 1 through p, or by the distributive law it would divide 1, and that is impossible.   Therefore, if the prime factor is of this form, it is a prime larger than p.   But if the prime factor of N has the form $4n + 1$, there is a complementary factor of the form $4n - 1$, for the complementary factor must also be odd, and the product

$$(4s + 1)(4t + 1) = 4k + 1$$

does not yield the form $4n - 1$, whereas the product

$$(4s + 1)(4t - 1) = 4k - 1$$

does.   We observe immediately that this complementary factor $4t - 1$ has a prime factor.

The argument is now repeated with reference to this last prime factor. Since the size of each of the positive factors having the form $4n - 1$ decreases as the argument proceeds, we must finally arrive at a factor having the form $4n - 1$ that has only itself and 1 as positive factors. This integer is, therefore, a prime.   It is of the proper form, and it is not one of the primes from 1 through p.   It is, therefore, larger than p, and, as a result, the number of primes of the form $4n - 1$ is infinite.

Dirichlet (1805−1859) showed by using advanced methods that the arithmetic progression determined by $an + b$, where a and b are fixed integers and $(a, b) = 1$, while n has all integral values, contains an infinite number of primes.   Although for many years elementary proofs were known for special cases of this theorem, such as $4n - 1$, no proof of the general theorem that did not make use of the methods of analysis employed by Dirichlet had been developed until 1949.   About this time certain mathematicians (Paul Erdös, Atle Selberg, H. N. Shapiro, and H. Zassenhaus), working on the prime number theorem and in the theory of algebraic numbers, developed methods that produce new proofs of Dirichlet's theorem.   These are, however, beyond the scope of this text.

Theorem 3-5. If $2^n - 1$ is a prime, n is a prime.

Suppose that n is a composite and that $n = n_1 n_2$, where $1 < n_1 < n$. Then $2^{n_1 n_2} - 1$ has the factor $2^{n_1} - 1$ which is neither 1 nor $2^n - 1$. Consequently, n must be a prime if $2^n - 1$ is a prime.

Notice, however, that when p is a prime, $2^p - 1$ need not be a prime, for when $p = 11$, $2^{11} - 1$ has the factor 23.

EXERCISES

1. Show that all primes except ± 2, ± 3 are represented by the forms $6n - 1$ and $6n + 1$.

2. Show that there is an infinite number of primes of the form $6n - 1$.

3. Prove that $n^4 + 4$ is composite when $n > 1$.

4. Show that if $2^n + 1$ is an odd prime, n is a power of 2.

5. Determine whether or not 1781 and 4079 are primes.

3-4. Unique Factorization. We have previously proved by means of a rather long discussion that when $m \mid ab$ and $(m, a) = 1$, then $m \mid b$. In the case where m is a prime this theorem can also be proved in the following manner:

Theorem 3-6. If p is a prime and p does not divide a or b, then p does not divide ab.

Take a, b, and p positive integers, and consider the case in which $a < p$, and $b < p$. We shall prove that the prime p does not divide ab by assuming the contrary and showing that we arrive at an impossibility. According to the principle of Archimedes there exists a positive integer k such that for $a > 1$

$$ka < p < (k + 1)a$$

where the equality sign is omitted because p is a prime. Therefore

$$0 < p - ka < a$$

and

$$0 < (p - ka)b < ab$$

But if p divides ab, then p divides $pb - kab$ and this positive integer is a smaller multiple of b than is ab. This argument leads to the conclusion that there is always a positive multiple of b that is divisible by p and is at the same time smaller than the one last found. Accordingly there would be an infinite number of multiples of b between b and ab. The result is, of course, impossible, and consequently $p \nmid ab$.

Suppose now that not both a and b are less than p. Then

$$a = m_1 p + r_1$$
$$b = m_2 p + r_2 \qquad 0 < r_1, r_2 < p$$

Thus

$$ab = Kp + r_1r_2$$

and if $p \mid ab$, it follows that $p \mid r_1r_2$, where both r_1 and r_2 are positive and less than p. We know this division is impossible, and therefore $p \nmid ab$. The result implies that if $p \mid ab$, p divides at least one of a and b.

Theorem 3-7. If p is a prime and p does not divide a_i, where $i = 1, 2,$ . . . , n, then p does not divide the product of the a_i.

If p divides $a_1a_2 \cdots a_n$, then p divides a_1 or $a_2a_3 \cdots a_n$. But p does not divide a_1, and so it divides $a_2a_3 \cdots a_n$. In like manner p divides a_2 or $a_3 \cdots a_n$. Finally, p would have to divide a_n, but it does not, and therefore p does not divide the given product.

Theorem 3-8. Fundamental theorem of arithmetic. Except for associated primes and the order of the factors, a composite can be factored into primes in one and only one way.

Assuming that m is a positive composite, according to Theorem 3-1, m has a positive prime factor p_1 so that $m = p_1m_1$. If m_1 is not a prime, we again apply this theorem and obtain $m_1 = p_2m_2$ and $m = p_1p_2m_2$. Since $m > m_1 > m_2 > \cdots > 0$, we need carry out this process only a finite number of times until we have factored m into positive primes. Thus $m = p_1p_2 \cdots p_n$.

Suppose that there is a second factorization of m into positive primes so that $m = q_1q_2 \cdots q_r$, where $n \geq r$. Then

$$p_1p_2 \cdots p_n = q_1q_2 \cdots q_r$$

Therefore, p_1 divides the product $q_1q_2 \cdots q_r$ and must divide one of the primes q_j, where $j = 1, 2, \ldots, r$. Suppose p_1 divides q_1. The only divisors of q_1 are ± 1 and $\pm q_1$, and since p_1 and q_1 are positive primes, $p_1 = q_1$. Hence,

$$p_2p_3 \cdots p_n = q_2q_3 \cdots q_r$$

Continuing this process, we see that when $n = r$, each p_i, where $i = 1,$ $2, \ldots, n$, is identical with a corresponding q_j, but when $n > r$, we finally have

$$p_{r+1} \cdots p_n = 1$$

and each of the integers $p_{r+1}, \ldots, p_n$ must be a unit. Therefore, the factorization of the positive composite m into positive primes is unique.

It is obvious, then, that if we gather the equal primes together into the power form p^s, any composite m can be written in the form $\pm p_1^{n_1}p_2^{n_2} \cdots$ $p_r^{n_r}$, where the factorization is unique except for the use of an associate in the place of any prime and the order of the factors.

The reader may well remember that an algebraic factorization of an expression shows factors of all integers represented by the expression, and the factorization may, therefore, be used to demonstrate a property of all these integers. For instance, by using the factors $a + 1$ and $a - 1$, we can show that, for $a > 2$, $a^2 - 1$ never represents a prime. In factoring an integer that is written in polynomial form into the product of two integers, however, one must recall that while the expression may not be factorable algebraically into rational factors or may be factorable in just one way besides itself and 1, a particular integer represented by the expression may have several factorizations. It is evident that although the expression $a^2 + 1$ lacks factors in our domain, yet, for the particular value $a = 5$, $a^2 + 1 = 26$ has the factors 2 and 13. Again, an integer represented by $a^2 - 1$ may have factors other than those given by the only rational factors $a - 1$ and $a + 1$ of $a^2 - 1$. For instance, when $a = 5$, $a^2 - 1 = 24$ and this integer has the factors 3 and 8, 2 and 12, as well as 4 and 6. Hence, we must be careful to avoid drawing the conclusion that an integer lacks factors just because the algebraic expression of which it is a value fails to produce the factors.

EXERCISES

1. Show that if both x and y are odd, there is no z such that $x^2 + y^2 = z^2$.

2. Show that if $(a, b) = 1$ and $ab = c^n$, then $a = s^n$, $b = t^n$.

3. Show that an integer can be represented as a difference of two squares if and only if it is of the form $2n + 1$ or $4n$. Show also that the representation is unique when the integer is a prime.

4. Find the positive integers x that make $x(x + 42)$ a perfect square.

5. Find the positive integers x that make $x(x + 84)$ a perfect square.

3-5. Fermat's Method of Infinite Descent. Although it was fairly easy to show in Exercise 3 of the last set that a prime of the form $4n + 1$ can be represented uniquely as a difference of two squares, the problem of expressing a prime of the form $4n + 1$ as a sum of two squares attracted the attention of mathematicians for many years. Fermat claimed in 1641 that he had proved the theorem by the inductive method, called the *method of infinite descent*, which was exhibited in the proof of Theorem 3-6. Thus he said, "If a prime $4n + 1$ is not a sum of two squares, there is a smaller prime of the same nature, then a third still smaller, etc., until the number 5 is reached."[*] Since 5 is the smallest positive prime of the form $4n + 1$, and since it can be written $5 = 1^2 + 2^2$, the method leads to a contradiction and consequently each prime of the form $4n + 1$ is a sum of two squares. Whether or not Fermat actually proved the theorem we do not know, but Euler is generally credited with developing the first proof together with the proof of the unicity of the representation. It was not until 1843, however, that he established a point that he needed

[*] L. E. Dickson, "History of the Theory of Numbers," Vol. 2, p. 228.

for a rigorous proof. In the meantime by 1801 Gauss had applied the theory of binary biquadratic forms to show the existence of the representation.*

But Fermat's method of infinite descent used, as he claimed, in the proof of the above theorem is of particular interest. He admitted that it could be applied with more facility to prove the impossibility of certain relations, of which Theorem 3-6 is an example, than to show affirmative statements. He made use of the method in the one specimen of a detailed proof that has been left by him when he showed that if integers a, b, c are the sides of a right triangle, the area cannot be a perfect square.

3-6. The Euclidean Algorithm. An *algorithm* is a method of obtaining a result by repeated applications of an operation and is such that an element determined by one application of the operation is used at least once in a succeeding application until the desired result has been found.

It is important to have a method for finding the greatest common divisor of two integers a and b. If one integer is zero, the greatest common divisor is evidently the positive associate of the other integer, and if either or both integers are negative, the greatest common divisor is the same as it is for the positive associates. Taking both a and b positive, therefore, with $a > b$, we shall set up the Euclidean algorithm for finding the greatest common divisor of a and b.

Applying the theorem of Euclid, we have

$$a = m_1 b + r_1 \qquad 0 < r_1 < b$$
$$b = m_2 r_1 + r_2 \qquad 0 < r_2 < r_1$$
$$r_1 = m_3 r_2 + r_3 \qquad 0 < r_3 < r_2$$
$$\cdot \; \cdot \; \cdot \; \cdot \; \cdot \; \cdot \; \cdot \; \cdot \; \cdot \; \cdot \; \cdot \; \cdot \; \cdot \; \cdot$$
$$r_{i-2} = m_i r_{i-1} + r_i \qquad 0 < r_i < r_{i-1}$$
$$\cdot \; \cdot \; \cdot \; \cdot \; \cdot \; \cdot \; \cdot \; \cdot \; \cdot \; \cdot \; \cdot \; \cdot \; \cdot \; \cdot$$
$$r_{k-2} = m_k r_{k-1} + r_k \qquad 0 < r_k < r_{k-1}$$
$$r_{k-1} = m_{k+1} r_k$$

Because $b > r_1 > r_2 > \cdots > r_i > 0$, it is evident that after k applications of the theorem we must arrive at a remainder r_k that is a divisor of r_{k-1}. Then r_k is the greatest common divisor of a and b, for first of all $r_k \mid r_{k-2}$ since it divides r_{k-1}. In like manner because r_k divides r_{k-1} and r_{k-2}, it must divide r_{k-3}. Using the steps of the algorithm in reverse order, we observe, therefore, that r_k divides each r_i and finally that it is a common divisor of b and a. But any common divisor of a and b divides r_1, and by the second step it also divides r_2. Proceeding in this manner, we see that any common divisor of a and b divides r_k. Therefore, r_k is the greatest common divisor of a and b.

The first step of the algorithm shows that r_1 can be expressed linearly

* *Ibid.*, p. 233.

in terms of a and b, for

$$r_1 = a - m_1 b$$

Moreover, $r_2 = b - m_2 r_1$, so that $r_2 = b - m_2(a - m_1 b) = (1 + m_1 m_2)b - m_2 a$. Thus from the equations

$$r_{i-1} = M_1 a + M_2 b$$
$$r_i = N_1 a + N_2 b$$

we see that since

$$r_{i+1} = r_{i-1} - m_{i+1} r_i$$

then

$$r_{i+1} = Q_1 a + Q_2 b$$

Hence, as was shown by a different method in Chap. 2, r_k, the greatest common divisor of a and b, can be expressed as a linear function of a and b with integral coefficients.

In the special case where $b \mid a$ so that $r_1 = 0$, it is evident that b is the greatest common divisor of a and b and that $b = a(0) + b(1)$.

By applying the unique factorization theorem, it is also apparent that if the integers a_i, where $i = 1, 2, \ldots, n$, are factored into powers of distinct primes so that

$$a_i = \prod_{j=1}^{r} p_j^{m_{ij}}$$

the exponents being positive integers or zero, the greatest common divisor of the a_i is $\prod_{j=1}^{r} p_j^{s_j}$, where each s_j is the smallest exponent that occurs for p_j in the factorizations of the a_i.

Example. Find the greatest common divisor of 573 and 291.

$$573 = 291 + 282, \quad 291 = 282 + 9, \quad 282 = (31)(9) + 3, \quad 9 = (3)(3)$$

Hence, the greatest common divisor is 3.

EXERCISES

1. Find the greatest common divisor of 5040 and 4704.

2. Express the greatest common divisor of 168 and 525 as a linear function of these numbers.

3. If $d = (a, b)$, then d is the number of integers in the sequence $a, 2a, 3a, \ldots, ba$ that are divisible by b. Prove it.

4. Show that the sum of a finite number of rational fractions in their lowest terms cannot be an integer if the denominators are prime each to each.

5. Prove that two integers having the form $2^{2^n} + 1$ are relatively prime. From this fact develop another proof that there are infinitely many primes. (Integers of the form $2^{2^n} + 1$ are called *Fermat numbers*. He believed erroneously that the formula generated primes for all integral values of n.)

6. Prove that the number of divisions required to find the greatest common divisor of two positive integers written in the scale of 10 by means of the Euclidean algorithm does not exceed five times the number of digits in the smaller integer.

3-7. The Least Common Multiple

Theorem 3-9. If d is the greatest common divisor of the positive integers a and b so that $a = a_0 d$, $b = b_0 d$, the least common multiple of a and b is $a_0 b_0 d$.

Any common multiple of a and b is a multiple of a and therefore has the form ma. But it is also a multiple of $b = b_0 d$. Thus $b_0 d \mid m a_0 d$, and because $(a_0, b_0) = 1$, it follows that $b_0 \mid m$. Hence, any common multiple of a and b has the form $k a_0 b_0 d$.

However, $a_0 b_0 d \mid k a_0 b_0 d$, and in order that an integer be a common multiple of a and b, it is sufficient that it have the factors a_0 and $b_0 d$. Therefore, the positive common multiple of a and b that divides every common multiple is $a_0 b_0 d$.

Corollary 1. If a and b are relatively prime, their least common multiple is the positive associate of their product ab.

Corollary 2. An integer is the least common multiple of the nonzero integers a and b if and only if it is the smallest positive integer that is a common multiple of them.

Theorem 3-10. If the least common multiple of a_1 and a_2 is L_{12}, then the least common multiple of a_1, a_2, and a_3 is the least common multiple of L_{12} and a_3.

Let L be the least common multiple of L_{12} and a_3. Then L is a common multiple of a_1, a_2, and a_3. But any common multiple of a_1 and a_2 is a multiple of their least common multiple L_{12}. For the same reason, if besides being a multiple of L_{12} an integer is a multiple of a_3, it is a multiple of L. Thus any common multiple of a_1, a_2, and a_3 is a multiple of L. Therefore, L is the least common multiple of a_1, a_2, and a_3, for it is a common multiple of them, and it divides all their common multiples.

In like manner we can extend the theorem to show that:

Theorem 3-11. The least common multiple of the set of integers a_1, a_2, . . . , a_{n-1}, a_n is the least common multiple of a_n and the integer that is the least common multiple of the set a_1, a_2, . . . , a_{n-1}.

Corollary. Any common multiple of the nonzero integers a_1, a_2, . . . , a_n is a multiple of the smallest positive integer of which each a_i is a factor.

It is obvious that when $a_i = \prod_{j=1}^{r} p_j{}^{m_{ij}}$, where $i = 1, 2, . . . , n$, the least common multiple of the a_i is $\prod_{j=1}^{r} p_j{}^{G_j}$, where G_j is the exponent of the highest power of p_j occurring in the factorizations of the a_i.

EXERCISES

1. If $d = (a, b)$, where a and b are positive, show that ab is equal to the product of d and the least common multiple of a and b.

2. Show that if 2^k is the highest power of 2 that is a factor of an integer of the set 1, 2, 3, . . . , n, then that integer of the set that is a multiple of 2^k is 2^k itself and is the only integer in the set that is divisible by 2^k.

3. Prove that $\frac{1}{2} + \frac{1}{3} + \cdots + 1/n$ is not an integer.

4. A necessary and sufficient condition that a positive common multiple M of the nonzero integers a_i, where $i = 1, 2, \ldots , n$, be their least common multiple is that the quotients M/a_i be relatively prime. Prove it.

5. Show that the product of n positive integers is equal to the product of their least common multiple and the greatest common divisor of all possible products that can be formed by taking the integers $n - 1$ at a time.

6. If m_i, where $i = 1, 2, \ldots , r$, is a set of integers having $(m_i, m_j) = d_{ij}$, where $j = 1, 2, \ldots , r$, and if A_i is the least common multiple of $m_1, m_2, \ldots , m_{i-1}$, $m_{i+1}, \ldots$, and m_r, then the greatest common divisor of m_i and A_i is the least common multiple of $d_{i1}, d_{i2}, \ldots , d_{i,i-1}, d_{i,i+1}, \ldots , d_{ir}$.

3-8. The Divisors of an Integer.

When we refer to the number of divisors of an integer m, we mean the number of positive divisors of that integer and we designate it by $\tau(m)$. Thus $\tau(6) = \tau(-6) = 4$. We also use the symbol $\sigma(m)$ to represent the sum of the positive divisors of m.

It is evident that the number of divisors of a prime p is 2 and the sum of the divisors is just $p + 1$ if $p > 0$.

Moreover, the divisors of p^α are $1, p, p^2, \ldots , p^\alpha$, and so their number is $\alpha + 1$, and their sum is $1 + p + p^2 + \cdots + p^\alpha$.

Theorem 3-12. If $0 < m = p_1^{\alpha_1} p_2^{\alpha_2} \cdots p_r^{\alpha_r}$, the number of divisors of m is $(\alpha_1 + 1)(\alpha_2 + 1) \cdots (\alpha_r + 1)$ and the sum of the divisors of m is

$$\frac{p_1^{\alpha_1+1} - 1}{p_1 - 1} \cdot \frac{p_2^{\alpha_2+1} - 1}{p_2 - 1} \cdots \frac{p_r^{\alpha_r+1} - 1}{p_r - 1}$$

If $m = \prod_{i=1}^{r} p_i^{\alpha_i}$, it is evident that each divisor of m which is also a divisor of $p_1^{\alpha_1}$ is a term in the expression

$$1 + p_1 + p_1^2 + \cdots + p_1^{\alpha_1} \tag{1}$$

Moreover, only these terms are divisors of both m and $p_1^{\alpha_1}$. In like manner the terms of

$$1 + p_2 + p_2^2 + \cdots + p_2^{\alpha_2} \tag{2}$$

give all and only the divisors common to m and $p_2^{\alpha_2}$. If we multiply these two sums together, each of the terms of the result is a divisor of $p_1^{\alpha_1} p_2^{\alpha_2}$ and furthermore these terms give all the common divisors of $p_1^{\alpha_1} p_2^{\alpha_2}$ and m. This product of (1) and (2) is

$$1 + p_1 + p_1^2 + \cdots + p_1^{\alpha_1} + p_2 + p_1 p_2 + p_1^2 p_2 + \cdots +$$
$$p_1^{\alpha_1} p_2 + \cdots + p_1^{\alpha_1} p_2^{\alpha_2}$$

and it has $(\alpha_1 + 1)(\alpha_2 + 1)$ terms.

Continuing the reasoning in this manner, we see that the terms of the expansion of the product

$$(1 + p_1 + \cdots + p_1^{\alpha_1})(1 + p_2 + \cdots + p_2^{\alpha_2}) \cdots$$
$$(1 + p_r + \cdots + p_r^{\alpha_r}) \quad (3)$$

give all and only divisors of m. There are

$$\tau(m) = (\alpha_1 + 1)(\alpha_2 + 1) \cdots (\alpha_r + 1) = \prod_{i=1}^{r} (\alpha_i + 1)$$

terms in this result, and therefore that is the number of divisors of m.

The sum of the divisors of m is the sum of the terms in the same product (3) and is, therefore,

$$\sigma(m) = \prod_{i=1}^{r} (1 + p_i + \cdots + p_i^{\alpha_i}) = \prod_{i=1}^{r} \frac{p_i^{\alpha_i + 1} - 1}{p_i - 1}$$

EXERCISES

1. Prove that the sum of the nth powers of the divisors of $m = \prod_{i=1}^{r} p_i^{\alpha_i}$ is

$$\prod_{i=1}^{r} \frac{p_i^{n(\alpha_i + 1)} - 1}{p_i^n - 1}$$

2. Find the smallest positive integer with 6 divisors.

Since $6 = 6 \cdot 1 = 2 \cdot 3 = (\alpha_1 + 1)(\alpha_2 + 1)$, the exponents of the prime factors of the required number are either the pair 5, 0 or the pair 1, 2. Evidently $2^2 \cdot 3 = 12$ is smaller than 2^5.

3. Find some integers having 10 divisors.

4. Find the smallest positive integer with 15 divisors.

5. Prove that if $n = n_1 n_2$, with $n_1 \geq n_2 > 1$, so that both 2^{n-1} and $2^{n_1-1} 3^{n_2-1}$ have n divisors, then $2^{n-1} > 2^{n_1-1} 3^{n_2-1}$.

6. Prove that if $n = n_1 n_2 n_3$, with $1 < n_1 < n_2 < n_3$, then $2^{n_3-1} 3^{n_2-1} 5^{n_1-1}$ is less than $2^{n_2 n_3-1} 3^{n_1-1}$ and both have n divisors. Consider the cases in which $n_2 = n_3$, in which $n_1 = n_2$, and in which $n_1 = n_2 = n_3$.

7. Find by trial positive integers n such that the sum of the divisors of n is a perfect square.

8. Find all primes that are one less than a perfect square. Is there a prime that is one less than a perfect cube? Can you find a prime that is one less than n^4? Prove a general statement to cover these results.

9. Find by trial positive integers n such that the sum of the divisors of n is a multiple of n.

10. Prove that a positive integer is the sum of consecutive positive integers if and only if it is not a power of 2.

11. Prove that the number of divisors of a positive integer is odd or even according as the integer is or is not a square.

12. Prove that the product of the divisors of a positive integer n is $n^{s/2}$, where s is the number of divisors of n.

13. Prove that if r is the number of distinct prime factors of $n > 0$, the number of ways in which n can be factored into two relatively prime factors is 2^{r-1}.

3-9. Perfect Numbers. Examine the divisors of 6, and you will notice the interesting fact that their sum is 12. Observe also that the sum of the divisors of 28 is 56. A positive integer is said to be *perfect* if the sum of its divisors is double itself. Besides 6 and 28, the integers 496, 8128, 130,816, 2,096,128, and 33,550,336 are perfect. Notice that all these perfect numbers are even. Although no odd perfect number has ever been found, mathematicians have not been able to prove that none exists. It has been shown, however, that if one does exist, it is greater than 10 billion.* On the other hand, we can prove:

Theorem 3-13. An even integer is perfect if and only if it has the form $2^{p-1}(2^p - 1)$, where $2^p - 1$ is a prime.

If an integer is of the given form, which is due to Euclid, the sum of its divisors is

$$(1 + 2 + \cdots + 2^{p-1})(1 + 2^p - 1) = 2^p(2^p - 1)$$

and hence the integer is perfect.

The converse was first proved by Euler, but we shall present a method due essentially to L. E. Dickson. Assume that m is of the form $2^k q$, where q is odd. If, further, m is perfect, by letting s represent the sum of all the divisors of q except q itself, we have

$$2^{k+1}q = (2^{k+1} - 1)(q + s)$$

But $2^{k+1} - 1$ is odd, and hence 2^{k+1} divides $q + s$, so that

$$q + s = 2^{k+1}n$$

Upon substituting this value in the first equation, we obtain

$$q = (2^{k+1} - 1)n$$

Consequently, n is a divisor of q. But by subtracting q from $q + s$ we find that $s = n$. Now let us suppose that $s = n = q$. Then the equation $q = (2^{k+1} - 1)q$ gives $1 = 2^{k+1} - 1$, and $k = 0$. In this case the original integer $2^k q$ would not be even. But if we suppose that n is a divisor of q that is not q and not 1, then $n = s$ is at least the sum of the divisors n and 1. However, it is impossible that $n \geq n + 1$. Accordingly, $n = 1$, and the only divisors of q are q and 1. Thus q is a prime. Since $q = 2^{k+1} - 1$, the exponent $k + 1$ is a prime. Therefore, every even perfect number has the form $2^{p-1}(2^p - 1)$, in which both $2^p - 1$ and p are primes.

* A. Brauer, *Bull. Am. Math. Soc.*, Vol. 49, No. 10, pp. 712–718, 1943. H. A. Bernhard, *Am. Math. Monthly*, Vol. 56, No. 9, pp. 628–629, 1949.

Integers of the form $2^p - 1$ with p a prime less than or equal to 257 are called *Mersenne numbers** after the mathematician Marin Mersenne, who lived from 1588 to 1648. Mersenne was interested in discovering which of these numbers $2^p - 1$ are primes and made certain decisions about their primality even though he lacked the modern facilities for testing numbers of this magnitude. It has taken many years to decide that exactly 12† of the Mersenne numbers are primes. In 1944, six Mersenne numbers corresponding to the primes $p = 157, 167, 193, 199, 227$, and 229 remained to be tested. The tremendous task of investigating the character of these 6 numbers was carried out by H. S. Uhler. He completed the work in 1947, finding no prime among them. We now know that only the primes $p = 2, 3, 5, 7, 13, 17, 19, 31, 61, 89, 107$, and 127 determine Mersenne primes of the form $2^p - 1$ and hence that only these 12 Mersenne numbers yield perfect numbers. The largest of these perfect numbers has 77 digits‡ when written in the scale of 10.

The author is indebted to D. H. Lehmer for the information that during the year 1952 it was demonstrated by the electronic calculator SWAC that $2^p - 1$ is prime for $p = 521, 607, 1279, 2203$, and 2281. Consequently, five more integers are now known to be perfect. It is particularly interesting to notice the large gaps between some of these primes.

Doubtless you have noticed that each of the first seven perfect numbers given above ends in 6 or 28. It has been proved that all perfect numbers of Euclid's type end in this way.

A *multiply perfect number* is an integer n the sum of whose positive divisors is a multiple of n. The first integer n the sum of whose divisors is $3n$ is 120. Fermat found the second one, which is 672. The third is 523,776. The first integer the sum of whose divisors is four times itself is 30,240. Recently some new multiply perfect numbers have been discovered.§

Two integers are said to be *amicable* if their sum is the sum of the divisors of each one. The smallest pair of amicable numbers is 220 and 284. Another pair, 17,296 and 18,416, was found by Fermat.

3-10. Scales of Notation. Have you thought of 5347 in the form of the polynomial $5x^3 + 3x^2 + 4x + 7$, where $x = 10$?

Theorem 3-14. Any positive integer m can be written uniquely in the form $m = a_0 r^n + a_1 r^{n-1} + \cdots + a_n$, where $r > 1$ and the coefficients are such that $0 < a_0 < r$ and $0 \leq a_i < r$ for $i = 1, 2, \ldots, n$.

* R. C. Archibald, *Scripta Mathematica*, Vol. 3, No. 2, pp. 112–119, 1937.

† D. H. Lehmer, *Bull. Am. Math. Soc.*, Vol. 53, No. 2, pp. 164–169, 1947. H. S. Uhler, *Bull. Am. Math. Soc.*, Vol. 53, No. 2, pp. 163–164, 1947; *ibid.*, Vol. 54, No. 4, pp. 378–380, 1948; *Scripta Mathematica*, Vol. 18, No. 2, pp. 122–131, 1952; *Proc. Natl. Acad. Sci. U.S.*, Vol. 34, No. 3, pp. 102–103, 1948.

‡ H. Gupta, *Am. Math. Monthly*, Vol. 42, No. 3, pp. 163–164, 1935.

§ B. Franqui and M. Garcia, *Am. Math. Monthly*, Vol. 60, No. 7, pp. 459–462, 1953.

When m is written in the form $a_0 r^n + a_1 r^{n-1} + \cdots + a_n$ with the conditions designated in the theorem, m is said to be expressed in the *scale* of r and r is called the *base*, or *radix*.

For a given m and $r > 1$, we know that

$$m = q_1 r + a_n$$
$$q_1 = q_2 r + a_{n-1}$$
$$\cdot \cdot \cdot \cdot \cdot \cdot \cdot \cdot$$
$$q_i = q_{i+1} r + a_{n-i}$$
$$\cdot \cdot \cdot \cdot \cdot \cdot \cdot \cdot \cdot$$
$$q_{n-1} = q_n r + a_1$$
$$q_n = a_0$$

where $0 \leq a_i < r$, for $i = 1, 2, \ldots, n$. Furthermore, we must finally arrive at q_n, which is positive and less than r, because $m > q_1 > q_2 > \cdots > 0$. Then

$$q_{n-1} = a_0 r + a_1$$
$$q_{n-2} = a_0 r^2 + a_1 r + a_2$$
$$\cdot \cdot \cdot \cdot \cdot \cdot \cdot \cdot \cdot \cdot \cdot$$
$$m = a_0 r^n + a_1 r^{n-1} + \cdots + a_n$$

This representation is unique, for if $n \geq s$ and

$$a_0 r^n + a_1 r^{n-1} + \cdots + a_n = b_0 r^s + b_1 r^{s-1} + \cdots + b_s$$

with $0 \leq b_j < r$ and $j = 0, 1, \ldots, s$, then

$$r(a_0 r^{n-1} + \cdots + a_{n-1} - b_0 r^{s-1} - \cdots - b_{s-1}) = b_s - a_n$$

Therefore, r divides $b_s - a_n$, and $b_s = a_n$. Continuing in this manner, we find that each $b_{s-j} = a_{n-j}$, until, if $n = s$, we have $b_0 = a_0$, but if $n > s$, $b_0 = a_{n-s}$, and then

$$a_0 r^{n-s-1} + \cdots + a_{n-s-1} = 0$$

Since $r > 0$, the remaining coefficients must all be 0 and the representation is unique.

It is on the basis of this theorem that we know we can write an integer in just one way in the Hindu-Arabic system, which uses the scale of 10 and the digits 0, 1, 2, 3, 4, 5, 6, 7, 8, and 9. The integer 363 in the ordinary scale becomes 2423 in the scale of 5, while it is 101,101,011 in the scale of 2.

Corollary. Any positive integer n can be expressed in one and only one way as a sum of distinct powers of 2.

We can apply this corollary to show that for weighing approximately any load not exceeding 127 lb but seven weights of 1, 2, 4, 8, 16, 32, and 64 lb each are needed for the scales, for 127 is written 1,111,111 in the scale of 2.

It is interesting to notice that the Egyptians recognized that an integer can be expressed as a sum of powers of 2 and that they made use of this fact in doing multiplication. Suppose, for instance, that 237 was to be multiplied by 45. They would first determine that $45 = 32 + 8 + 4 + 1$ and then compute the corresponding multiples of 237 by the process of doubling. Accordingly, the calculations would be:

1	237
2	474
4	948
8	1896
16	3792
32	7584

Then all that was necessary was to find the sum, $237 + 948 + 1896 + 7584 = 10,665.$

They carried out division in a similar manner. If 539 was to be divided by 41, they used the process of doubling on the divisor until they could find suitable multiples of it which, when added, would give a result smaller than 539 but less than 41 units from it. Their work might be indicated as follows:

1	41
2	82
4	164
8	328

But $328 + 164 + 41 = 533$, and so $539 = 8(41) + 4(41) + 1(41) + 6$, or $539 = 13(41) + 6.$

The digital idea is the basis for many of our computing machines. Indeed even the abacus, which was probably the earliest mathematical machine, makes use of it. Each rod of the abacus corresponds to the place a digit occupies when the number is written in the scale of 10, and the beads on the rods correspond to the digits. Corresponding to the digital places, some of the calculating machines use the contrivance of a series of gearwheels that rotate when certain levers are pressed. Each such cogwheel has 10 teeth to correspond to the 10 digits, and upon a complete rotation of a given wheel there is a mechanism that turns the wheel corresponding to the next higher digital place through one-tenth of a rotation.

In setting up some of the modern electrical calculating machines it has been found practical to use the binary rather than the denary system of notation. In spite of the increased number of digital positions necessary for representing any number greater than one in the scale of 2 as compared with the scale of 10, fewer electronic tubes are required by machines constructed on the basis of this system, for but two digits, 0 and 1, are needed in each position. The mechanism is, therefore, decidedly simpler. The calculator at the Institute for Advanced Study in Princeton is of this type.*

EXERCISES

1. Prove that any positive integer can be expressed uniquely as a sum of distinct powers of 3 with coefficient -1, 0, or $+1$. From this representation show that a set of five weights is sufficient to weigh any load of at most 121 lb if a balance scale having two pans is used.

2. Set up multiplication tables for the scale of 5. Then write 42 and 352 in the scale of 5, and find their product when they are so written. Check the answer by converting the result to the ordinary scale of 10.

3. If 42 and 352 are in the scale of 6, find their sum and product in that scale.

4. Explain the ordinary process of multiplication by writing 382 and 73 as polynomials in 10 and finding the product of the polynomials.

5. In what scale is 374 written if it is the square of an integer?

6. Prove that the fraction a/b with $(a, b) = 1$ and $a < b$ can be expressed uniquely in decimal form. Show that the decimal either terminates or repeats in cycles of not more than $b - 1$ digits. For what values of b will the decimal terminate?

7. If $(a, b) = 1$ with $a < b$ and if in calculating the value of a/b in decimal form a remainder $b - a$ occurs, show that half of the repeating cycle of digits has been found and that the remainder of the cycle can be determined by finding in order the differences between 9 and the digits already established.

3-11. The Highest Power of a Prime That Is a Factor of $n!$.

If a is a positive integer, $\left[\dfrac{n}{a}\right]$ is the largest integer α such that $\alpha a \leq n$. This definition is equivalent to saying that $\left[\dfrac{n}{a}\right] = \alpha$, where $n = \alpha a + r$ with $0 \leq r < a$. Thus $\left[\dfrac{12}{5}\right] = 2$, and $\left[\dfrac{-12}{5}\right] = -3$.

Theorem 3-15. For any a and b greater than 0,

$$\left[\frac{\left[\dfrac{n}{a}\right]}{b}\right] = \left[\frac{n}{ab}\right]$$

Let $\left[\dfrac{n}{a}\right] = \alpha$ and $\left[\dfrac{\alpha}{b}\right] = \beta$, so that

$$n = \alpha a + r_1 \qquad 0 \leq r_1 < a$$
$$\alpha = \beta b + r_2 \qquad 0 \leq r_2 < b$$

Therefore,

$$n = \beta ab + a r_2 + r_1$$

---

* Mathematical Machines, *Sci. American*, April, 1949, pp. 29–39.

and

$$\left[\frac{n}{ab}\right] = \beta + \left[\frac{ar_2 + r_1}{ab}\right]$$

However, r_2 is at most $b - 1$, and r_1 is at most $a - 1$, and thus $ar_2 + r_1$ is at most $a(b - 1) + a - 1 = ab - 1$. Therefore,

$$\left[\frac{n}{ab}\right] = \beta = \left[\frac{\alpha}{b}\right]$$

Corollary 1. If p is a positive prime,

$$\left[\frac{\left[\frac{n}{p^s}\right]}{p^t}\right] = \left[\frac{n}{p^{s+t}}\right]$$

Corollary 2. If $n \geq a > 0$ and $b > 1$, then

$$\left[\frac{n}{a}\right] > \left[\frac{n}{ab}\right]$$

Corollary 3. If m, n, and a are positive,

$$\left[\frac{mn}{a}\right] \geq m\left[\frac{n}{a}\right]$$

Corollary 4. If $n = n_1 + n_2 + \cdots + n_t$, where the n_i, for $i = 1$, $2, \ldots, t$, are positive, then $\left[\frac{n}{a}\right] \geq \left[\frac{n_1}{a}\right] + \left[\frac{n_2}{a}\right] + \cdots + \left[\frac{n_t}{a}\right]$.

Letting $\left[\frac{n_i}{a}\right] = \alpha_i$, we have $n_i = \alpha_i a + r_i$ with $0 \leq r_i < a$. Therefore,

$$n = (\alpha_1 + \alpha_2 + \cdots + \alpha_t)a + r_1 + r_2 + \cdots + r_t$$

and

$$\left[\frac{n}{a}\right] = \alpha_1 + \alpha_2 + \cdots + \alpha_t + \left[\frac{r_1 + \cdots + r_t}{a}\right]$$

Hence,

$$\left[\frac{n}{a}\right] \geq \left[\frac{n_1}{a}\right] + \left[\frac{n_2}{a}\right] + \cdots + \left[\frac{n_t}{a}\right]$$

If p is a positive prime, let $E_p(m)$ be the exponent of the highest power of the prime p that is a divisor of m. Using this symbol, we shall prove the following theorem due to Legendre (1752–1833). It will help you to appreciate how $E_p(n!)$ increases as n increases.

Theorem 3-16. If both n and the prime p are positive, the exponent of the highest power of p that divides $n!$ is

$$E_p(n!) = \left[\frac{n}{p}\right] + \left[\frac{n}{p^2}\right] + \cdots + \left[\frac{n}{p^s}\right] \qquad \left[\frac{n}{p^{s+1}}\right] = 0$$

Consider the set of integers

$$1, 2, \ldots, p, \ldots, 2p, \ldots, p^k, \ldots, n \qquad (4)$$

The last integer of the set that is divisible by p is $\left[\dfrac{n}{p}\right] p$, and the coefficient of p shows that there are $\left[\dfrac{n}{p}\right]$ multiples of p in this set. All other integers of the set are prime to p. Hence,

$$E_p(n!) = E_p\left(p \cdot 2p \cdot \ \cdots \ \cdot p^k \cdot \ \cdots \ \cdot \left[\frac{n}{p}\right] p\right)$$

Now take out one factor p from each of these multiples of p that are in the set (4), thereby obtaining the factor $p^{\left[\frac{n}{p}\right]}$. Therefore,

$$E_p(n!) = \left[\frac{n}{p}\right] + E_p\left(1 \cdot 2 \cdot \ \cdots \ \cdot \left[\frac{n}{p}\right]\right)$$

But the last integer of the new set $1, 2, \ldots, \left[\dfrac{n}{p}\right]$ that is a multiple of p is

$\left[\dfrac{\left[\dfrac{n}{p}\right]}{p}\right] p = \left[\dfrac{n}{p^2}\right] p$. We can, as before, remove the factor $p^{\left[\frac{n}{p^2}\right]}$ from the product of the integers of the new set, showing that

$$E_p(n!) = \left[\frac{n}{p}\right] + \left[\frac{n}{p^2}\right] + E_p\left(1 \cdot 2 \cdot \ \cdots \ \cdot \left[\frac{n}{p^2}\right]\right)$$

Likewise, we remove the factors $p^{\left[\frac{n}{p^3}\right]}$, $p^{\left[\frac{n}{p^4}\right]}$, $\ldots$ until we find that $p^s \leq n < p^{s+1}$, so that $\left[\dfrac{n}{p^s}\right] \neq 0$, while $\left[\dfrac{n}{p^{s+1}}\right] = 0$. Therefore,

$$E_p(n!) = \left[\frac{n}{p}\right] + \left[\frac{n}{p^2}\right] + \cdots + \left[\frac{n}{p^s}\right]$$

Corollary. If $n = ab$, $E_p((ab)!) \geq aE_p(b!)$.

Theorem 3-17. If $n > 0$ is written in the scale of the prime p so that $n = a_0 p^s + \cdots + a_s$, then

$$E_p(n!) = \frac{n - \displaystyle\sum_{i=0}^{s} a_i}{p - 1}$$

Because $n = a_0p^s + a_1p^{s-1} + \cdots + a_s$ with $0 < a_0 < p$ and $0 \leq a_i < p$ for $i = 1, 2, \ldots, s$,

$$\left[\frac{n}{p}\right] = a_0p^{s-1} + a_1p^{s-2} + \cdots + a_{s-2}p + a_{s-1}$$

$$\left[\frac{n}{p^2}\right] = a_0p^{s-2} + a_1p^{s-3} + \cdots + a_{s-2}$$

$$\cdots \cdots \cdots \cdots \cdots$$

$$\left[\frac{n}{p^s}\right] = a_0$$

Therefore,

$$\left[\frac{n}{p}\right] + \cdots + \left[\frac{n}{p^s}\right] = a_0\frac{p^s - 1}{p - 1} + a_1\frac{p^{s-1} - 1}{p - 1} + \cdots + a_{s-1}$$

or

$$E_p(n!) = \frac{a_0p^s + a_1p^{s-1} + \cdots + a_{s-1}p - a_0 - a_1 - \cdots - a_{s-1}}{p - 1}$$

$$= \frac{a_0p^s + \cdots + a_{s-1}p + a_s - a_0 - \cdots - a_{s-1} - a_s}{p - 1}$$

$$= \frac{n - (a_0 + a_1 + \cdots + a_s)}{p - 1}$$

Example. Find the exponent of the highest power of 5 in 138!.

$138 = (27)5 + 3;$ $\left[\dfrac{138}{5}\right] = 27;$ $27 = (5)5 + 2;$ $\left[\dfrac{138}{5^2}\right] = 5;$ $5 = (1)5 + 0;$ $\left[\dfrac{138}{5^3}\right] = 1.$ Hence $E_5(138!) = 27 + 5 + 1 = 33.$

We may also use the second formula for $E_p(n!)$. Writing 138 in the scale of 5, we have $5^3 + 0(5^2) + 2(5) + 3$. Therefore $E_5(138!) = (138 - 6)/4 = 33.$

Theorem 3-18. The expression $n!/a_1!a_2! \cdots a_t!$, where $\sum_{i=1}^{t} a_i = n$, is an integer.

We shall show that $n!/a_1!a_2! \cdots a_t!$ is an integer by proving that the highest power of any prime contained in the denominator is at least equaled by the highest power of that prime contained in the numerator. We know that

$$E_p(n!) = \left[\frac{n}{p}\right] + \left[\frac{n}{p^2}\right] + \cdots + \left[\frac{n}{p^k}\right] + \cdots$$

$$+ \left[\frac{n}{p^s}\right] \qquad \left[\frac{n}{p^{s+1}}\right] = 0 \quad (5)$$

Since $a_1 + a_2 + \cdots + a_t = n$, if p^{s+1} exceeds n, it exceeds each a_i, and therefore $\left[\dfrac{a_i}{p^{s+1}}\right] = 0$ for $i = 1, 2, \ldots, t$. Hence,

$$E_p(a_1!) = \left[\frac{a_1}{p}\right] + \left[\frac{a_1}{p^2}\right] + \cdots + \left[\frac{a_1}{p^k}\right] + \cdots + \left[\frac{a_1}{p^s}\right]$$

where, of course, some $\left[\dfrac{a_1}{p^m}\right]$, for $m < s + 1$, may be 0, in which case all the integers that follow it in the sum are also 0. Likewise,

$$E_p(a_2!) = \left[\frac{a_2}{p}\right] + \cdots + \left[\frac{a_2}{p^k}\right] + \cdots + \left[\frac{a_2}{p^s}\right]$$

$$\cdots \cdots \cdots \cdots \cdots \cdots \cdots \cdots \cdots \cdots \cdots \cdots$$

$$E_p(a_t!) = \left[\frac{a_t}{p}\right] + \cdots + \left[\frac{a_t}{p^k}\right] + \cdots + \left[\frac{a_t}{p^s}\right] \tag{6}$$

But by Corollary 4 above,

$$\left[\frac{n}{p^k}\right] \geq \left[\frac{a_1}{p^k}\right] + \left[\frac{a_2}{p^k}\right] + \cdots + \left[\frac{a_t}{p^k}\right]$$

As a result of summing by columns the expressions (6) for the $E_p(a_i!)$, we conclude from Eq. (5) that

$$E_p(n!) \geq E_p(a_1!) + E_p(a_2!) + \cdots + E_p(a_t!)$$

and thus the given expression is an integer.

Corollary 1. The product of any n consecutive positive integers is divisible by $n!$.

The expression $k(k + 1)(k + 2) \cdots (k + n - 1)/n! = (k + n - 1)!/(k - 1)!n!$ and therefore is an integer.

This corollary shows that the coefficients in the expansion of $(a + b)^n$ with n a positive integer are themselves integers, a fact otherwise known from the multiplication itself. As a matter of fact Theorem 3-18 proves that the coefficients in the expansion of $(b_1 + b_2 + \cdots + b_r)^n$, for $n > 0$, obtained by means of the multinomial theorem are integers, for any term of the expansion takes the form

$$\frac{n!}{a_1!a_2! \cdots a_r!} b_1{}^{a_1}b_2{}^{a_2} \cdots b_r{}^{a_r}$$

where $a_1 + a_2 + \cdots + a_r = n$.

In particular it is now evident that:

Corollary 2. If p is a positive prime, all the coefficients of $(b_1 + b_2 + \cdots + b_r)^p$ except the coefficients of the $b_i{}^p$, where $i = 1, 2, \ldots, r$, are multiples of p.

The expression $p!/a_1!a_2! \cdots a_r!$, with $a_1 + a_2 + \cdots + a_r = p$, is an integer, and furthermore since each a_i either is positive and less than p or is 0, there is no factor p in the denominator. Hence, $(p-1)!/a_1!a_2! \cdots a_r! = M$ is an integer, and the required coefficient is Mp.

EXERCISES

1. If $a^p - b^p$, where p is a positive prime, is divisible by p, prove that it is divisible by p^2.

2. Prove that if m, n, and a are positive integers,

$$\left[\frac{2m}{a}\right] + \left[\frac{2n}{a}\right] \geq \left[\frac{m}{a}\right] + \left[\frac{n}{a}\right] + \left[\frac{m+n}{a}\right]$$

3. If x is a real number and $[x]$ is the largest integer that is less than or equal to x, show that:

　　a. $[(1 + \sqrt{3})^n]$, for $n \geq 0$, is odd or even according as n is even or odd.

　　b. $[(1 + \sqrt{3})^{2n}] + 1$ is divisible by 2^{n+1} for $n \geq 0$.

　　c. $[(3 + \sqrt{5})^n] + 1$ is divisible by 2^n.

4. For which values of n is $[4^n - (2 + \sqrt{2})^n]$ divisible by 112?

5. Is there a positive integer n such that 3^{200} is the highest power of 3 contained in $n!$?

Applying Theorem 3-17, let $(n-1)/2 = 200$, for the sum of the coefficients of the powers of 3 necessary to express n in the scale of 3 is at least 1. Then n is at least 401. But the highest power of 3 contained in 401! is 3^{196}. However, 402 has the factor 3, so that 402!, 403!, and 404! have the factor 3^{197}, but 405 has the factor 3^4, so that 405! has the factor 3^{201}. Hence, there is no n such that $n!$ has the factor required.

6. Find a positive integer n such that 5^{19} is the highest power of 5 contained in $n!$.

7. Show that 95! ends with 22 zeros. With how many zeros does 100! end?

8. Find the highest power of 12 contained in 500!.

9. Prove that the exponent of the highest power of 3 contained in $(3^r - 2)!$ is $(3^r - 2r - 1)/2$.

10. Find the exponent of the highest power of 5 that is a factor of $(5^r - 1)!$.

11. If $m > 0$ and $\tau(m)$ means the number of positive divisors of m, show that

$$\tau(1) + \tau(2) + \cdots + \tau(n) = \left[\frac{n}{1}\right] + \left[\frac{n}{2}\right] + \cdots + \left[\frac{n}{n}\right]$$

12. If $m > 0$ and $\sigma(m)$ is the sum of the positive divisors of m, prove that

$$\sigma(1) + \sigma(2) + \cdots + \sigma(n) = \left[\frac{n}{1}\right] + 2\left[\frac{n}{2}\right] + 3\left[\frac{n}{3}\right] + \cdots + n\left[\frac{n}{n}\right]$$

13. When $a > 0$ and $b > 0$, prove that if $m = ab$, then $m!$ is divisible by $(a!)^b$.

14. If $m = ab$ with a and b positive integers, prove that $m!$ is divisible by the least common multiple of $(a!)^b$ and $(b!)^a$.

15. Prove that when $(m, n) = 1$ and m and n are positive integers,

$$\frac{(m+n-1)!}{m!n!}$$

is an integer.

16. Prove that when m and n are positive integers,

$$\frac{(2m)!(2n)!}{m!n!(m+n)!}$$

is an integer.

17. If $n = a_1 + a_2 + \cdots + a_r$ with all $a_i > 0$ and $(a_1, a_2, \ldots, a_r) = d$, then

$$\frac{d(n-1)!}{a_1! a_2! \cdots a_r!}$$

is an integer.

18. If m, n, and a are positive integers, under what conditions will

$$\left[\frac{mn}{a}\right] \geq \left[\frac{n}{a}\right] + n\left[\frac{m}{a}\right]$$

19. Prove that $(x-1)(x^2-1) \cdots (x^r-1)$ is a factor of $(x^n-1)(x^{n+1}-1)$ $\cdots (x^{n+r-1}-1)$ when n is a positive integer.

3-12. Some Theorems on Primes.

We have already found some polynomials like $4x - 1$ that represent an infinite number of primes for integral values of x, but we have noticed that not all the values of these polynomials obtained when integers are substituted for the variable are primes. For instance, $4x - 1$ gives 15 when $x = 4$. The polynomial $x^2 - x + 41$ is extraordinary, for it produces primes for $x = 0, \pm 1, \pm 2, \pm 3, \ldots, \pm 39$, and 40. Mathematicians have not yet produced an integral polynomial of the second degree in one variable that can be shown to represent an infinite number of primes, nor have they proved that such a polynomial does not exist. On the other hand, certain quadratic forms represent an infinitude of primes.

If $f(x)$ is a function of x whose value is a prime whenever x is a positive integer, then $f(x)$ is a *prime-representing function*.

Mathematicians have recently developed prime-representing functions* that require the symbol $[x]$, denoting the largest integer less than or equal to x, but it is interesting to observe that no algebraic expression that represents an infinite number of distinct primes, and only primes, has been discovered. Euler $(1707-1783)$ showed that Fermat $(1601-1665)$ was in error in thinking that all integers of the form $2^{2^n} + 1$ are primes by showing that $2^{32} + 1 = 4,294,967,297$ has the factor 641. It has been proved, however, that no rational function of x except a constant can be a prime-representing function.† We shall prove the corresponding well-known theorem about a polynomial.

Theorem 3-19. An integral polynomial of at least the first degree cannot represent primes alone.

Suppose that, for $x = x'$, where $x' > 0$, $f(x) = a_0 x^n + \cdots + a_n$ represents the prime p. Substituting $x = x' + mp$ in $f(x)$, we obtain

$$f(x' + mp) = a_0(x' + mp)^n + a_1(x' + mp)^{n-1} + \cdots + a_n$$

where the coefficients in the expansions are integers and in each expansion

---

* W. H. Mills, *Bull. Am. Math. Soc.*, Vol. 53, No. 6, p. 604, 1947. E. M. Wright, *Am. Math. Monthly*, Vol. 58, No. 9, pp. 616–618, 1951.

† R. C. Buck, *Am. Math. Monthly*, Vol. 53, No. 5, p. 265, 1946.

every term except the first is a multiple of p. Therefore,

$$f(x' + mp) = a_0 x'^n + a_1 x'^{n-1} + \cdots + a_n + Kp$$

or

$$f(x' + mp) = p + Kp$$

Hence, $p \mid f(x' + mp)$, and $f(x' + mp)$ is not a prime unless $f(x' + mp)$ is p or $-p$. Suppose that, for $m = 0, 1, 2, \ldots, n - 1$, $f(x' + mp) = p$. Then no other value of m can yield p, or the equation $f(x) = p$ of degree n would have more than n roots. In like manner, but n values of m can yield $-p$. Consequently, there is a value of m for which $x' + mp > 0$ and $f(x' + mp) \neq \pm p$.

Moreover, if the integral polynomial $f(x_1, x_2, \ldots, x_n)$ represented primes alone, then for $x_2 = a_2, \ldots, x_n = a_n$ the integral polynomial $f(x_1, a_2, \ldots, a_n)$ having but one variable would represent primes for all positive values of x_1. The given polynomial is thus not a prime-representing function.

In the proof given above it has been necessary to refer to the theorem on the number of roots of a rational integral algebraic equation which depends upon analysis for its validity. A property of the whole set of complex numbers is accordingly made use of in order to show a characteristic of the rational integers. Such cases, in which we use a domain that includes as part of itself the one with which we are particularly concerned, are not rare in mathematics. Can you name some of them?

EXERCISE

Prove that for integral values of x an integral polynomial $a_0 x^n + a_1 x^{n-1} + \cdots + a_n$ of degree $n > 0$ has an infinite number of distinct prime factors. (Assuming the number is finite, substitute multiples of $a_n \displaystyle\prod_{i=1}^{k} p_i$ for x.)

*Theorem 3-20 (Legendre). The number of positive primes not exceeding the positive integer n is

$$\pi(n) = n + r - 1 - \sum_{i=1}^{r} \left[\frac{n}{p_i} \right] + \sum_{\substack{i,j=1 \\ i<j}}^{r} \left[\frac{n}{p_i p_j} \right] - \cdots$$

$$+ (-1)^r \left[\frac{n}{p_1 p_2 \cdots p_r} \right]$$

where $p_1, p_2, \ldots, p_r$ are all the positive primes such that $p_i^2 \leq n$, where $i = 1, 2, \ldots, r$.

Determine I so that I is the largest integer whose square is less than or equal to n. Then find all positive primes $p_1, p_2, \ldots, p_r$ that are less

than or equal to I. Since exactly $M_1 = \left[\dfrac{n}{p_1}\right]$ of the integers $1, 2, \ldots,$
n are divisible by p_1, none of these multiples of p_1, except p_1 itself, is a
prime. In like manner, $\left[\dfrac{n}{p_2}\right]$ integers from 1 through n are divisible by
p_2. Of these multiples of p_2, however, $\left[\dfrac{n}{p_1 p_2}\right]$ are divisible by both p_1
and p_2, and hence

$$M_2 = \left[\frac{n}{p_1}\right] + \left[\frac{n}{p_2}\right] - \left[\frac{n}{p_1 p_2}\right]$$

is the number of integers from 1 through n that are divisible by either of
the first two primes, p_1 and p_2.

Assuming then that

$$M_k = \left[\frac{n}{p_1}\right] + \cdots + \left[\frac{n}{p_k}\right] - \left[\frac{n}{p_1 p_2}\right] - \left[\frac{n}{p_1 p_3}\right] - \cdots - \left[\frac{n}{p_{k-1} p_k}\right]$$
$$+ \left[\frac{n}{p_1 p_2 p_3}\right] + \cdots + (-1)^{k-1} \left[\frac{n}{p_1 p_2 \cdots p_k}\right] \quad (7)$$

is the number of integers from 1 through n that are divisible by at least
one of the first k primes $p_1, p_2, \ldots, p_k$, we shall find the number of
integers from 1 through n that are divisible by the next prime p_{k+1} and
that are prime to all the first k primes.

The number of integers from 1 through n that are divisible by p_{k+1} is
$\left[\dfrac{n}{p_{k+1}}\right]$. Of these integers, $\left[\dfrac{\left[\dfrac{n}{p_{k+1}}\right]}{p_1}\right]$ are also divisible by p_1, for if we
examine the set of multiples of p_{k+1},

$$p_{k+1}, 2p_{k+1}, \ldots, \left[\frac{n}{p_{k+1}}\right] p_{k+1}$$

the coefficients of p_{k+1}, which are $1, 2, \ldots, \left[\dfrac{n}{p_{k+1}}\right]$, determine whether
or not the integers are divisible by p_1. Likewise, if we wish to determine
how many of these integers are divisible by $p_1, p_2, \ldots,$ or p_r, we must
operate on $\left[\dfrac{n}{p_{k+1}}\right]$ just as we operated on n above. Hence,

$$M_k' = \left[\frac{\left[\dfrac{n}{p_{k+1}}\right]}{p_1}\right] + \cdots + \left[\frac{\left[\dfrac{n}{p_{k+1}}\right]}{p_k}\right] - \left[\frac{\left[\dfrac{n}{p_{k+1}}\right]}{p_1 p_2}\right] - \cdots$$
$$- \left[\frac{\left[\dfrac{n}{p_{k+1}}\right]}{p_{k-1} p_k}\right] + \cdots + (-1)^{k-1} \left[\frac{\left[\dfrac{n}{p_{k+1}}\right]}{p_1 p_2 \cdots p_k}\right]$$

is the number of integers from 1 through n that are divisible by p_{k+1} and also by at least one of the primes p_1, p_2, . . . , p_k. Using the fact that

$$\frac{\left[\dfrac{n}{p_{k+1}}\right]}{p_1 p_2 \, \cdot \, \cdot \, p_t} = \left[\frac{n}{p_1 p_2 \, \cdot \, \cdot \, p_t p_{k+1}}\right]$$

and subtracting M'_k from $\left[\dfrac{n}{p_{k+1}}\right]$, we have

$$\left[\frac{n}{p_{k+1}}\right] - \left[\frac{n}{p_1 p_{k+1}}\right] - \cdot \cdot \cdot - \left[\frac{n}{p_k p_{k+1}}\right] + \left[\frac{n}{p_1 p_2 p_{k+1}}\right] + \cdot \cdot \cdot$$
$$+ \, (-1)^k \left[\frac{n}{p_1 \, \cdot \, \cdot \, p_k p_{k+1}}\right] \quad (8)$$

as the number of integers from 1 through n that are divisible by p_{k+1} but not by any of the primes p_1, p_2, . . . , p_k. Adding this number (8) to the number (7) of integers from 1 through n that are divisible by at least one of p_1, p_2, . . . , p_k, we find that

$$M_{k+1} = \left[\frac{n}{p_1}\right] + \cdot \cdot \cdot + \left[\frac{n}{p_k}\right] + \left[\frac{n}{p_{k+1}}\right] - \left[\frac{n}{p_1 p_2}\right] - \cdot \cdot \cdot$$
$$- \left[\frac{n}{p_k p_{k+1}}\right] + \cdot \cdot \cdot + (-1)^k \left[\frac{n}{p_1 p_2 \, \cdot \, \cdot \, p_k p_{k+1}}\right]$$

is the number of integers from 1 through n that are divisible by at least one of the primes p_1, p_2, . . . , p_k, p_{k+1}. This formula (7) with $k = r$, therefore, holds for the first r primes. But by Theorem 3-2 any positive integer less than or equal to n and greater than p_r is a prime unless it is divisible by one of these first r primes. Hence, $n - M_r$ is the number of integers from 1 through n that are prime to p_1, p_2, . . . , and p_r. Consequently, this number counts the integer 1 and all primes greater than p_r, but it does not include the primes p_1, p_2, . . . , p_r themselves. Therefore

$$\pi(n) = n - M_r + r - 1$$

is the number of positive primes that are less than or equal to n.

Sometimes the symbol $\phi(n,r)$ is used to indicate the number of positive integers not exceeding n and prime to the first r primes. Then $\phi(n,r) = n - M_r$, and the number of positive primes not exceeding n can be written

$$\pi(n) = \phi(n,r) + r - 1$$

where r is the number of positive primes not exceeding $\sqrt{n}$.

This formula obviously becomes impracticable when n is large. In 1870 Meissel developed another formula the use of which is less cumbersome, but even though his method has been improved upon,* no expeditious method for finding the exact number of positive primes less than a large n has been discovered.

On the other hand, due to the work of Legendre and Gauss (1777–1855) in applying analysis to the theory of numbers, we have formulas which approximate the number of primes not exceeding x. Legendre stated the empirical formula

$$F(x) = \frac{x}{\log x - 1.08366}$$

which agrees very well with $\pi(x)$ so long as x is not greater than 1,000,000. Gauss discovered "the integral logarithm of x,"

$$\text{Li } (x) = \int_2^x \frac{dt}{\log t}$$

but we have no reason to believe that he developed a proof of it. Basing their work on that of Riemann (1826–1866), mathematicians succeeded in developing an asymptotic formula that is a refinement of Gauss' observation. By 1900 they had proved what is called "the prime number theorem,"

$$\lim_{x \to \infty} \frac{\pi(x)}{x/\log x} = 1$$

As recently as 1948 Paul Erdös and Atle Selberg developed new and more elementary methods for showing this limit.

As a matter of fact although many theorems about primes have been demonstrated, we can still state a large number of theories that mathematicians believe to be true but which remain unproved. We have seen that Euclid established an interval within which there must be a prime. Again it has been proved that if $p_1, p_2, \ldots, p_{n-1}$ are the first $n - 1$ primes, when $n > 4$, the next prime p_n is such that

$$p_n^2 < p_1 p_2 \cdots p_{n-1}$$

Furthermore, Tchebysheff (1821–1894) developed a better result by proving that for a real number $n > \frac{7}{2}$ there is always at least one prime between n and $2n - 2$. But the problem of naming the next prime after any given prime remains unsolved. Likewise, we have no formula for finding even one prime greater than a given one.

It has been previously pointed out that Dirichlet (1805–1859) proved that there is an infinite number of primes among the terms of any arithmetic progression in which the first term and the difference are relatively prime. Kronecker (1823–1891) later showed an interval within which the next prime after a given one of such a progression must lie.

* A. Brauer, *Am. Math. Monthly*, Vol. 53, No. 5, pp. 521–523, 1946.

Kronecker remarked, but there is no proof, that every positive even integer can be represented as the difference of two positive primes in infinitely many ways. If this theorem is true, it means that there are infinitely many pairs of primes that differ by 2, and hence no matter how far out we go in the sequence of consecutive positive integers there will always be primes that are as close to each other as it is possible for them to be. Of course the frequency of the appearance of such primes decreases as the primes increase in size. We can show, moreover, that if we take sufficiently large positive integers, we can find as many consecutive integers as we please all of which are composites, for none of the integers

$$n! + 2, n! + 3, \ldots , n! + n$$

is a prime when $n > 1$. Hence, as we move out in the sequence of positive integers, there must be consecutive primes whose difference is larger than any assigned integer.

Euler mentioned that Goldbach (1742) had stated the empirical theorem that every even integer greater than 2 can be represented as the sum of two positive primes. Although the truth of this conjecture has been verified in many cases, it has never been proved. Goldbach also said that every odd integer greater than or equal to 9 is the sum of three odd primes. In 1937 Vinogradov proved by analytical means that this theorem is true for sufficiently large odd integers.

If we examine a table of primes, we notice that there is at least one prime between any two consecutive squares n^2 and $(n + 1)^2$, but whether or not this statement is always true, we do not know. Again, we do not know whether or not there is an infinite number of primes of the form $(2n)^2 + 1$.

TABLE OF PRIMES

2	233	547	877	1229	1597	1993	2371	2749
3	239	557	881	1231	1601	1997	2377	2753
5	241	563	883	1237	1607	1999	2381	2767
7	251	569	887	1249	1609	2003	2383	2777
11	257	571	907	1259	1613	2011	2389	2789
13	263	577	911	1277	1619	2017	2393	2791
17	269	587	919	1279	1621	2027	2399	2797
19	271	593	929	1283	1627	2029	2411	2801
23	277	599	937	1289	1637	2039	2417	2803
29	281	601	941	1291	1657	2053	2423	2819
31	283	607	947	1297	1663	2063	2437	2833
37	293	613	953	1301	1667	2069	2441	2837
41	307	617	967	1303	1669	2081	2447	2843
43	311	619	971	1307	1693	2083	2459	2851
47	313	631	977	1319	1697	2087	2467	2857
53	317	641	983	1321	1699	2089	2473	2861
59	331	643	991	1327	1709	2099	2477	2879
61	337	647	997	1361	1721	2111	2503	2887
67	347	653	1009	1367	1723	2113	2521	2897
71	349	659	1013	1373	1733	2129	2531	2903
73	353	661	1019	1381	1741	2131	2539	2909
79	359	673	1021	1399	1747	2137	2543	2917
83	367	677	1031	1409	1753	2141	2549	2927
89	373	683	1033	1423	1759	2143	2551	2939
97	379	691	1039	1427	1777	2153	2557	2953
101	383	701	1049	1429	1783	2161	2579	2957
103	389	709	1051	1433	1787	2179	2591	2963
107	397	719	1061	1439	1789	2203	2593	2969
109	401	727	1063	1447	1801	2207	2609	2971
113	409	733	1069	1451	1811	2213	2617	2999
127	419	739	1087	1453	1823	2221	2621	3001
131	421	743	1091	1459	1831	2237	2633	3011
137	431	751	1093	1471	1847	2239	2647	3019
139	433	757	1097	1481	1861	2243	2657	3023
149	439	761	1103	1483	1867	2251	2659	3037
151	443	769	1109	1487	1871	2267	2663	3041
157	449	773	1117	1489	1873	2269	2671	3049
163	457	787	1123	1493	1877	2273	2677	3061
167	461	797	1129	1499	1879	2281	2683	3067
173	463	809	1151	1511	1889	2287	2687	3079
179	467	811	1153	1523	1901	2293	2689	3083
181	479	821	1163	1531	1907	2297	2693	3089
191	487	823	1171	1543	1913	2309	2699	3109
193	491	827	1181	1549	1931	2311	2707	3119
197	499	829	1187	1553	1933	2333	2711	3121
199	503	839	1193	1559	1949	2339	2713	3137
211	509	853	1201	1567	1951	2341	2719	3163
223	521	857	1213	1571	1973	2347	2729	3167
227	523	859	1217	1579	1979	2351	2731	3169
229	541	863	1223	1583	1987	2357	2741	3181

CHAPTER 4

PROPERTIES OF CONGRUENCES

4-1. Congruent Integers. We have shown that when n and $m \neq 0$ are given, the integer n can be expressed uniquely in the form

$$n = qm + r \qquad 0 \leq r < |m|$$

Now we separate all integers n into $|m|$ classes according to the remainders r that they yield upon being divided by m. We say that two integers are *congruent modulo m* if and only if the integers produce the same least nonnegative remainder upon being divided by $m \neq 0$.

Gauss (1777–1855) introduced this idea of congruence, and it was he who suggested the notation: $a \equiv b(\bmod\ m)$, which is read, "a is congruent to b modulo m," or "a is congruent to b for the modulus m." The value of this concept and its symbol is that emphasis is placed upon the important integers in the equations

$$a = q_1 m + r$$

and

$$b = q_2 m + r \qquad 0 \leq r < |m|$$

Since the definition requires that when $a \equiv b(\bmod\ m)$ the remainders in the above equations be identical, it follows immediately that the difference $a - b$ is divisible by m. Conversely, if $a - b = km$, then $a \equiv b(\bmod\ m)$, for if $a = q_1 m + r_1$ and $b = q_2 m + r_2$, where $0 \leq r_1$, $r_2 < |m|$, then $a - b = m(q_1 - q_2) + r_1 - r_2$, and $r_1 - r_2$ is divisible by m. Therefore, $r_1 = r_2$. Thus we have:

Theorem 4-1. Two integers are congruent modulo m if and only if their difference is divisible by $m \neq 0$.

If a and b have distinct remainders r_1 and r_2, where $0 \leq r_1, r_2 < |m|$, upon being divided by m, then a and b are said to be *incongruent modulo m*. The difference between two incongruent integers modulo m is, therefore, not divisible by m. In this case we write: $a \not\equiv b(\bmod\ m)$.

When two integers are congruent to each other modulo m, each is said to be a *residue* of the other for that modulus. Thus, because $12 \equiv 2(\bmod\ 10)$, 2 is a residue of 12, and 12 is a residue of 2 modulo 10.

The totality of integers congruent to a given integer for the modulus m constitutes a *residue class modulo m*.

These definitions imply that each integer belongs to exactly one residue class for a given modulus and that each residue class modulo m contains one and only one of the integers 0, 1, 2, . . . , $|m| - 1$. Hence, there are exactly $|m|$ residue classes modulo m.

Any set of $|m|$ integers selected so that no two of them belong to the same residue class modulo m forms a *complete residue system modulo m*. Thus for the modulus m the set of integers 0, 1, 2, . . . , $|m| - 1$ or the set 1, 2, 3, . . . , $|m|$ is often chosen to represent the classes of which the individual integers are members. The class represented by 0 contains all and only multiples of m, and the class represented by r consists of all the integers of the form $km + r$. Any set of $|m|$ integers containing one and only one integer represented by each of the forms km, $km + 1$, $km + 2$, . . . , $km + |m| - 1$ is, therefore, a complete residue system modulo m.

Since, as we have already shown, an integer is or is not prime to m according as the remainder obtained upon its division by m is or is not prime to m, the set of remainders from 1 through $|m| - 1$ which are prime to m represents all and only the integers that are prime to m. These integers, prime to m, are thus separated into residue classes modulo m that are in one-to-one correspondence with the positive integers from 1 through $|m| - 1$ that are prime to m.

Any set of integers prime to m and selected so that one and only one of them belongs to each of the residue classes of integers prime to m for the modulus m constitutes a *reduced residue system modulo m*. For the modulus 5 the set 1, 2, 3, 4 is a reduced residue system, but for the modulus 6 the integers 1 and 5, as well as the set 1 and -1, form such a system.

It is evident also that the residue classes for the modulus m are identical with the residue classes modulo $-m$, for when the sign of m is changed, we need change only the sign of q in the equation

$$a = qm + r \qquad 0 \leq r < |m|$$

Thus any congruence that holds for either m or $-m$ as modulus holds for the other one. It is convenient, therefore, to use only positive integers as moduli, and we shall hereafter adhere to this convention without making a specific statement of the fact in the discussion.

4-2. Basic Properties of Congruences. The relation of congruence has some properties similar to those of equality:

1. For any modulus m, $a \equiv a \pmod{m}$.
2. If $a \equiv b \pmod{m}$, then $b \equiv a \pmod{m}$.
3. If $a \equiv b \pmod{m}$ and $b \equiv c \pmod{m}$, then $a \equiv c \pmod{m}$.
4. If $a \equiv b \pmod{m}$ and $c \equiv d \pmod{m}$, then $a \pm c \equiv b \pm d \pmod{m}$. From the equations $a = b + km$, $c = d + tm$, we have $a \pm c = b \pm d + Lm$.
5. If $a \equiv b \pmod{m}$ and $c \equiv d \pmod{m}$, then $ac \equiv bd \pmod{m}$.

6. If $a \equiv b \pmod{m}$, then $a^n \equiv b^n \pmod{m}$, where n is a positive integer.

7. If $a \equiv b \pmod{m}$ and $f(x) = a_0 x^n + a_1 x^{n-1} + \cdots + a_n$ is an integral rational function of x with integral coefficients, then $f(a) \equiv f(b) \pmod{m}$.

The first three statements show that the congruence relation is reflexive, symmetric, and transitive. It is also clear that when $a + b \equiv c \pmod{m}$ and $b \equiv d \pmod{m}$, then $a + d \equiv c \pmod{m}$. In a congruence the laws thus permit the substitution of a number or expression in the place of a term congruent to it for the given modulus. The application of the fifth statement allows us to conclude that when $ac + b \equiv 0 \pmod{m}$ and $c \equiv e \pmod{m}$, then $ae + b \equiv 0 \pmod{m}$. Accordingly, we infer that for a given modulus a congruent number or expression may be substituted for a factor of a term of a congruence.

When "equality" is the relation, substitutions of the above types are just two of those covered by the familiar postulate, "Equals may be substituted for equals in any operation." It is, however, not true that integers which are congruent for a modulus m may always be substituted one for the other in a congruence modulo m. If $a^s \equiv b \pmod{m}$ and $s \equiv t \pmod{m}$, it need not happen that $a^t \equiv b \pmod{m}$, for a^s need not be congruent to a^t modulo m. Notice that $5^2 \equiv 4 \pmod{7}$ and that $2 \equiv 9 \pmod{7}$ but $5^9 \equiv 6 \pmod{7}$, so that $5^2 \not\equiv 5^9 \pmod{7}$.

The congruence relation also has the following properties that pertain to division:

1. If d is a divisor of m and $a \equiv b \pmod{m}$, then $a \equiv b \pmod{d}$.

2. If $a \equiv b \pmod{m_1}$ and $a \equiv b \pmod{m_2}$, then $a \equiv b \pmod{L}$, where L is the least common multiple of m_1 and m_2.

3. If $ac \equiv bc \pmod{m}$ and $c \neq 0$ is such that $(c, m) = 1$, then $a \equiv b \pmod{m}$.

4. If $ac \equiv bc \pmod{m}$ and $(c, m) = d$, then $a \equiv b \pmod{m_0}$, where $m = m_0 d$.

Examples. 1. We can find the remainder when 2^{30} is divided by 17 by simple operations on congruences. Since $2^4 \equiv 16 \pmod{17}$ and $16 \equiv -1 \pmod{17}$, we have $2^4 \equiv -1 \pmod{17}$. Raising each member of the congruence to the seventh power, we obtain $2^{28} \equiv -1 \pmod{17}$. But $2^2 \equiv 4 \pmod{17}$, and therefore $2^{30} \equiv -4 \pmod{17}$, or $2^{30} \equiv 13 \pmod{17}$.

2. We know that $10 \equiv 1 \pmod{3}$. Accordingly, $a_0(10)^n + a_1(10)^{n-1} + \cdots + a_n \equiv a_0 + a_1 + \cdots + a_n \pmod{3}$. Thus a number written in the scale of 10 is divisible by 3 if and only if the sum of its digits is divisible by 3.

EXERCISES

1. Find the remainder when 7^{10} is divided by 51; when 3^{10} is divided by 51; when 21^{10} is divided by 51.

2. Find the remainder when 5^{21} is divided by 127. Do the same for 5^{65}.

3. Prove that $2^{11} - 1$ has the factor 23 and that $2^{23} - 1$ has the factor 47.

4. If $a \equiv b \pmod{m}$, prove that the greatest common divisor of a and m is the greatest common divisor of b and m. State this result in terms of the integers of a residue class modulo m.

5. If $a + b \equiv c \pmod{m}$ and $b \equiv d \pmod{m}$, show that $a + d \equiv c \pmod{m}$.

6. If $ab \equiv c \pmod{m}$ and $b \equiv d \pmod{m}$, show that $ad \equiv c \pmod{m}$.

7. Since $2^4 \equiv 1 \pmod 5$ and $4 \equiv 9 \pmod 5$, is $2^9 \equiv 1 \pmod 5$? Explain.

8. Prove that an integer is divisible by 9 if and only if the sum of its digits is divisible by 9.

9. Prove that an integer is divisible by 8 if and only if the number formed by its last three digits is divisible by 8.

10. Prove that an integer is divisible by 11 if and only if the sum of the digits in the odd-numbered places diminished by the sum of the digits in the even-numbered places is divisible by 11.

11. If an integer N is written in the scale of r and then its digits are rearranged in any way to form the integer M, the difference $N - M$ is divisible by $r - 1$.

4-3. The Residue Classes. The properties of congruences stated above show that as far as the operations of addition, subtraction, and multiplication are concerned the elements in any two residue classes for the modulus m combine to give results that are always in the residue class designated by carrying out the very operations on any convenient representatives of the classes. Thus if an element a of class A is added to an element b of class B and the result $a + b$ is in the class C, then if any element of A is added to any element of B, the result will be in class C. Because subtraction is always possible, it follows, moreover, that when $a + b$ is an element of class C, any element $a + b + km$ of C can be expressed as the sum of an element of A and one of B.

It is important to notice, however, that although the result of multiplying any element of class A by an element of class B is always in the same class D, say, yet each element of D need not be a product of an element from A and an element from B. Take, for instance, the residue classes modulo 10. When any element of the class represented by 2 is multiplied by an element of the class of 3, the result is an element in the class represented by 6. Yet the particular element 16, which is congruent to 6 modulo 10, cannot be written as the product of two factors, one from the class of 2 and the other from the class of 3, for if

$$16 = (2 + 10k)(3 + 10t)$$

an odd number would divide 16.

It is interesting to notice also that $2 \cdot 5 \equiv 4 \pmod 6$ as well as $2 \cdot 2 \equiv 4 \pmod 6$; that is, the same least positive residue $2 \not\equiv 0 \pmod 6$ can be multiplied by either one of the distinct least positive residues 2 and 5 to produce a number of the class of 4 modulo 6. If we examine the least positive residues of any prime, we find that no such thing happens when we do not choose the first factor from the class of zero for the given prime. To prove this statement, let p be a prime, and suppose that $ac_1 \equiv b(\bmod\ p)$ and $ac_2 \equiv b(\bmod\ p)$. Therefore, $ac_1 \equiv ac_2(\bmod\ p)$, and since $(a, p) = 1$, $c_1 \equiv c_2(\bmod\ p)$. Hence, c_1 and c_2 must come from the same residue class modulo p.

When we select the integers a and b and ask whether or not there is an integer x such that $ax \equiv b(\bmod\ m)$, it is evident that we are dealing with a problem in division, the inverse of multiplication. We have, therefore, shown that when we divide b by a for the modulus m, it is possible to have results that do not belong to the same residue class for that modulus. It may happen, of course, that all answers are in but one residue class as is true in the case of the congruence $5x \equiv 1(\bmod\ 6)$. But it is also possible that there be no answer whatever, for a solution of $2x \equiv 1(\bmod\ 6)$ would demand that $2x = 1 + 6k$ and that 2 divide 1. Consequently, we must proceed with care, for division modulo m is not always possible and, when it is, need not yield a unique result.

One of the important ideas of arithmetic is that if $ab = 0$ and $a \neq 0$, then b must be 0. Suppose that

$$ab \equiv 0(\bmod\ m)$$

Is it necessary that either a or b be in the class of 0 for the modulus m? When the modulus is 6, we notice immediately that $2 \cdot 3 \equiv 0(\bmod\ 6)$ and that neither 2 nor 3 is congruent to 0 modulo 6. But when the modulus is a prime p and $ab \equiv 0(\bmod\ p)$, both a and b cannot come from the set of integers $1, 2, 3, \ldots, p - 1$, for the product of any two of these integers is prime to p. Consequently, we see that in this case a product is not congruent to 0 unless at least one factor is in the class of 0 for the given modulus. When the modulus m is composite, however, by factoring $m \neq 0$ so that $m = n_1 n_2$, where $1 < n_1 < m$, it follows that $n_1 n_2 \equiv 0(\bmod\ m)$.

We call any integers n_1 and n_2, neither one of which is in the class of 0 modulo m, but whose product is congruent to 0 for the modulus m, *divisors of zero modulo m*. The existence of divisors of zero for a composite modulus again reminds us of the need of caution in applying the idea of division to the notion of congruence.

EXERCISES

1. Show that although $2(6) \equiv 26(\bmod\ 14)$, 26 cannot be factored into integers such that one is in the class of 2 and the other in the class of 6 modulo 14.

2. Find numbers in the class of 10 modulo 11 that can, and some that cannot, be expressed as a product of two integers, one from the class of 2 and the other from the class of 5 modulo 11.

3. How many solutions do each of the following congruences have?

$$2x \equiv 6 \pmod{10}$$
$$2x \equiv 3 \pmod{4}$$
$$2x \equiv 3 \pmod{5}$$
$$3x \equiv 6 \pmod{15}$$

4. Find some divisors of zero modulo 12.

5. Compare the residue classes of the powers of 2, 4, and 7 modulo 15 with those of the powers of 3, 5, and 6 modulo 15. Can you find a law that governs them?

4-4. Euler's ϕ Function. Leonhard Euler (1707–1783) worked in many fields of pure and applied mathematics. His voluminous publications were concerned with algebra, the calculus of finite differences, the differential and integral calculus, the calculus of variations, astronomy, and analytical mechanics besides the theory of numbers. In the latter field he discovered the theorems which taken together make up the quadratic reciprocity law, supplied the proof and generalization of Fermat's theorem, showed that every prime of the form $4n + 1$ is expressible as a sum of two squares in exactly one way, as well as making many less startling but nevertheless important discoveries, one of which is the ϕ function.

The *indicator* $\phi(m)$ of an integer $m \neq 0$ is the number of positive integers less than or equal to $|m|$ and prime to m. Thus $\phi(m)$ is the number of integers in a reduced residue system modulo m, and $\phi(m) = \phi(-m)$. Because of this last fact, it will be sufficient to use only positive integers m in considering the ϕ function.

Examples. $\phi(1) = 1$, $\phi(5) = 4$, $\phi(6) = 2$.

It is evident that when p is a positive prime, $\phi(p)$ is $p - 1$.

Theorem 4-2. If p is a positive prime and n is a positive integer, $\phi(p^n) = p^{n-1}(p - 1)$.

To find $\phi(p^n)$, consider the set of integers

$$1, 2, \ldots, p, \ldots, 2p, \ldots, p^r, \ldots, p^n$$

Each of these integers is either divisible by p or is prime to p. But p^{n-1} of them are divisible by p. Therefore, $p^n - p^{n-1} = p^{n-1}(p - 1)$ of the integers from 1 through p^n are prime to p.

Any function of the variables x_i, where $i = 1, 2, \ldots, r$, is *arithmetic* if it assumes only integral values for the sets of integral values of the variables x_i for which the function is defined. The function $\phi(x)$ is arithmetic, as are the integral polynomials.

A single-valued arithmetic function $f(x)$ is said to be *regular* or *multiplicative* if, for any a and b which are relatively prime, $f(ab) = f(a)f(b)$. We shall show that the ϕ function is multiplicative.

Theorem 4-3. If a and b are relatively prime, $\phi(ab) = \phi(a)\phi(b)$.

We suppose that the integers a and b are positive and arrange the integers from 1 through $m = ab$ in the following array suggested by the residue classes modulo a:

1	2	3	k	a
$a + 1$	$a + 2$	$a + 3$	$a + k$	$2a$
$2a + 1$	$2a + 2$	$2a + 3$	$2a + k$	$3a$
. . . .	. . . .	. . . .	. . . .	. .
$(b - 1)a + 1$	. . . . .	. . . . .	$(b - 1)a + k$	ba

Because an integer is prime to m if and only if it is prime to both a and b, we shall determine first the number of integers in the above array that are prime to a and then find how many of these are also prime to b.

We know that there are $\phi(a)$ integers prime to a in the first row. Moreover, each integer in the column headed by an integer k, from 1 through a, is of the form $sa + k$. Furthermore,

$$sa + k \equiv k \pmod{a}$$

Therefore, if the integer k at the top of a column has a divisor in common with a, every integer in that column has that divisor in common with a, and if k is prime to a, every integer in that column is prime to a. There are then $\phi(a)$ columns of integers that are prime to a. How many of these integers are prime to b?

Consider the set of b integers in any column,

$$k \quad a + k \quad 2a + k \quad \ldots \quad (b - 1)a + k$$

No two of these integers are congruent modulo b, for if

$$sa + k \equiv ta + k \pmod{b}$$
$$(t - s)a \equiv 0 \pmod{b}$$

and

$$t - s \equiv 0 \pmod{b}$$

since $(a, b) = 1$. But t and s range through the residue system 0, 1, 2, . . . , $b - 1$ modulo b, so that unless $t = s$, $t \not\equiv s \pmod{b}$. The b integers of any column are, therefore, in some order congruent modulo b to the integers 1, 2, . . . , b. But then exactly $\phi(b)$ of them are prime to b.

Since $\phi(b)$ integers in each of the $\phi(a)$ columns of integers prime to a are also prime to b, the number of integers from 1 through ab that are prime to both a and b is $\phi(a)\phi(b)$.

Theorem 4-4. If $m = p_1^{n_1}p_2^{n_2} \cdots p_r^{n_r}$, where the p_i, for $i = 1, 2, \ldots, r$, are positive primes, $\phi(m) = p_1^{n_1-1}p_2^{n_2-1} \cdots p_r^{n_r-1}(p_1 - 1)(p_2 - 1) \cdots (p_r - 1)$.

Since m has been factored into powers of distinct primes,

$$\phi(m) = \phi(p_1^{n_1})\phi(p_2^{n_2} \cdots p_r^{n_r})$$

By repeating this process, we find

$$\phi(m) = \phi(p_1^{n_1})\phi(p_2^{n_2}) \cdots \phi(p_r^{n_r})$$

from which we infer the desired result.

Corollary. If $m > 2$, $\phi(m)$ is even.

Example. The number of positive integers less than 360 and prime to 360 is $\phi(360) = 2^2 \cdot 3 \cdot (2 - 1)(3 - 1)(5 - 1) = 96$.

EXERCISES

1. Show that the formulas for the number of divisors of an integer m and the sum of the divisors are multiplicative functions.

2. Show that, for $n > 1$, the sum of the positive integers less than n and prime to n is $(n/2)\phi(n)$.

3. Show that the sum of the squares of the positive integers less than n and prime to n is

$$\frac{n^3}{3}\left(1 - \frac{1}{p_1}\right)\left(1 - \frac{1}{p_2}\right) \cdots \left(1 - \frac{1}{p_r}\right) + \frac{n}{6}(1 - p_1)(1 - p_2) \cdots (1 - p_r)$$

where $p_1, p_2, \ldots,$ and p_r are the distinct positive prime factors of n.

4. Prove that if $n = p_1 p_2 p_3$, where the p_i, with $i = 1, 2, 3$, are distinct primes, then the product of all the positive integers less than n and prime to n is

$$\frac{(n - 1)! \displaystyle\prod_{i=1}^{3} (p_i - 1)!}{\displaystyle\prod_{\substack{i,j=1 \\ i<j}}^{3} (p_i p_j - 1)! \displaystyle\prod_{\substack{i=1 \\ i \neq j \neq k}}^{3} p_i^{(p_j-1)(p_k-1)}}$$

Use the method so developed to find the product of all positive integers less than n and prime to $n = p_1^{\alpha_1} p_2^{\alpha_2} \cdots p_r^{\alpha_r}$.

5. Set up a method for finding by trial all integers x such that $\phi(x) = n$. Use your method to find the solutions of $\phi(x) = 16$.

6. If $G(n) = \displaystyle\sum_{d|n} \phi(d)$, show that $G(n)$ is multiplicative.

Note that the symbol $\displaystyle\sum_{d|n} \phi(d)$ is read "the sum over the divisors of n of $\phi(d)$," and we understand that we use only the positive divisors of n.

Theorem 4-5. If $m = p_1^{n_1} p_2^{n_2} \cdots p_k^{n_k} \cdots p_r^{n_r}$, where the p_i, $i = 1, 2, \ldots, r$, are distinct positive primes, the number of integers from 1 through m that are prime to $p_1, p_2, \ldots, p_k$ is $m(1 - (1/p_1))(1 - (1/p_2)) \cdots (1 - (1/p_k))$.

It is sometimes important to find the number of positive integers not greater than the positive integer m and prime to some but not all of the prime factors of m. For instance, we may wish to know the number of positive integers less than 360 and prime to 2 and 5.

When $m = p_1^{n_1}p_2^{n_2} \cdots p_r^{n_r}$, it is evident that the number of integers from 1 through m that are divisible by p_1 is m/p_1, leaving then $m - (m/p_1) = m(1 - (1/p_1))$ integers that are prime to p_1.

Proceeding by induction, suppose that the number of integers from 1 through m that are prime to p_1, p_2, . . . , and p_k is

$$m\left(1 - \frac{1}{p_1}\right)\left(1 - \frac{1}{p_2}\right) \cdots \left(1 - \frac{1}{p_k}\right) \tag{1}$$

Some of these integers, however, are divisible by p_{k+1}. We wish, therefore, to subtract from the above number the number of integers from 1 through m that are divisible by p_{k+1} and at the same time are prime to p_1, p_2, . . . , p_k. To find this number, first consider the integers of the set from 1 through m that are multiples of p_{k+1}. They are

$$p_{k+1}, 2p_{k+1}, 3p_{k+1}, \ . \ . \ . \ , \frac{m}{p_{k+1}} \, p_{k+1}$$

Since any integer cp_{k+1} is or is not prime to p_1, p_2, . . . , and p_k according as its coefficient c is or is not prime to p_1, p_2, . . . , and p_k, we must ask how many integers of the set

$$1, 2, 3, \ . \ . \ . \ , \frac{m}{p_{k+1}}$$

are prime to p_1, p_2, . . . , and p_k. Referring to our inductive assumption (1), we consequently know that

$$\frac{m}{p_{k+1}}\left(1 - \frac{1}{p_1}\right)\left(1 - \frac{1}{p_2}\right) \cdots \left(1 - \frac{1}{p_k}\right) \tag{2}$$

is the number of integers from 1 through m/p_{k+1} that are prime to p_1, p_2, . . . , and p_k and is, therefore, the number of integers from 1 through m divisible by p_{k+1} and also prime to p_1, p_2, . . . , p_k. Subtracting this last number (2) from the number (1) of integers prime to p_1, p_2, . . . , p_k, we have

$$m\left(1 - \frac{1}{p_1}\right)\left(1 - \frac{1}{p_2}\right) \cdots \left(1 - \frac{1}{p_k}\right)$$
$$- \frac{m}{p_{k+1}}\left(1 - \frac{1}{p_1}\right)\left(1 - \frac{1}{p_2}\right) \cdots \left(1 - \frac{1}{p_k}\right)$$
$$= m\left(1 - \frac{1}{p_1}\right)\left(1 - \frac{1}{p_2}\right) \cdots \left(1 - \frac{1}{p_k}\right)\left(1 - \frac{1}{p_{k+1}}\right)$$

as the number of integers from 1 through m that are prime to $p_1, p_2, \ldots,$ p_k and also p_{k+1}. Thus by induction we may write this formula so that it includes the number of integers from 1 through m that are prime to some or all of the distinct prime factors of m.

Example. If $m = 2^3 \cdot 3^2 \cdot 5^3$, the number of integers from 1 through m that are prime to 2 and 5 is $2^3 \cdot 3^2 \cdot 5^3(1 - \frac{1}{2})(1 - \frac{1}{5}) = 3600$.

Theorem 4-6. If the positive integer $m = kd$, the number of integers n from 1 through m having the property that d is the greatest common divisor of n and m is $\phi(k)$.

Consider the integers $1, 2, \ldots, d, \ldots, 2d, \ldots, kd$. There are k multiples of d in this set, but the integers td and $m = kd$ have the greatest common divisor d if and only if t and k are relatively prime. Since t has the values $1, 2, \ldots, k$, there are exactly $\phi(k)$ integers from 1 through m that have with m the greatest common divisor d.

Theorem 4-7. If $d_1, d_2, \ldots, d_r$ are the distinct positive divisors of $m \neq 0$, then $\sum_{d \mid m} \phi(d) = \phi(d_1) + \phi(d_2) + \cdots + \phi(d_r) = |m|$.

Each integer n in the set $1, 2, \ldots, |m|$ has with m one and only one of the d_i, where $i = 1, 2, \ldots, r$, as greatest common divisor. Consequently, if we pick from this set the integers n such that $(n, m) = d_i$, where $|m| = d_i d_j$, there will be exactly $\phi(d_j)$ of them. As d_i ranges through all the positive divisors of m, so does d_j, and each integer from 1 through $|m|$ will thereby have been put into one and only one class defined by the greatest common divisor it has with m. Recalling that the symbol $\sum_{d \mid m} \phi(d)$ is read, "the sum over the divisors of m of $\phi(d)$," the sum of the numbers indicating the sizes of these classes is $\sum_{d \mid m} \phi(d) = |m|$.

Examples. 1. If $m = 90$, the number of integers n from 1 through 90 such that $(n, 90) = 6$ is $\phi(15) = 8$. The integers are 6, 12, 24, 42, 48, 66, 78, and 84.

2. The positive divisors of 70 are 1, 2, 5, 7, 10, 14, 35, and 70. Moreover, $\phi(1) = 1$; $\phi(2) = 1$; $\phi(5) = 4$; $\phi(7) = 6$; $\phi(10) = 4$; $\phi(14) = 6$; $\phi(35) = 24$; $\phi(70) = 24$; and the sum of these integers is 70.

4-5. Residue Systems Modulo m. Take any integer a prime to $m > 1$, and let

$$r_1, r_2, \ldots, r_m$$

be a complete residue system modulo m. Form the products

$$ar_1, ar_2, \ldots, ar_m$$

No two of these m integers are congruent modulo m, for if $i \neq j$ and

$$ar_i \equiv ar_j (\bmod\ m)$$

then

$$r_i \equiv r_j(\text{mod } m)$$

which is contrary to our assumption. Consequently, these integers represent the m residue classes modulo m.

Moreover, if

$$r_1, r_2, \ldots, r_{\phi(m)}$$

is a reduced residue system modulo m and $(a, m) = 1$, the set

$$ar_1, ar_2, \ldots, ar_{\phi(m)}$$

is also a reduced residue system modulo m, for this set contains exactly $\phi(m)$ integers, all of which are incongruent modulo m, and each integer is itself prime to m.

Example. The set $0, 5, 5 \cdot 2, 5 \cdot 3, \ldots, 5 \cdot 11$, or $0, 5, 10, 15, \ldots, 55$, is a complete residue system modulo 12, while $5, 25, 35, 55$ is a reduced residue system modulo 12.

Again if $r_1, r_2, \ldots, r_m$ is a complete residue system modulo m,

$$a + r_1, a + r_2, \ldots, a + r_m$$

for any $a \neq 0$ is another complete residue system, for there are m integers in the set, and if two of them were congruent modulo m, when $i \neq j$,

$$a + r_i \equiv a + r_j(\text{mod } m)$$

then

$$r_i \equiv r_j(\text{mod } m)$$

Sometimes it is convenient to use the integers of smallest numerical value to represent the residue classes modulo m. If we write any integer a in the form

$$a = km + r \qquad 0 \leq r < m$$

for this system we keep the values of r which do not exceed $m/2$, that is, the integers from 0 through $m/2$ or $(m - 1)/2$ depending upon whether m is even or odd. But those values of r which exceed $m/2$ are replaced by the negative integers of least numerical value to which they are congruent for the modulus m. Since

$$m - r \equiv -r(\text{mod } m)$$

this complete residue system modulo m, when m is even, is

$$0, 1, 2, \ldots, \frac{m}{2}, 1 - \frac{m}{2}, 2 - \frac{m}{2}, \ldots, -2, -1$$

and when m is odd, it is

$$0, 1, 2, \ldots, \frac{m - 1}{2}, -\frac{m - 1}{2}, -\frac{m - 3}{2}, \ldots, -2, -1$$

Examples. For the modulus 14 the set $-6, -5, -4, \ldots, -1, 0,$ $1, 2, \ldots, 7$ is a complete residue system, but for the modulus 15 the system using least numerical values is $-7, -6, \ldots, -1, 0, 1, 2, \ldots,$ 7.

In Theorem 4-3 we showed that the integers

$$k, k + d, k + 2d, \ldots, k + (b - 1)d$$

of the arithmetic progression in which $(b, d) = 1$ form a complete residue system modulo b.

Furthermore, we can generate a complete residue system modulo ab by using the form $ax + y$, where x takes all the values in a complete residue system

$$r_1, r_2, \ldots, r_b \tag{3}$$

for the modulus b, and y takes all values in a complete residue system

$$k_1, k_2, \ldots, k_a \tag{4}$$

modulo a. It is evident that the form thereby gives ab integers. These integers are, moreover, incongruent modulo ab, for if

$$ar_i + k_j \equiv ar_s + k_t \pmod{ab}$$

then

$$a(r_i - r_s) \equiv k_t - k_j \pmod{ab}$$

and $a \mid (k_t - k_j)$, so that

$$k_t \equiv k_j \pmod{a}$$

But since no two of the integers of (4) are congruent modulo a, $k_t = k_j$. Hence,

$$a(r_i - r_s) \equiv 0 \pmod{ab}$$

and

$$r_i - r_s \equiv 0 \pmod{b}$$

so that, as above, $r_i = r_s$. Consequently, two integers formed as described cannot be congruent modulo ab unless they are identical, and the set, therefore, forms a complete residue system modulo ab.

Again when $(a, b) = 1$, if we use the form $ax + by$, letting x have the values of (3) and y have the values of (4), the resulting ab integers form a complete residue system modulo ab, for if

$$ar_i + bk_j \equiv ar_s + bk_t \pmod{ab}$$

then

$$a(r_i - r_s) \equiv b(k_t - k_j) \pmod{ab}$$

But then $a \mid (k_t - k_j)$, and therefore $k_t = k_j$. Also $b \mid (r_i - r_s)$, so that $r_i = r_s$. Hence, the given ab integers are distinct modulo ab.

It is easy to show also that if x has the values in (3) that are prime to b while y has the values in (4) that are prime to a, then when $(a, b) = 1$, the integers $ax + by$ form a reduced residue system modulo ab.

EXERCISES

1. Use the form $ax + by$ with $(a, b) = 1$ to show that $\phi(ab) = \phi(a)\phi(b)$.

2. Prove Theorem 4-5 by setting up the integers 1 through $m = p_1{}^{n_1}p_2{}^{n_2} \cdots p_k{}^{n_k} s$ in an array of s complete residue systems modulo $p_1{}^{n_1}p_2{}^{n_2} \cdots p_k{}^{n_k}$.

3. Show that $a^{n-1}x + y$ generates a complete residue system modulo a^n if x has the values in a complete residue system modulo a while y has the values in a complete residue system modulo a^{n-1}.

4. If $f(x)$ is an integral polynomial and if there are $\psi(m)$ integers prime to m in the set $f(1), f(2), \ldots, f(m)$, prove that when $(a, b) = 1$, $\psi(ab) = \psi(a)\psi(b)$.

5. Find the number of integers prime to m in the set:

a. $1 \cdot 2,\ 2 \cdot 3,\ \ldots,\ m(m + 1)$.

b. $\dfrac{1 \cdot 2}{2},\ \dfrac{2 \cdot 3}{2},\ \ldots,\ \dfrac{m(m + 1)}{2}$.

6. For $m > 0$ set up all the permutations k at a time with repetitions allowed of the positive integers not greater than m. Then the number of these sets of k integers whose greatest common divisor is prime to m is $\phi_k(m)$. Find a formula for $\phi_k(p^n)$, and show that this function is multiplicative.

7. Without using an enumeration according to size, show that if a, b, and c are positive integers and $a = bc$, there are in a complete residue system modulo a exactly c integers that are divisible by b. (Let $c_1, c_2, \ldots, c_c$ be a complete residue system modulo c. Then consider the set $bc_1, bc_2, \ldots, bc_c$.)

8. Can you find an integer the powers of which set up a complete residue system modulo 13? Can all integers prime to 13 be used to form such a set?

9. By expanding $(1 + 1 + \cdots + 1)^p$, prove that if p is a prime, $a^p \equiv a \pmod{p}$ and hence that when $(a, p) = 1$, $a^{\phi(p)} \equiv 1 \pmod{p}$.

CHAPTER 5

THE SOLUTION OF CONGRUENCES

5-1. Identical and Conditional Congruences. In Sec. 4-3 the consideration of the manner in which residue classes combine led to setting up a congruence in which we used the symbol x to represent an integer. For instance, when we asked whether or not there is an integer which when multiplied by 2 would give an integer in the class of 4 modulo 6, we were dealing with a congruence of the form $2x \equiv 4 \pmod 6$. In such congruences we shall hereafter think of x not as just a symbol for an unknown integer but as a variable whose values are the rational integers. By substituting such values in the congruence $2x \equiv 4 \pmod 6$ it has already been verified that both 2 and 5 are values of x that satisfy this congruence. In the general case we shall say that if the constants $a_1, a_2, \ldots, a_n$ are substituted, respectively, for the variables $x_1, x_2, \ldots, x_n$ (all of whose values are integers) in the congruence

$$f_1(x_1, x_2, \ldots, x_n) \equiv f_2(x_1, x_2, \ldots, x_n) \pmod m$$

where f_1 and f_2 are integral polynomials in these variables, and if

$$f_1(a_1, a_2, \ldots, a_n) \equiv f_2(a_1, a_2, \ldots, a_n) \pmod m$$

then $x_1 = a_1, x_2 = a_2, \ldots, x_n = a_n$ is a *solution* of the given congruence.

If two integral polynomials f_1 and f_2 in the variables $x_1, x_2, \ldots, x_n$ are such that the coefficients of like terms are congruent to each other for the given modulus m, then these expressions are said to be *identically congruent* for the modulus m, and we sometimes write

$$f_1(x_1, x_2, \ldots, x_n) \equiv f_2(x_1, x_2, \ldots, x_n) \pmod m$$

calling this congruence an *identical congruence* although very often we use only the ordinary sign of congruence to express this relation. Correspondingly, an integral rational algebraic function $f(x_1, x_2, \ldots, x_n)$ with integral coefficients is *identically congruent to zero for the modulus m* if and only if all its coefficients are divisible by m. All the congruences that involve only constants, such as $a \equiv b \pmod m$, are necessarily identical congruences. $9x^2 - 2x + 5 \equiv 3x^2 + 4x - 1 \pmod 6$ is an identical congruence in the single variable x. It is evident that an identical con-

66

gruence will be satisfied regardless of the integral values that are assigned to the variables.

On the other hand, we shall call a congruence of the above form, but in which the left- and right-hand members f_1 and f_2 are not identically congruent for the modulus m, a *conditional congruence*.

We shall be concerned chiefly with congruences of the form $f_1(x) \equiv f_2(x) \pmod{m}$, where $f_1(x)$ and $f_2(x)$ are integral polynomials in x. We know from the properties of congruences that when r is a solution of such a congruence, every integer in the class with r for the modulus m also satisfies the congruence, for $f_i(r) \equiv f_i(r + km) \pmod{m}$. This whole class of integers is considered just one solution of the congruence, and consequently a solution is itself written in the form of a congruence, $x \equiv r \pmod{m}$.

Example. The congruence $2x \equiv 6 \pmod{10}$ is satisfied by 3 and 8. Hence, the complete solutions are written in the form $x \equiv 3 \pmod{10}$ and $x \equiv 8 \pmod{10}$.

Let us recall that in algebra* two polynomials $f_1(x)$ and $f_2(x)$ are said to be identically equal if and only if they are equal for all values of x, and hence if and only if corresponding terms have the same coefficients. In particular, a polynomial vanishes identically if and only if it vanishes for all values of x, which means if and only if all its coefficients are zero. In contrast, consider the congruence $x^3 - x \equiv 0 \pmod{3}$, and observe that although for the modulus 3 the polynomial $x^3 - x$ is congruent to zero for all values of x, yet not all its coefficients are congruent to zero modulo 3. Again, both members of the congruence $x^3 - 2 \equiv x + 1 \pmod{3}$ have the same values modulo 3 for all values of x, but the members are not identically congruent modulo 3. In other words a congruence may be satisfied by all integers and still not be an identical congruence according to the above definition. Examples of such conditional congruences are

$$x^5 - x \equiv 0 \pmod{5}$$
$$x^3 + 3x^2 + 2x \equiv 0 \pmod{6}$$

Likewise,

$$2x \equiv 4 \pmod{6}$$

and

$$x^2 \equiv 2 \pmod{5}$$

are conditional congruences, the first one having two incongruent solutions modulo 6, while the second has no solution whatever.

On the other hand,

$$x^2 - (x - 2)(x + 2) \equiv 0 \pmod{4}$$

* M. Bocher, "Introduction to Higher Algebra," Chap. 1, The Macmillan Company, New York, 1931.

and
$$6x^2 + x - 15 \equiv x + 3 (\text{mod } 6)$$
are identical congruences.

EXERCISES

Determine whether the following congruences are identical or conditional, and find the solutions by trial if there are any.

1. $2x^2 + 3x \equiv 5 (\text{mod } 7)$.
2. $x^4 + x^2 \equiv 0 (\text{mod } 10)$.
3. $x^3 + x^2 \equiv x^3 - x^2 (\text{mod } 2)$.
4. $2x^3 + 3x^2 + x \equiv 0 (\text{mod } 6)$.
5. $x^2 - 4 \equiv 0 (\text{mod } 5)$.
6. $x^4 - 1 \equiv (x - 1)(x - 2)(x - 3)(x - 4) (\text{mod } 5)$.

5-2. Equivalent Congruences. Having performed on a congruence an operation listed among the properties of the congruence relation (Sec. 4-2), if a second one of these operations can be performed on the result so as to restore the original congruence, the first operation is said to be reversible. The following operations on a congruence can be reversed:

1. Adding to or subtracting from each member of a congruence congruent integers or other expressions that are identically congruent for the given modulus.

2. Substituting $F(x)$ for $f(x)$ in a term $f(x)g(x)$ of a congruence if $F(x)$ is identically congruent to $f(x)$ for the given modulus.

3. Multiplying or, when possible, dividing the coefficients of each member of a congruence by an integer that is prime to the modulus.

4. Multiplying or, when possible, dividing the coefficients of each member of a congruence as well as the modulus by the same integer.

If any of these operations is performed a finite number of times on a congruence $f_1(x_1,x_2,\ldots,x_n) \equiv f_2(x_1,x_2,\ldots,x_n) (\text{mod } m_1)$ and the resulting congruence is $g_1(x_1,x_2,\ldots,x_n) \equiv g_2(x_1,x_2,\ldots,x_n) (\text{mod } m_2)$, then the two congruences are said to be *equivalent*. For instance, when $f(x) \equiv F(x) (\text{mod } m)$ identically, then $f(x)g(x) \equiv k(x) (\text{mod } m)$ is equivalent to $F(x)g(x) + m[h(x)] \equiv k(x) (\text{mod } m)$.

Accordingly, any congruence

$$f_1(x_1,x_2,\ldots,x_n) \equiv f_2(x_1,x_2,\ldots,x_n) (\text{mod } m)$$

can be reduced to an equivalent congruence of the form $f(x_1,x_2,\ldots,x_n) \equiv 0 (\text{mod } m)$. For example, the congruence $x^2 + 10 \equiv 7x (\text{mod } 6)$ is equivalent to each of the congruences $x^2 - x + 4 \equiv 0 (\text{mod } 6)$, $5x^2 - 5x + 2 \equiv 0 (\text{mod } 6)$, and $3x^2 - 3x + 12 \equiv 0 (\text{mod } 18)$.

When a congruence has been written in the form $f(x_1,x_2,\ldots,x_n) \equiv 0 (\text{mod } m)$, the *degree of the congruence* is defined as the degree of the term or terms of highest degree in $f(x_1,x_2,\ldots,x_n)$ whose coefficient or coefficients are not congruent to zero for the modulus m. Thus

$$6x^3 + 10x^2 - 7x + 9 \equiv 0(\mathrm{mod}\ 12)$$

is of degree three, although

$$12x^3 + 3x^2 - 5x + 7 \equiv 0(\mathrm{mod}\ 12)$$

is of only the second degree and can be written

$$3x^2 - 5x + 7 \equiv 0(\mathrm{mod}\ 12)$$

It is evident that when two conditional congruences are equivalent, any integer that satisfies one of them necessarily satisfies the other. Take, for instance, the congruence $x^2 \equiv 4(\mathrm{mod}\ 5)$ that has the solutions $x \equiv 2(\mathrm{mod}\ 5)$ and $x \equiv 3(\mathrm{mod}\ 5)$. The congruence $5x^3 + 3x^2 \equiv 2(\mathrm{mod}\ 5)$ has the same solutions, for the two are equivalent. Again, consider the congruence $2x \equiv 4(\mathrm{mod}\ 6)$. Every integer that satisfies this congruence also satisfies the equivalent congruence $x \equiv 2(\mathrm{mod}\ 3)$. The distinction lies in the fact that all the integers that satisfy the latter congruence are in the class of 2 for the modulus 3, but these integers are separated into the classes of the residues 2 and 5 for the modulus 6. The first congruence, therefore, has two incongruent solutions modulo 6, while the second one has but one solution modulo 3.

It is not true, however, that two congruences that have the same solutions for a given modulus are necessarily equivalent. Both $2x \equiv 4(\mathrm{mod}\ 6)$ and $x^2 - x + 4 \equiv 0(\mathrm{mod}\ 6)$ have the solutions $x \equiv 2(\mathrm{mod}\ 6)$ and $x \equiv 5(\mathrm{mod}\ 6)$, yet they are not equivalent.

A single conditional congruence may be equivalent to a set of simultaneous congruences. When $f(x) \equiv 0(\mathrm{mod}\ m)$ and $m = m_1 m_2 \cdots m_r$, where $(m_i, m_j) = 1$, with $i, j = 1, 2, \ldots, r$, and $i \neq j$, then the congruence can be broken up into the set of congruences $f(x) \equiv 0(\mathrm{mod}\ m_i)$. Conversely, if $(m_i, m_j) = 1$, the set of congruences $f(x) \equiv 0(\mathrm{mod}\ m_i)$ can be combined to form $f(x) \equiv 0(\mathrm{mod}\ m)$. We shall say in this case that $f(x) \equiv 0(\mathrm{mod}\ m)$ is equivalent to the set $f(x) \equiv 0(\mathrm{mod}\ m_i)$. For example, $5x \equiv 1(\mathrm{mod}\ 12)$ is equivalent to the set of two congruences $5x \equiv 1(\mathrm{mod}\ 3)$ and $5x \equiv 1(\mathrm{mod}\ 4)$. It follows that if $x \equiv x_0(\mathrm{mod}\ 12)$ is a solution of the first congruence, then x_0 also satisfies the last two. Conversely, any simultaneous solution of the set of two congruences implies that the original congruence has the same solution, for the moduli 3 and 4 are relatively prime, and thus when $5x_0 - 1$ is divisible by both 3 and 4, it is divisible by their product.

But when two congruences are themselves not equivalent, the existence of a solution of either one of them may often be determined by showing the existence of a solution of the other one. In that case we speak of the problems of the existence of the solutions as being equivalent. Notice that if the congruence $2x \equiv 3 \pmod 9$ has a solution, then $2x \equiv 1 \pmod 3$ has a solution, and conversely. This statement is valid, for any solution $x \equiv x_0 \pmod 9$ of the first congruence would have to be a multiple of 3, and consequently each $x_0/3$ satisfies the second congruence. On the other hand, the second congruence is satisfied by all integers in the class of 2 modulo 3, and none of these integers is a multiple of 3. However, where $x \equiv x' \pmod 3$ is a solution of $2x \equiv 1 \pmod 3$, $x \equiv 3x' \pmod 9$ must be a solution of $2x \equiv 3 \pmod 9$. Thus the questions of the existence of solutions of these congruences are mutually dependent.

Example. To determine whether or not the congruences $3x^2 - x + 7 \equiv 0 \pmod{15}$ and $9x^2 - 8x + 11 \equiv 0 \pmod{15}$ are equivalent, we try to find a multiplier prime to the modulus that will change the leading coefficient of the first congruence into the one we want. What value of y will satisfy $3y \equiv 9 \pmod{15}$? The solutions are 3, 8, and 13 modulo 15. We reject 3 since it is not prime to 15. Multiplying each member of the first congruence by 8, we have $24x^2 - 8x + 56 \equiv 0 \pmod{15}$, which reduces to $9x^2 - 8x + 11 \equiv 0 \pmod{15}$. Thus the congruences are equivalent.

EXERCISES

1. Is $x^3 - 2 \equiv 0 \pmod 3$ equivalent to $x^3 + 1 \equiv 0 \pmod 3$?

2. Show that $2x^3 - x^2 + 2 \equiv 0 \pmod 5$ is equivalent to $2x^3 + 4x^2 \equiv 3 \pmod 5$.

3. Show that $x^2 - 2x + 1 \equiv 0 \pmod 3$ is equivalent to $2x^2 - x + 2 \equiv 0 \pmod 3$.

4. Show that $3x^2 - 6 \equiv 0 \pmod{15}$ is equivalent to $x^2 - 2 \equiv 0 \pmod 5$.

5. Are $2x^2 + x - 4 \equiv 0 \pmod 5$ and $x^2 + 3x - 2 \equiv 0 \pmod 5$ equivalent?

6. Is the congruence $x^3 - 2 \equiv 0 \pmod 3$ equivalent to the congruence $2x^3 - x - 2 \equiv 0 \pmod 3$? Are the solutions the same?

7. Develop two congruences equivalent to $x^2 - 9 \equiv 0 \pmod{12}$.

8. Are the congruences $x^3 - x \equiv 0 \pmod 3$ and $x^4 + 2x^2 \equiv 0 \pmod 3$ equivalent? Are the solutions the same?

9. Note that $2x \equiv 8 \pmod{10}$ and $x^2 - 3x + 6 \equiv 0 \pmod{10}$ have the same solutions. Are they equivalent?

5-3. Linear Congruences. Can the double of an integer give the remainder 7 when it is divided by 52? Has $2x \equiv 7 \pmod{52}$ a solution?

Theorem 5-1. When a is prime to m, the congruence $ax \equiv 1 \pmod m$ has one and only one solution modulo m and this solution is prime to m.

The congruence $ax \equiv 1 \pmod m$ is equivalent to the equation $ax + my = 1$, which we have shown always has a solution in integers when $(a, m) = 1$. There can be but one solution modulo m, moreover, for if both x_1 and x_2 satisfy $ax \equiv 1 \pmod m$,

$$ax_1 \equiv ax_2 \pmod m$$

and

$$x_1 \equiv x_2 \pmod m$$

Furthermore, when $ax_1 \equiv 1(\mathrm{mod}\ m)$, it is clear that x_1 is prime to m.

Theorem 5-2. When a is prime to m, the congruence $ax \equiv b(\mathrm{mod}\ m)$ has one and only one solution modulo m.

Now consider the congruence $ax \equiv b(\mathrm{mod}\ m)$ with $(a,\ m) = 1$. We know that $ax \equiv 1(\mathrm{mod}\ m)$ has a solution $x \equiv x_1(\mathrm{mod}\ m)$. Then

$$ax_1b \equiv b(\mathrm{mod}\ m)$$

shows that $x \equiv x_1b(\mathrm{mod}\ m)$ satisfies the original congruence.

Again, as proved above, there can be but one solution modulo m, but notice that it is not necessarily prime to m.

Theorem 5-3. If d is the greatest common divisor of a and m, the congruence $ax \equiv b(\mathrm{mod}\ m)$ has a solution if and only if d divides b. When d does divide b, there are exactly d incongruent solutions modulo m.

Let $(a,\ m) = d$, $a = a_0d$, and $m = m_0d$. If $ax \equiv b(\mathrm{mod}\ m)$ has a solution, it is evident that d divides b. On the other hand, if d divides b, let $b = cd$, and reduce the congruence to the equivalent congruence

$$a_0x \equiv c(\mathrm{mod}\ m_0)$$

In this case $(a_0,\ m_0) = 1$, and there is but one solution $x \equiv x_1(\mathrm{mod}\ m_0)$. Consider this class of integers all of which are of the form $x_1 + km_0$ and obviously satisfy the given congruence. We wish to know whether these integers constitute one or more solutions modulo m; that is, we should like to know for which values of k these integers are in the same residue class modulo m. We see that

$$x_1 + km_0 \equiv x_1 + sm_0(\mathrm{mod}\ m)$$

if and only if

$$m_0(k - s) \equiv 0(\mathrm{mod}\ m)$$

that is, if and only if $k - s \equiv 0(\mathrm{mod}\ d)$. Consequently, when k ranges from 0 through $d - 1$, the integers $x_1 + km_0$ represent exactly d solutions that are incongruent for the modulus m and all solutions of the given congruence lie in one of these d classes modulo m.

Example. Solve: $15x \equiv 12(\mathrm{mod}\ 36)$.

Since $(15,\ 36) = 3$ and $3 \mid 12$, we reduce the congruence to $5x \equiv 4(\mathrm{mod}\ 12)$ of which there is one solution $x \equiv 8(\mathrm{mod}\ 12)$. Hence, the solutions of the original congruence are $x \equiv 8,\ 20,\ 32(\mathrm{mod}\ 36)$.

EXERCISES

State with reasons the number of distinct solutions of the following congruences, and find the solutions.

1. $3x \equiv 5(\mathrm{mod}\ 9)$.   **2.** $5x \equiv 3(\mathrm{mod}\ 27)$.
3. $6x \equiv 3(\mathrm{mod}\ 18)$.   **4.** $49x \equiv 23(\mathrm{mod}\ 125)$.
5. $12x \equiv 36(\mathrm{mod}\ 56)$.

5-4. Division of Polynomials. If $f_1(x)$ and $f_2(x)$ are integral polynomials and if it is possible to divide $f_1(x)$ or $f_1(x) + m \cdot g(x)$, where $g(x)$ is an integral polynomial, by $f_2(x)$, obtaining integral polynomials $q(x)$ and $r(x)$ so that

$$f_1(x) \equiv f_2(x)q(x) + r(x)(\text{mod } m)$$

is an identical congruence, and if the division is continued until $r(x)$ is either lower in degree than is $f_2(x)$ or is congruent to zero modulo m, then $q(x)$ is said to be the *quotient* and $r(x)$ the *remainder in the division modulo m* of $f_1(x)$ by $f_2(x)$. When $r(x) \equiv 0(\text{mod } m)$ identically, the division is said to be *exact* and both $f_2(x)$ and $q(x)$ are *factors modulo m* of $f_1(x)$ or *divisors modulo m* of $f_1(x)$. Moreover, $f_1(x)$ is a *multiple modulo m* of $f_2(x)$.

Notice, for example, that if we divide $2x^2 - x - 3$ by $x - 3$ using ordinary long division, we find that there is a remainder 12 which is, of course, in the class of 0 for the modulus 6, and therefore we say that $x - 3$ is a divisor modulo 6 of $2x^2 - x - 3$.

As it stands, we cannot divide $x^2 - 1$ by $3x - 2$ modulo 6, for if there were a quotient $ax + b$ that would make $(3x - 2)(ax + b) + r \equiv x^2 - 1(\text{mod } 6)$ an identical congruence, then $3a \equiv 1(\text{mod } 6)$. But there is no value of a that will satisfy this congruence.

On the other hand, the division of $4x^2 + x$ by $2x - 5$ modulo 6 is possible, but it is not exact, for

$$
\begin{array}{r}
2x - 5| \overline{4x^2 + 1} \qquad\quad | \underline{2x + 2} \\
\underline{4x^2 - 10x} \\
10x + 1 \equiv 4x + 1(\text{mod } 6) \\
\underline{4x - 10} \\
11 \equiv 5(\text{mod } 6)
\end{array}
$$

Hence, $4x^2 + 1 \equiv (2x - 5)(2x + 2) + 5(\text{mod } 6)$.

If we try to divide $4x^2 + x + 1$ by $2x - 5$ modulo 6, we find we cannot carry out the division far enough to obtain a remainder of the required form, for

$$
\begin{array}{r}
2x - 5| \overline{4x^2 + \quad x + 1} \qquad | \underline{2x} \\
\underline{4x^2 - 10x} \\
11x + 1 \equiv 5x + 1(\text{mod } 6)
\end{array}
$$

But $2y \equiv 5(\text{mod } 6)$ has no solution, and the best we can do is to write the identical congruence $4x^2 + x + 1 \equiv (2x - 5)(2x) + 5x + 1(\text{mod } 6)$.

However, if we change the form of the above divisor using $-4x - 5$ instead of $2x - 5$, we have

$$\underline{-4x - 5|}\ 4x^2 + \ x + 1 \qquad \underline{|\ -x + 1}$$
$$\underline{4x^2 + 5x}$$
$$- 4x + 1$$
$$\underline{- 4x - 5}$$
$$6 \equiv 0(\mathrm{mod}\ 6)$$

Hence, $4x^2 + x + 1 \equiv (-4x - 5)(-x + 1)(\mathrm{mod}\ 6)$.

We could obtain a like result by first adding $6x^2$ to $4x^2 + x + 1$, for we find that

$$\underline{2x - 5|}\ 10x^2 + \ \ x + 1 \qquad \underline{|\ 5x + 1}$$
$$\underline{10x^2 - 25x}$$
$$26x + 1 \equiv 2x + 1(\mathrm{mod}\ 6)$$
$$\underline{2x - 5}$$
$$6 \equiv 0(\mathrm{mod}\ 6)$$

We, therefore, have $4x^2 + x + 1 \equiv (2x - 5)(5x + 1)(\mathrm{mod}\ 6)$.

Notice, furthermore, that when the modulus is 6, we can divide $3x^3 + 1$ by $3x^2 - 1$, getting three distinct quotients and three distinct remainders, for

$$3x^3 + 1 \equiv (3x^2 - 1)(x) + x + 1(\mathrm{mod}\ 6)$$
$$3x^3 + 1 \equiv (3x^2 - 1)(3x) + 3x + 1(\mathrm{mod}\ 6)$$

and

$$3x^3 + 1 \equiv (3x^2 - 1)(5x) + 5x + 1(\mathrm{mod}\ 6)$$

When the modulus is a prime and the polynomials are not constants, it is easy to show that the division modulo p of $f_1(x)$ by $f_2(x)$ can always be accomplished, for any term present in either one of these polynomials has a coefficient that is prime to the modulus and the congruence $ay \equiv b(\mathrm{mod}\ p)$ has exactly one solution when $(a,p) = 1$. The remainder $r(x)$ will, therefore, be congruent either to zero modulo p or to an expression that is at least one degree lower than the degree of the divisor. In this case, moreover, both $q(x)$ and $r(x)$ are unique, for if

$$f_1(x) \equiv f_2(x)q_1(x) + r_1(x)(\mathrm{mod}\ p)$$

and

$$f_1(x) \equiv f_2(x)q_2(x) + r_2(x)(\mathrm{mod}\ p)$$

then

$$f_2(x)[q_1(x) - q_2(x)] \equiv r_2(x) - r_1(x)(\mathrm{mod}\ p)$$

If $q_1(x) - q_2(x) \not\equiv 0(\mathrm{mod}\ p)$, let its leading coefficient be $b_0 \not\equiv 0(\mathrm{mod}\ p)$, and let the leading coefficient of $f_2(x)$ be $a_0 \not\equiv 0(\mathrm{mod}\ p)$. Then the leading coefficient of $f_2(x)[q_1(x) - q_2(x)]$ is $a_0b_0 \not\equiv 0(\mathrm{mod}\ p)$, and the degree of this expression is at least that of $f_2(x)$, thereby exceeding the degree of $r_2(x) - r_1(x)$. This is impossible, and we infer that $q_1(x) \equiv q_2(x)(\mathrm{mod}\ p)$ identically and likewise that $r_1(x) \equiv r_2(x)(\mathrm{mod}\ p)$.

EXERCISES

1. Explain why $x^2 + 3$ cannot be divided by $4x - 2$ modulo 8. Carry out the division modulo 5.

2. Divide $x^2 - 2x + 5$ by $2x - 3$ modulo 7.

3. Divide $3x^2 - 2x + 4$ by $2x - 1$ modulo 15.

4. Divide $x^3 - 2x^2 + 5x - 1$ by $2x - 3$ modulo 11.

5. Divide $2x^2 - 2x + 5$ by $-2x - 3$ modulo 6, and then change the divisor to the form $4x - 3$ and carry out the division modulo 6.

6. Divide $4x^3 - 3x^2 + 2x + 1$ by $3x - 1$ modulo 11.

7. If $f(x) = a_0x^n + a_1x^{n-1} + \cdots + a_n$ and $g(x) = b_0x^t + b_1x^{t-1} + \cdots + b_t$ are integral polynomials with $t \leq n$, and if $(b_0, m) = 1$, do polynomials $q(x)$ and $r(x)$ exist so that $f(x) \equiv g(x)q(x) + r(x)(\bmod m)$ with $r(x)$ lower in degree than $g(x)$? If so, are these polynomials unique modulo m?

Theorem 5-4. If $x \equiv r(\bmod m)$ is a solution of the congruence $f(x) \equiv 0(\bmod m)$, where the polynomial $f(x) = a_0x^n + a_1x^{n-1} + \cdots + a_n$ with $a_0 \not\equiv 0(\bmod m)$, then $x - r$ is a factor of $f(x)$ for the modulus m, and conversely.

According to the remainder theorem of algebra, $f(r)$ is the remainder when $f(x)$ is divided by $x - r$. Consequently,

$$f(x) = (x - r)q(x) + f(r)$$

or

$$f(x) - f(r) = (x - r)q(x)$$

identically, and $q(x)$ is a polynomial $b_0x^{n-1} + b_1x^{n-2} + \cdots + b_{n-1}$. But $f(r)$ is an integer, and furthermore $f(r) \equiv 0(\bmod m)$, for r satisfies the given congruence. Therefore, the coefficients of $f(x) - f(r)$ are integers. Moreover, it is evident from a consideration of the process of long division or from the following argument that the coefficients of $q(x)$ are integers. Because the leading coefficient of $f(x)$ is an integer, the product $(x - r)q(x)$ shows that $b_0 = a_0$ is an integer. If b_1 were not an integer, the coefficient $a_1 = b_1 - rb_0$, where rb_0 is an integer, would not be an integer. In like manner the fact that b_{i-1} and $b_i - rb_{i-1}$, where $i = 1, 2, \ldots, n$, are integers implies that b_i is also an integer. Thus $q(x)$ is an integral polynomial. Hence,

$$f(x) - f(r) \equiv (x - r)q(x)(\bmod m)$$

and so

$$f(x) \equiv (x - r)q(x)(\bmod m)$$

identically, showing that $x - r$ is a factor of $f(x)$ for the modulus m.

Conversely, if

$$f(x) \equiv (x - r)q(x)(\bmod m)$$

then

$$f(r) \equiv 0(\bmod m)$$

and $x \equiv r(\bmod m)$ is a solution of $f(x) \equiv 0(\bmod m)$.

It is easy to show that when $x - r$ is a factor modulo m of $f(x)$, the quotient is unique.

5-5. The Number and Multiplicity of the Solutions of a Congruence. We have shown that the congruence $2x - 4 \equiv 0 \pmod 6$ has the solutions $x \equiv 2 \pmod 6$ and $x \equiv 5 \pmod 6$. Therefore, Theorem 5-4 shows that $x - 2$ and $x - 5$ are factors modulo 6 of $2x - 4$. Thus $2x - 4 \equiv 2(x - 2) \pmod 6$, and $2x - 4 \equiv 2(x - 5) \pmod 6$. Notice, however, that the product $(x - 2)(x - 5)$ is not a factor modulo 6 of $2x - 4$. On the other hand, if the modulus is a prime, the proof of the following theorem brings out the fact that when $r_1, r_2, \ldots, r_s$ are incongruent integers modulo p that satisfy $f(x) \equiv 0 \pmod p$, the product $(x - r_1)(x - r_2) \cdots (x - r_s)$ is a factor modulo p of $f(x)$.

The eminent mathematician Lagrange (1736–1813) improved the work of his teacher Euler in the calculus of variations, did extensive work in the solution of algebraic equations, and expanded the theory of differential equations. In the theory of numbers he was the first to prove Wilson's theorem and the first to prove that every integer is a sum of at most four squares. He gave a complete proof of the method of solving the equation $x^2 - by^2 = 1$ in integers. Again, he made important contributions to the theory of quadratic residues and binary quadratic forms. The next theorem is credited to him and reflects his interest in the solution of equations as well as congruences.

Theorem 5-5 (Lagrange's Theorem). If p is a prime and $f(x)$ is an integral polynomial $a_0 x^n + a_1 x^{n-1} + \cdots + a_n$ in which $a_0 \not\equiv 0 \pmod p$, then the congruence $f(x) \equiv 0 \pmod p$ has at most n incongruent solutions modulo p.

We have observed that the congruence $f(x) \equiv 0 \pmod p$ need have no solution, but if there is a solution $x \equiv r_1 \pmod p$, it follows from Theorem 5-4 that $x - r_1$ is a factor of $f(x)$ for the modulus p. If it should happen that $(x - r_1)^{n_1}$, where $1 < n_1 \leq n$, is a factor modulo p of $f(x)$ and if this power is the highest power of $x - r_1$ contained as a factor in $f(x)$, then $x \equiv r_1 \pmod p$ is said to be a solution of multiplicity n_1, and

$$f(x) \equiv (x - r_1)^{n_1} q_1(x) \pmod p$$

with $q_1(x)$ of degree $n - n_1$ and leading coefficient $b_0 \equiv a_0 \pmod p$.

If $n_1 < n$ and if the original congruence has another solution $x \equiv r_2 \pmod p$ with r_2 incongruent to r_1 modulo p, then

$$f(r_2) \equiv (r_2 - r_1)^{n_1} q_1(r_2) \pmod p$$

But since $f(r_2) \equiv 0 \pmod p$ and $r_1 \not\equiv r_2 \pmod p$, it is evident that $q_1(r_2) \equiv 0 \pmod p$ and, as above,

$$q_1(x) \equiv (x - r_2)^{n_2} q_2(x) \pmod p$$

so that

$$f(x) \equiv (x - r_1)^{n_1}(x - r_2)^{n_2}q_2(x)(\text{mod } p)$$

identically.

If $f(x) \equiv 0(\text{mod } p)$ has one or more other distinct solutions for the modulus p, we continue in this manner until either all the solutions which are fewer than n in number have been found or we have at most n linear factors modulo p of $f(x)$. In the latter case we find the identical congruence

$$f(x) \equiv a_0(x - r_1)^{n_1}(x - r_2)^{n_2} \cdots (x - r_k)^{n_k}(\text{mod } p) \qquad (1)$$

where $n_1 + n_2 + \cdots + n_k = n$, and hence there are n solutions, for a solution of multiplicity n_i, where $i = 1, 2, \ldots, k$, is counted n_i times.

If we now substitute for x in (1) any integer s not congruent to any r_i, where $i = 1, 2, \ldots, k$, for the modulus p, we find

$$f(s) \equiv a_0(s - r_1)^{n_1}(s - r_2)^{n_2} \cdots (s - r_k)^{n_k}(\text{mod } p) \qquad (2)$$

But $s - r_i \not\equiv 0(\text{mod } p)$, and $a_0 \not\equiv 0(\text{mod } p)$. Consequently, $f(s) \not\equiv 0(\text{mod } p)$, and $x \equiv s(\text{mod } p)$ is not a solution of $f(x) \equiv 0(\text{mod } p)$. Therefore, there can be no more than n solutions.

It is easy to show, furthermore, that the solutions are the same regardless of the order in which they are found.

Moreover, the multiplicity of each solution is unique regardless of the order in which the factors are obtained, for if

$$f(x) \equiv (x - r_1)^u q_1(x) \equiv (x - r_1)^v q_2(x)(\text{mod } p)$$

where neither $q_1(x)$ nor $q_2(x)$ is divisible modulo p by $x - r_1$, and if $u > v$, we have the identical congruence

$$(x - r_1)^v[(x - r_1)^{u-v}q_1(x) - q_2(x)] \equiv 0(\text{mod } p)$$

But if the leading coefficient of the expansion of $(x - r_1)^{u-v}q_1(x) - q_2(x)$ is not congruent to zero modulo p, the leading coefficient of the last congruence written in the expanded form cannot be congruent to zero modulo p. The congruence states, however, that when it is written in the form $a_0x^n + a_1x^{n-1} + \cdots + a_n \equiv 0(\text{mod } p)$, all its coefficients are multiples of p. Consequently, the leading coefficient and, in like manner, each of the other coefficients of the expansion of $(x - r_1)^{u-v}q_1(x) - q_2(x)$ are congruent to zero modulo p. Therefore, we have the identical congruence

$$(x - r_1)^{u-v}q_1(x) \equiv q_2(x)(\text{mod } p)$$

Substituting r_1 for x, we find

$$(r_1 - r_1)^{u-v}q_1(r_1) \equiv q_2(r_1)(\text{mod } p)$$

As a result $q_2(r_1) \equiv 0 \pmod{p}$, and $x - r_1$ is a factor modulo p of $q_2(x)$, which is contrary to our assumption.

It is obvious, of course, that when $n > p$, the congruence $f(x) \equiv 0 \pmod{p}$ can have no more than p distinct solutions modulo p.

Again, let us observe that if we place no condition on the a_0 of $f(x) \equiv 0 \pmod{p}$ and assume that the congruence has an $(n + 1)$st solution $x \equiv s \pmod{p}$ that is distinct from each r_i, where $i = 1, 2, \ldots, k$, for the modulus p, the congruence (2) requires that a_0 be congruent to zero modulo p. Consequently, the identical congruence (1) implies that every coefficient of $f(x)$ is congruent to zero modulo p. Hence, we conclude:

Theorem 5-6. If the congruence $a_0 x^n + a_1 x^{n-1} + \cdots + a_n \equiv 0 \pmod{p}$, with p a prime, has more than n solutions (a solution of multiplicity m being counted m times), each a_i, where $i = 0, 1, \ldots, n$, is congruent to zero modulo p and the congruence is an identical congruence.

Example. Find by trial the solutions of $x^4 + x^2 - x + 2 \equiv 0 \pmod{5}$. If $f(x) = x^4 + x^2 - x + 2$, $f(-1) = 5$. Hence, $x + 1$ is a factor of $f(x)$ modulo 5. By using synthetic division we find $f(x) \equiv (x + 1)(x^3 - x^2 + 2x - 3) \pmod{5}$. Let $f_1(x) = x^3 - x^2 + 2x - 3$. Then $f_1(-3) = -45$, and therefore $f(x) \equiv (x + 1)(x + 3)(x^2 - 4x + 4) \pmod{5}$. It is now evident that $f(x) \equiv (x + 1)(x + 3)(x - 2)^2 \pmod{5}$ and that besides the solutions $x \equiv -1 \pmod{5}$, $x \equiv -3 \pmod{5}$, there is a double solution $x \equiv 2 \pmod{5}$.

Theorem 5-7. If p is a prime, the congruence $f(x) \equiv 0 \pmod{p}$ of degree $n < p$ has a solution $x \equiv a \pmod{p}$ of multiplicity $r \leq n$ if and only if $f(a) \equiv 0 \pmod{p}$, $f'(a) \equiv 0 \pmod{p}$, $\ldots$, $f^{(r-1)}(a) \equiv 0 \pmod{p}$, and $f^{(r)}(a) \not\equiv 0 \pmod{p}$.

We recall that $x \equiv a \pmod{p}$ is a solution of multiplicity r of $f(x) \equiv 0 \pmod{p}$ if and only if $(x - a)^r$ is a factor modulo p of the polynomial $f(x)$, but $(x - a)^{r+1}$ is not a factor modulo p of $f(x)$. Furthermore, we notice that if we define the derivative with respect to x of $f(x) \equiv a_0 x^n + a_1 x^{n-1} + \cdots + a_n$ as $f'(x) = a_0 n x^{n-1} + a_1(n - 1)x^{n-2} + \cdots + a_{n-1}$, the application of Taylor's theorem to the polynomial $f(x)$ sets up the identity

$$f(x) = f(a) + (x - a)f'(a) + (x - a)^2 \frac{f''(a)}{2!} + \cdots + (x - a)^n \frac{f^{(n)}(a)}{n!}$$

If $f(a) \equiv 0 \pmod{p}$, $f'(a) \equiv 0 \pmod{p}$, $\ldots$, and $f^{(r-1)}(a) \equiv 0 \pmod{p}$, but $f^{(r)}(a) \not\equiv 0 \pmod{p}$ for $r \leq n$, then, the $f^{(i)}(a)/i!$ being integers, we have

$$f(x) \equiv (x - a)^r \frac{f^{(r)}(a)}{r!} + \cdots + (x - a)^n \frac{f^{(n)}(a)}{n!} \pmod{p}$$

and

$$f(x) \equiv (x - a)^r Q(x) \pmod{p}$$

If $(x - a)^{r+1}$ were a factor modulo p of $f(x)$, then

$$(x - a)^{r+1}q(x) \equiv (x - a)^r Q(x) \pmod{p}$$

and the identical congruence

$$(x - a)^r[(x - a)q(x) - Q(x)] \equiv 0 \pmod{p}$$

implies that

$$(x - a)q(x) \equiv Q(x) \pmod{p}$$

Hence, $[f^{(r)}(a)/r!] + \cdots + (x - a)^{n-r}[f^{(n)}(a)/n!]$ has the factor $x - a$ modulo p, and so $f^{(r)}(a) \equiv 0 \pmod{p}$, which is contrary to the hypothesis.

To prove the converse of the theorem, first call to mind the rule for differentiating a product of two functions, and remember that when a polynomial has been factored into two polynomials, this rule enables us to set up an identity between two forms of $f'(x)$, for if

$$f(x) = a_0x^n + a_1x^{n-1} + \cdots + a_n = (b_0x^r + \cdots + b_r)(c_0x^s + \cdots + c_s)$$

then

$$f'(x) = a_0nx^{n-1} + a_1(n - 1)x^{n-2} + \cdots + a_{n-1} = (b_0x^r + \cdots + b_r)(c_0sx^{s-1} + \cdots + c_{s-1}) + (b_0rx^{r-1} + \cdots + b_{r-1})(c_0x^s + \cdots + c_s)$$

On this basis the method of induction shows that it is valid to apply Leibnitz's rule for the kth derivative of a product to this case. If u and v are polynomials in x, we may, therefore, write

$$\frac{d^k(uv)}{dx^k} = v\frac{d^ku}{dx^k} + k\frac{dv}{dx}\frac{d^{k-1}u}{dx^{k-1}} + \frac{k(k - 1)}{2!}\frac{d^2v}{dx^2}\frac{d^{k-2}u}{dx^{k-2}} + \cdots + u\frac{d^kv}{dx^k}$$

Consequently, if $f(x) \equiv (x - a)^r q(x) \pmod{p}$, then the formula verifies the statement that $f^{(k)}(a) \equiv 0 \pmod{p}$ for $k < r$, because clearly each $d^s(x - a)^r/dx^s$ has a factor $x - a$ when $s < r$. But $(x - a)^{r+1}$ is not a factor modulo p of $f(x)$, and so we infer from $q(a) \not\equiv 0 \pmod{p}$ and

$$\frac{d^r[(x - a)^r q(x)]}{dx^r} = (x - a)^r q^{(r)}(x) + \cdots + r(r!)(x - a)q'(x) + (r!)q(x)$$

that $f^{(r)}(a) \not\equiv 0 \pmod{p}$.

To make it plain that the restriction which Theorem 5-7 places on the degree of $f(x) \equiv 0 \pmod{p}$ is a necessary one, consider the congruence $x^{10} - x^5 \equiv 0 \pmod{5}$. Its only solutions are $x \equiv 0 \pmod{5}$ of multiplicity 5 and the simple solution $x \equiv 1 \pmod{5}$. Nevertheless, $f^{(k)}(0)$ and $f^{(k)}(1)$ are congruent to 0 modulo 5 for all positive values of k.

When we are solving a congruence by trial, it is often helpful to make use of the following two theorems to eliminate some of the possible solutions:

*Theorem 5-8.** If r satisfies the congruence $a_0x^n + a_1x^{n-1} + \cdots + a_n \equiv 0(\text{mod } m)$, then r is a factor modulo m of a_n.

Since r is a solution of the congruence, $a_0x^n + a_1x^{n-1} + \cdots + a_n \equiv (x - r)Q(x)(\text{mod } m)$, where $Q(x) \equiv b_0x^{n-1} + \cdots + b_{n-1}(\text{mod } m)$ and $b_0 \equiv a_0(\text{mod } m)$. Hence, $a_n \equiv -rb_{n-1}(\text{mod } m)$, and thus r is a factor modulo m of a_n.

*Theorem 5-9.** If r satisfies the congruence $f(x) \equiv 0(\text{mod } m)$, then $r - a$ divides $f(a)$ modulo m.

The hypothesis implies that $f(x) \equiv (x - r)Q(x)(\text{mod } m)$. Substituting a for x, we derive $f(a) \equiv (a - r)Q(a)(\text{mod } m)$.

Example. Solve $f(x) \equiv x^3 - 4x^2 - 11x + 6 \equiv 0(\text{mod } 12)$ by trial.

Applying Theorem 5-8, the possible solutions are obtained by considering the congruences $rx \equiv 6(\text{mod } 12)$ for $r = 1, 2, \ldots, 11$. The values $r = 4$ and 8 are immediately ruled out, for the corresponding linear congruences have no solution.

Then we find that $f(1) = -8$, and we apply Theorem 5-9. The values $r = 7$ and 10 are thereby eliminated, for there is no y such that $(r - 1)y \equiv -8(\text{mod } 12)$. The possible solutions are, therefore, narrowed to 2, 3, 5, 6, 9, and 11 modulo 12, and the substitution of these values in $f(x)$ shows that each one is a solution of the given congruence.

5-6. The Chinese Remainder Theorem. The problem of finding an integer that yields certain remainders upon being divided by given integers was familiar to the Chinese as early as the first century. The solution is now easily effected by using congruences. When the integers $m_1, m_2, \ldots, m_n$ are relatively prime in pairs, we wish to find an integer x such that

$$\begin{aligned} x &\equiv a_1(\text{mod } m_1) \\ x &\equiv a_2(\text{mod } m_2) \\ &\cdots\cdots\cdots \\ x &\equiv a_n(\text{mod } m_n) \end{aligned} \tag{3}$$

Let $M = \prod_{i=1}^{n} m_i$ and $M_i = M/m_i$, where $i = 1, 2, \ldots, n$. Then set up the n congruences

$$M_i x \equiv 1(\text{mod } m_i) \tag{4}$$

In each case $(M_i, m_i) = 1$, and there is exactly one solution $x \equiv x_i(\text{mod } m_i)$ of each congruence (4). Now consider

$$X \equiv M_1x_1a_1 + M_2x_2a_2 + \cdots + M_nx_na_n(\text{mod } M)$$

and substitute X for x in $x \equiv a_1(\text{mod } m_1)$. Since M and each M_i except M_1 are congruent to 0, and M_1x_1 is congruent to 1 for the modulus m_1, every integer of the form $X + kM$ satisfies $x \equiv a_1(\text{mod } m_1)$. In like manner the integers in the residue class of X modulo M satisfy all the given congruences.

But this class of integers is the only simultaneous solution of the set of congruences, for if there were a second solution X_1, the substitution of X and X_1 in the given congruences (3) shows that

$$X \equiv X_1 (\bmod \; m_i)$$

and since the m_i are relatively prime in pairs,

$$X \equiv X_1 (\bmod \; M)$$

Hence, we have shown that:

Theorem 5-10. If the m_i, where $i = 1, 2, \ldots, n$, are relatively prime in pairs, the congruences $x \equiv a_i (\bmod \; m_i)$ have one and only one simultaneous solution modulo $M = \prod_{i=1}^{n} m_i$.

Example. Find all integers that give the remainders **2, 6, 5** when divided by **5, 7,** and **11,** respectively.

$$M = 385 \qquad M_1 = 77 \qquad M_2 = 55 \qquad M_3 = 35$$
$77x \equiv 1 (\bmod \; 5)$ or $2x \equiv 1 (\bmod \; 5)$ has the solution $x \equiv 3 (\bmod \; 5)$
$55x \equiv 1 (\bmod \; 7)$ or $6x \equiv 1 (\bmod \; 7)$ has the solution $x \equiv 6 (\bmod \; 7)$
$35x \equiv 1 (\bmod \; 11)$ or $2x \equiv 1 (\bmod \; 11)$ has the solution $x \equiv 6 (\bmod \; 11)$

Hence, $X \equiv (77)(3)(2) + (55)(6)(6) + (35)(6)(5) (\bmod \; 385)$, or $X \equiv 27 (\bmod \; 385)$.

5-7. Other Simultaneous Linear Congruences. We shall demonstrate a method for finding a solution, when it exists, of certain linear simultaneous congruences whose moduli are not relatively prime in pairs by proving the following theorem by induction:

*Theorem 5-11. The set of n linear congruences $x \equiv a_i (\bmod \; m_i)$ has a solution if and only if the greatest common divisor of any pair of moduli, m_i, m_j, i and j having the values $1, 2, \ldots, n$, with $i \neq j$, divides the corresponding $a_i - a_j$. When the integer X_0 satisfies each congruence of the set,† all common solutions take the form $X_0 + Lt$, where L is the least common multiple of the m_i and t is any integer.

Taking the two congruences

$$\begin{aligned} x &\equiv a_1 (\bmod \; m_1) \\ x &\equiv a_2 (\bmod \; m_2) \end{aligned} \tag{5}$$

† Oystein Ore gave the general form of the solution in *Am. Math. Monthly*, Vol. 59, No. 6, pp. 365–370, 1952.

with $d_{12} = (m_1, m_2)$, let us suppose that x_0 satisfies both of them. Then since

$$x_0 \equiv a_1(\text{mod } m_1)$$
$$x_0 \equiv a_2(\text{mod } m_2)$$

we infer that

$$x_0 \equiv a_1(\text{mod } d_{12})$$
$$x_0 \equiv a_2(\text{mod } d_{12})$$

and that

$$a_1 \equiv a_2(\text{mod } d_{12})$$

Conversely, if d_{12} divides $a_1 - a_2$, we can show that there is a solution of the first congruence that satisfies the second one. Every solution of the first congruence is of the form $a_1 + m_1 y$, and if any of these integers satisfy the second congruence, the values of y are determined by the congruence

$$a_1 + m_1 y \equiv a_2(\text{mod } m_2)$$

or

$$m_1 y \equiv a_2 - a_1(\text{mod } m_2)$$

But since $d_{12} \mid (a_2 - a_1)$, there is at least one value y_0 of y that produces a simultaneous solution $a_1 + m_1 y_0$ of the two congruences.

Moreover, if there are two integers x_0 and x_1 that satisfy the given congruences (5), substituting them in these congruences shows that

$$x_1 \equiv x_0(\text{mod } m_1)$$
$$x_1 \equiv x_0(\text{mod } m_2)$$

and hence that

$$x_1 \equiv x_0(\text{mod } L)$$

where L is the least common multiple of m_1 and m_2. Furthermore, any integer of the form $x_0 + Lt$ is a common solution of the congruences if x_0 is, for Lt is congruent to 0 for both the moduli m_1 and m_2.

Suppose now that the theorem is true for a set of $k - 1$ congruences of the given form. Then if there is a common solution X_0, all and only simultaneous solutions of the set are of the form $X_0 + L_{k-1}t$, where L_{k-1} is the least common multiple of $m_1, m_2, \ldots, m_{k-1}$, and t is the parameter.

If X is a solution of a set of k congruences of the required form, certainly X satisfies the first $k - 1$ congruences, and thus it is true that $d_{ij} = d_{ji} = (m_i, m_j)$ divides $a_i - a_j$ for $i, j = 1, 2, \ldots, k - 1$, and $i \neq j$. But

$$X \equiv a_i(\text{mod } m_i) \qquad i = 1, 2, \ldots, k - 1$$

and

$$X \equiv a_k(\text{mod } m_k)$$

Hence,

$$X \equiv a_i(\text{mod } d_{ik})$$
$$X \equiv a_k(\text{mod } d_{ik})$$

and therefore

$$a_i \equiv a_k(\text{mod } d_{ik})$$

Consequently, d_{ij} divides $a_i - a_j$ for $i, j = 1, 2, \ldots, k$, where $i \neq j$.

Conversely, if d_{ij} divides $a_i - a_j$ for $i, j = 1, 2, \ldots, k$, common solutions of the first $k - 1$ congruences exist and have the form $X_0 + L_{k-1}t$, where X_0 is a simultaneous solution. It is, moreover, possible to determine a value for the parameter t so that this expression will produce a solution of $x \equiv a_k(\text{mod } m_k)$. To prove this statement, consider the congruence

$$X_0 + L_{k-1}t \equiv a_k(\text{mod } m_k)$$

in the form

$$L_{k-1}t \equiv a_k - X_0(\text{mod } m_k)$$

We can show that this congruence has a solution $t \equiv t_0(\text{mod } m_k)$ by proving that the greatest common divisor of L_{k-1} and m_k divides $a_k - X_0$.

If p is a prime factor of any of the m_i, let m_i' be the exponent of the highest power of that prime contained in m_i. The highest power of this p in L_{k-1} is the highest power of p that is in any one of $m_1, m_2, \ldots, m_{k-1}$. Suppose it is $p^{m_r'}$, the power of p that occurs in m_r, where $1 \leq r \leq k - 1$. Then the exponent of the highest power of the prime p that is contained in $D = (m_k, L_{k-1})$ is the smaller of m_k' and m_r'. Let this integer be m_s'. But

$$X_0 - a_r \equiv 0(\text{mod } m_r)$$

and hence

$$X_0 - a_r \equiv 0(\text{mod } p^{m_r'})$$

Since $a_k - a_r$ is divisible by the greatest common divisor of m_k and m_r, it is divisible by that power of p determined by the smaller of the two exponents m_k' and m_r', that is, by m_s'. But from the above congruences $X_0 - a_r$ is divisible by the power of p designated by the smaller of the exponents m_k' and m_r'. Hence,

$$X_0 - a_r \equiv 0(\text{mod } p^{m_s'})$$

and

$$a_k - a_r \equiv 0(\text{mod } p^{m_s'})$$

Therefore,

$$X_0 - a_k \equiv 0(\text{mod } p^{m_s'})$$

Furthermore, since this congruence is true for any prime factor of $D = (m_k, L_{k-1})$, the integer $X_0 - a_k$ is divisible by the product of the very powers of the primes that are contained in D; that is, $X - a_k$ is divisible by D. Thus there is a value of t that forces a solution of the first $k - 1$ congruences to satisfy the kth one, $x \equiv a_k \pmod{m_k}$.

Again, any two solutions of the set of k congruences $x \equiv a_i \pmod{m_i}$ must be congruent modulo the least common multiple of $m_1, m_2, \ldots, m_k$, for two solutions X_0 and X_1 are such that

$$X_0 \equiv X_1 \pmod{L_{k-1}}$$
$$X_0 \equiv X_1 \pmod{m_k}$$

and hence

$$X_0 \equiv X_1 \pmod{L_k}$$

where L_k is the least common multiple of L_{k-1} and m_k and hence of m_1, $m_2, \ldots, m_k$. Moreover, all integers of the form $X_0 + L_k t$ satisfy each congruence of the given set if X_0 is a common solution.

Example. Solve:

$$x \equiv 7 \pmod{18}$$
$$x \equiv 10 \pmod{15}$$
$$x \equiv 1 \pmod{14}$$

Let $d_1 = (18, 15) = 3$, $d_2 = (18, 14) = 2$, $d_3 = (15, 14) = 1$. It is evident that $d_1 \mid (7 - 10)$, $d_2 \mid (7 - 1)$, $d_3 \mid (10 - 1)$. Therefore, a solution exists.

Substituting $7 + 18t$ in the second congruence, we find

$$18t \equiv 3 \pmod{15}$$

so that

$$t \equiv 1 \pmod{15}$$

Since 90 is the least common multiple of 18 and 15, we substitute $7 + 18 + 90s$ in the third congruence and have

$$90s \equiv -24 \pmod{14}$$

and therefore

$$s \equiv 3 \pmod{14}$$

Hence, the common solution is $X \equiv 295 \pmod{630}$.

EXERCISES

1. Find by trial all the solutions of $3x^4 - 3x^3 - 2x^2 + 3x + 6 \equiv 0 \pmod{7}$.

2. Find the solutions of $x^6 + 10x^5 + 4x^4 - x^3 + x + 6 \equiv 0 \pmod{11}$.

3. Decide whether or not the following congruences have multiple solutions.

a.
$$x^3 + x^2 + 3 \equiv 0 \pmod{5}$$
b.
$$2x^3 + 1 \equiv 0 \pmod{3}$$

4. Find the common solutions of the following sets of congruences.

a.
$$x \equiv 2(\text{mod } 11)$$
$$x \equiv 4(\text{mod } 15)$$
$$x \equiv 9(\text{mod } 14)$$

b.
$$x \equiv 11(\text{mod } 21)$$
$$x \equiv 2(\text{mod } 12)$$
$$x \equiv 4(\text{mod } 10)$$

c.
$$x \equiv 12(\text{mod } 46)$$
$$x \equiv 1(\text{mod } 31)$$
$$x \equiv 16(\text{mod } 28)$$

5. Find a multiple of 7 that has the remainders 1, 2, 3, 4, and 5 when it is divided, respectively, by 2, 3, 4, 5, and 6.

5-8. The Number of Solutions of the Congruence $f(x) \equiv 0(mod\ m)$.

If the p_i, where $i = 1, 2, \ldots, r$, are distinct primes and $m = p_1^{n_1} p_2^{n_2} \cdots p_r^{n_r}$, there is a solution of the congruence

$$f(x) \equiv 0(\text{mod } m) \tag{6}$$

where $f(x)$ is an integral polynomial, if and only if there is a simultaneous solution of the equivalent set of congruences

$$f(x) \equiv 0(\text{mod } p_1^{n_1})$$
$$f(x) \equiv 0(\text{mod } p_2^{n_2})$$
$$\cdots \cdots \cdots \cdots \tag{7}$$
$$f(x) \equiv 0(\text{mod } p_r^{n_r})$$

But if there is a solution of each of the individual congruences of (7), we can build up a simultaneous solution of the set by means of the Chinese remainder theorem. Suppose that integers x_i satisfy $f(x) \equiv 0(\text{mod } p_i^{n_i})$, where $i = 1, 2, \ldots, r$. Then find the common solution of the congruences

$$x \equiv x_i(\text{mod } p_i^{n_i}) \tag{8}$$

Let this solution be $x \equiv X_1(\text{mod } m)$. The integer X_1 satisfies both the set (7) and the original congruence (6) because for each i

$$X_1 \equiv x_i(\text{mod } p_i^{n_i})$$

and therefore

$$f(X_1) \equiv f(x_i)(\text{mod } p_i^{n_i})$$

But

$$f(x_i) \equiv 0(\text{mod } p_i^{n_i})$$

so that

$$f(X_1) \equiv 0(\text{mod } p_i^{n_i})$$

and

$$f(X_1) \equiv 0(\text{mod } m)$$

If in the set of congruences (8) we replace the solution of just one of the congruences of (7), say the first one, by a solution x_1' distinct from x_1 modulo $p_1^{n_1}$, the solution $x \equiv X_2(\bmod\ m)$ of the resulting set,

$$x \equiv x_1'(\bmod\ p_1^{n_1})$$
$$x \equiv x_j(\bmod\ p_j^{n_j}) \qquad j = 2, 3, \ldots, r$$

will be distinct modulo m from the solution X_1 of (8), for if the solutions were the same,

$$X_1 \equiv X_2(\bmod\ m)$$

would imply that

$$X_1 \equiv X_2(\bmod\ p_i^{n_i}) \qquad i = 1, 2, \ldots, r$$

Then

$$x_1 \equiv x_1'(\bmod\ p_1^{n_1})$$

whereas we assumed that these integers are incongruent solutions of $f(x) \equiv 0(\bmod\ p_1^{n_1})$. Hence, if each congruence of (7) has k_i solutions, by inserting them in (8), we see that there are $k_1 k_2 \cdots k_r$ solutions modulo m of $f(x) \equiv 0(\bmod\ m)$.

It is evident too that if one congruence of (7) fails to have a solution, there is no solution of $f(x) \equiv 0(\bmod\ m)$. Thus we have shown that:

Theorem 5-12. If the congruences $f(x) \equiv 0(\bmod\ p_i^{n_i})$, where $i = 1,$ 2, . . . , r, have $k_i \geq 0$ solutions, respectively, there are exactly $\prod\limits_{i=1}^{r} k_i$ incongruent solutions modulo m of $f(x) \equiv 0(\bmod\ m)$, where $m = \prod\limits_{i=1}^{r} p_i^{n_i}$ and the p_i are distinct primes.

We have, therefore, reduced the problem of solving a congruence $f(x) \equiv 0(\bmod\ m)$ to that of solving a congruence whose modulus is a power of a prime.

5-9. The Solution of $f(x) \equiv 0(\bmod\ p^s)$. Any integer that satisfies $f(x) \equiv 0(\bmod\ p^s)$, where p is a prime and $f(x)$ is an integral polynomial, evidently satisfies the congruence

$$f(x) \equiv 0(\bmod\ p^{s-1})$$

The converse, however, is not true, but it is obvious that if the second congruence fails to have a solution, $f(x) \equiv 0(\bmod\ p^s)$ can have no solution.

Suppose that $f(x) \equiv 0(\bmod\ p^{s-1})$ has a solution $x \equiv x'(\bmod\ p^{s-1})$. Under what conditions will one of these integers, $x' + kp^{s-1}$, be a solution of $f(x) \equiv 0(\bmod\ p^s)$? We must determine which values of k, if any, will satisfy the congruence

$$f(x' + kp^{s-1}) \equiv 0 \pmod{p^s}$$

When $f(x) = a_0 x^n + a_1 x^{n-1} + \cdots + a_n$ is a rational integral function of x, we have defined the derivative of $f(x)$ with respect to x as $a_0 n x^{n-1} + a_1(n-1)x^{n-2} + \cdots + a_{n-1}$. The expansion of $f(x + h)$ according to Taylor's theorem is finite and is of necessity valid for integral values of x. Consequently,

$$f(x' + kp^{s-1}) \equiv f(x') + kp^{s-1}f'(x') + k^2 p^{2s-2}\frac{f''(x')}{2!} + \cdots$$
$$+ k^n p^{ns-n}\frac{f^{(n)}(x')}{n!} \pmod{p^s}$$

is an identical congruence, the expressions $f^{(r)}(x')/r!$ having been shown to be integers. Moreover, if $s \geq 2$, then $p^{rs-r} \geq p^s$ for $r \geq 2$ and hence all except the first two terms of the expansion are congruent to 0 for the modulus p^s, so that

$$f(x' + kp^{s-1}) \equiv f(x') + kp^{s-1}f'(x') \pmod{p^s}$$

But if $x' + kp^{s-1}$ is to satisfy $f(x) \equiv 0 \pmod{p^s}$, this congruence shows that $f(x') + kp^{s-1}f'(x')$ must be divisible by p^s, and therefore k must be chosen to satisfy the congruence $f(x') + kp^{s-1}f'(x') \equiv 0 \pmod{p^s}$. We know that $f(x') = tp^{s-1}$, and therefore the last congruence can be reduced to the congruence $t + kf'(x') \equiv 0 \pmod{p}$.

When the greatest common divisor of $f'(x')$ and p is 1, the congruence $kf'(x') \equiv -t \pmod{p}$ has exactly one solution $k \equiv k_1 \pmod{p}$. This value of k yields exactly one solution $x \equiv x' + k_1 p^{s-1} \pmod{p^s}$ of $f(x) \equiv 0 \pmod{p^s}$.

When the greatest common divisor of $f'(x')$ and p is p, and p does not divide t, the solution $x \equiv x' \pmod{p^{s-1}}$ of $f(x) \equiv 0 \pmod{p^{s-1}}$ does not yield a solution of $f(x) \equiv 0 \pmod{p^s}$. But if p does divide t, $f(x')$ is a multiple of p^s, and when k has the values $0, 1, \ldots, p - 1$, each of the p integers $x' + kp^{s-1}$ is a distinct solution modulo p^s of $f(x) \equiv 0 \pmod{p^s}$. We have therefore proved:

Theorem 5-13. If $f(x) = a_0 x^n + a_1 x^{n-1} + \cdots + a_n$ and x' satisfies the congruence $f(x) \equiv 0 \pmod{p^{s-1}}$ and (1) if $(f'(x'),p) = 1$, there is exactly one value of k such that $x \equiv x' + kp^{s-1} \pmod{p^s}$ is a solution of $f(x) \equiv 0 \pmod{p^s}$, but (2) if $(f'(x'),p) = p$, no solution of $f(x) \equiv 0 \pmod{p^s}$ can be derived from x' unless x' itself satisfies $f(x) \equiv 0 \pmod{p^s}$, in which case $x' + kp^{s-1}$ yields exactly p incongruent solutions modulo p^s by letting k have all the values in a complete residue system modulo p.

According to this theorem, to solve $f(x) \equiv 0 \pmod{p^s}$, we first solve $f(x) \equiv 0 \pmod{p}$ and then determine by means of linear congruences modulo p the solutions, if there are any, of $f(x) \equiv 0(\mod p^2)$, $f(x) \equiv 0(\mod p^3)$, ...

Example. To solve $2x^2 - 3x - 1 \equiv 0(\mod 19^2)$, first take $f(x) = 2x^2 - 3x - 1 \equiv 0(\mod 19)$ and find the solutions $x \equiv 4, 7(\mod 19)$. Since $f(4) = 19$, $t = 1$. Also $f'(x) = 4x - 3$, and therefore $f'(4) = 13$. Hence, we must solve $1 + 13k \equiv 0(\mod 19)$. But $k \equiv -3(\mod 19)$, so that $x \equiv 4 - (3)(19) \equiv 308(\mod 19^2)$ is a solution of the original congruence.

Let the student show that $x \equiv 235(\mod 19^2)$ is the solution derived from $x \equiv 7(\mod 19)$.

After showing that $x \equiv 3(\mod 4)$ is the solution of $f(x) \equiv 0(\mod 4)$, apply the Chinese remainder theorem to find the solutions of $f(x) \equiv 0(\mod 2^2 \cdot 19^2)$.

EXERCISES

Solve the following congruences.

1. $3x^2 - 2x + 3 \equiv 0(\mod 72)$.
2. $4x^3 + 7x^2 + 16x - 2 \equiv 0(\mod 45)$.
3. $6x^2 + 17x - 20 \equiv 0(\mod 500)$.
4. $x^3 - 19x^2 + 32x + 34 \equiv 0(\mod 75)$.
5. $2x^3 - x^2 + 20x + 4 \equiv 0(\mod 1089)$.
6. $5x^2 - 24x - 9 \equiv 0(\mod 1350)$.
7. $x^3 - x^2 - 2x - 2 \equiv 0(\mod 2000)$.
8. $2x^3 + x^2 - 6x - 13 \equiv 0(\mod 340)$.
9. $x^3 - 2x^2 - 8x - 6 \equiv 0(\mod 357)$.
10. $x^3 - 5x^2 - 12x + 6 \equiv 0(\mod 1700)$.

CHAPTER 6

THE THEOREMS OF FERMAT AND WILSON AND THE MÖBIUS FUNCTION

6-1. Fermat's Theorem. Pierre de Fermat (1601–1665) was a profound scholar who was not especially attracted to mathematics until a translation of the work of Diophantus excited his interest. Once having embarked on the study of mathematics, he influenced its development in all the branches known at the time. With Pascal he originated basic ideas in the theory of probability, and independent of Descartes he developed the analytical geometry. He also helped to lay the foundations for the calculus. But he is renowned for his work in the theory of numbers. Unfortunately he failed to publish the many theorems he discovered about the integers, and when he announced his results in letters to other mathematicians, he usually concealed his methods of proof.

The Chinese knew as early as 500 B.C. that $2^p - 2$ is divisible by p if p is a prime, but it remained for Fermat in 1640 to state that if p is a prime and $(a, p) = 1$, then $a^{p-1} \equiv 1 \pmod{p}$. We do not have his demonstration of this fact, but by 1761 both this theorem and the more general one stated below had been proved by Euler.

The Chinese also believed that if n is not a prime, $2^n - 2$ is not divisible by n. Even Leibnitz (1646–1716) thought this statement to be true. Not until the latter part of the eighteenth century did mathematicians show signs of resolving the problem. The conjecture was finally disproved in 1819 when Sarrus found that 341, which is not a prime, is a factor of $2^{341} - 2$.* Since then it has been shown that there is an infinite number of composites n that will divide $2^n - 2$.

Theorem 6-1. If the integer a is prime to m, $a^{\phi(m)} \equiv 1 \pmod{m}$.

We showed in Chap. 4 that when $(a, m) = 1$ and $r_1, r_2, \ldots, r_{\phi(m)}$ is a reduced residue system modulo m, the set $ar_1, ar_2, \ldots, ar_{\phi(m)}$ is also a reduced residue system modulo m. The integers in the second set are, therefore, in some order congruent to those in the first set. Hence,

---

*L. E. Dickson, "History of the Theory of Numbers," Vol. 1, p. 92. D. H. Lehmer, *Am. Math. Monthly*, Vol. 43, No. 6, p. 347, 1936.

$$ar_1 \equiv r_{i1}(\text{mod } m)$$
$$ar_2 \equiv r_{i2}(\text{mod } m)$$
$$\cdot \cdot \cdot \cdot \cdot \cdot \cdot \cdot \cdot \cdot$$
$$ar_{\phi(m)} \equiv r_{i\phi(m)}(\text{mod } m)$$

Therefore,

$$a^{\phi(m)}r_1r_2 \cdot \cdot \cdot r_{\phi(m)} \equiv r_1r_2 \cdot \cdot \cdot r_{\phi(m)}(\text{mod } m)$$

and

$$a^{\phi(m)} \equiv 1(\text{mod } m)$$

Corollary 1. If p is a prime and a is prime to p, $a^{p-1} \equiv 1(\text{mod } p)$.

Corollary 2. If p is a prime and a is any integer, $a^p \equiv a(\text{mod } p)$.

Examples. $5^6 \equiv 1(\text{mod } 7)$; $2^{48} \equiv 1(\text{mod } 105)$.

EXERCISES

1. Find the remainder when 7^{48} is divided by 180; when 11^{50} is divided by 180.

2. What do you notice about the least positive residues of the powers of 3 modulo 7? Is the same fact true of the powers of 2 modulo 7?

3. Find the remainder when 2^{100} is divided by 11 and when 2^{105} is divided by 11.

4. Show that $n^{12} - 1$ is divisible by 7 when n is prime to 7.

5. Find the solutions of the congruence $x^4 - 1 \equiv 0(\text{mod } 12)$.

6. Prove that $n^{37} - n$ is divisible by the product of the primes 2, 3, 5, 7, 13, and 37 for any positive n.

7. Prove that $a^{18} - b^{18}$ is divisible by 133 if a and b are prime to 133.

8. Can you find integers all of whose digits are 9 that are divisible by 7? By other primes?

6-2. Applications of Fermat's Theorem

Theorem 6-2. The solution of $ax \equiv b(\text{mod } m)$, where $(a, m) = 1$, is $x \equiv ba^{\phi(m)-1}(\text{mod } m)$.

According to Fermat's theorem

$$a^{\phi(m)} \equiv 1(\text{mod } m)$$

Hence,

$$a^{\phi(m)}b \equiv b(\text{mod } m)$$

and therefore $x \equiv ba^{\phi(m)-1}(\text{mod } m)$ is the solution of $ax \equiv b(\text{mod } m)$.

Theorem 6-3. If $f(x)g(x) \equiv x^{p-1} - 1(\text{mod } p)$, where p is a prime greater than 2, each of the congruences $f(x) \equiv 0(\text{mod } p)$ and $g(x) \equiv 0(\text{mod } p)$ has the maximum number of incongruent solutions modulo p permitted by its degree.

Fermat's theorem shows that the congruence

$$x^{p-1} - 1 \equiv 0(\text{mod } p) \tag{1}$$

has exactly $p - 1$ distinct solutions modulo p. When $p > 2$, if we factor

$x^{p-1} - 1$ modulo p into $f(x)$ and $g(x)$ of degrees r and $p - 1 - r$, respectively, the congruence

$$f(x) \equiv 0(\text{mod } p) \tag{2}$$

has no more than r distinct solutions, and

$$g(x) \equiv 0(\text{mod } p) \tag{3}$$

has at most $p - 1 - r$ incongruent solutions modulo p. But since $f(x)g(x) \equiv 0(\text{mod } p)$ has exactly $p - 1$ distinct solutions, neither of the congruences (2) and (3) can have fewer than its maximum number of incongruent solutions modulo p.

For example, if $p > 2$,

$$x^{p-1} - 1 = (x - 1)(x^{p-2} + x^{p-3} + \cdots + 1)$$

Hence, the congruence

$$x^{p-2} + x^{p-3} + \cdots + 1 \equiv 0(\text{mod } p)$$

has exactly $p - 2$ incongruent solutions modulo p and they are 2, 3, $\ldots, p - 1$.

Corollary 1. If p is a prime greater than 2, each of the congruences $x^{(p-1)/2} - 1 \equiv 0(\text{mod } p)$ and $x^{(p-1)/2} + 1 \equiv 0(\text{mod } p)$ has exactly $(p - 1)/2$ solutions that are incongruent modulo p.

For $p > 2$,

$$x^{p-1} - 1 = (x^{(p-1)/2} - 1)(x^{(p-1)/2} + 1)$$

and therefore each of the congruences $x^{(p-1)/2} - 1 \equiv 0(\text{mod } p)$, and $x^{(p-1)/2} + 1 \equiv 0(\text{mod } p)$ has exactly $(p - 1)/2$ solutions that are distinct modulo p. Furthermore, since

$$(p - a)^{(p-1)/2} \equiv (-a)^{(p-1)/2}(\text{mod } p)$$

if p is of the form $4k + 1$ and $(p, a) = 1$, both a and $p - a$ satisfy the same congruence, but if p is of the form $4k - 1$, a satisfies one of the congruences while $p - a$ satisfies the other.

Corollary 2. If p is a prime greater than 2 and d divides $p - 1$, the congruence $x^d - 1 \equiv 0(\text{mod } p)$ has exactly d solutions that are incongruent modulo p.

EXERCISES

1. Write the solution of $3x \equiv 20(\text{mod } 35)$, and reduce it to a least positive residue modulo 35.

2. Find the solutions of $x^8 + 1 \equiv 0(\text{mod } 17)$ and $x^8 - 1 \equiv 0(\text{mod } 17)$, and also of $x^9 + 1 \equiv 0(\text{mod } 19)$ and $x^9 - 1 \equiv 0(\text{mod } 19)$.

3. How many solutions has the congruence $x^3 - 1 \equiv 0(\text{mod } 13)$? Find them.

4. Prove that the congruence $x^2 + 1 \equiv 0(\text{mod } p)$ in which p is a prime of the form $4n + 1$ has two distinct solutions modulo p.

*Theorem 6-4. Corresponding to any conditional congruence $f(x) \equiv a_0 x^n + a_1 x^{n-1} + \cdots + a_n \equiv 0 \pmod{p}$, where p is a prime, $a_0 \not\equiv 0 \pmod{p}$, $n \geq p$, and $f(x)$ is not a multiple of $x^p - x$ modulo p, there is a congruence that is lower than p in degree and has the same distinct solutions modulo p as the original congruence.

Using Fermat's theorem, we showed that

$$x^p - x \equiv 0 \pmod{p}$$

has all p distinct solutions permitted by the modulus. Moreover, if we divide $f(x)$ by $x^p - x$ until we have a remainder whose degree is less than p, we observe that both the quotient $Q(x)$ and the remainder $R(x)$ are integral polynomials and that

$$f(x) \equiv (x^p - x)Q(x) + R(x) \pmod{p}$$

is an identical congruence. Consequently, every distinct solution of $f(x) \equiv 0 \pmod{p}$ must satisfy

$$R(x) \equiv 0 \pmod{p}$$

and conversely.

Example. $2x^4 - x^2 - 1 \equiv 2x(x^3 - x) + x^2 - 1 \pmod{3}$, and therefore the congruence $x^2 - 1 \equiv 0 \pmod{3}$ has the same distinct solutions $x \equiv 1 \pmod{3}$ and $x \equiv 2 \pmod{3}$ as the congruence $2x^4 - x^2 - 1 \equiv 0 \pmod{3}$. Although these integers are simple solutions of the second congruence, they are double solutions of $2x^4 - x^2 - 1 \equiv 0 \pmod{3}$.

Notice that if $f(x) \equiv 0 \pmod{p}$ has p distinct solutions modulo p, $R(x) \equiv 0 \pmod{p}$ is an identical congruence, for it is lower than p in degree and yet has p incongruent solutions modulo p. Hence, $f(x)$ is a multiple of $x^p - x$ modulo p. Conversely, if $f(x)$ is a multiple of $x^p - x$ modulo p, $f(x) \equiv 0 \pmod{p}$ has p distinct solutions modulo p. Thus we have:

Corollary. The congruence $f(x) \equiv 0 \pmod{p}$ with p a prime has p distinct solutions modulo p if and only if $f(x)$ is a multiple of $x^p - x$ modulo p.

*Theorem 6-5. The congruence $f(x) \equiv a_0 x^n + a_1 x^{n-1} + \cdots + a_n \equiv 0 \pmod{p}$ with $a_0 \not\equiv 0 \pmod{p}$ and p a prime is equivalent to a congruence $b_0 x^n + b_1 x^{n-1} + \cdots + b_n \equiv 0 \pmod{p}$ in which $b_0 \equiv 1 \pmod{p}$.

Let x_0 satisfy the congruence

$$a_0 x \equiv 1 \pmod{p}$$

and multiply $f(x)$ by x_0 so that

$$x_0 a_0 x^n + x_0 a_1 x^{n-1} + \cdots + x_0 a_n \equiv x^n + b_1 x^{n-1} + \cdots + b_n \pmod{p}$$

Obviously, $x_0 f(x) \equiv 0 \pmod{p}$ is equivalent to $f(x) \equiv 0 \pmod{p}$, for $(x_0, p) = 1$.

Theorem 6-6. The congruence $f(x) \equiv a_0 x^n + a_1 x^{n-1} + \cdots + a_n \equiv 0 \pmod{p}$ with p a prime, $a_0 \not\equiv 0 \pmod{p}$, and $n < p$ has exactly n distinct solutions modulo p if and only if the remainder $R(x)$ obtained upon dividing $x^p - x$ by $f(x)$ modulo p is identically congruent to zero for the modulus p.

Dividing $x^p - x$ by $f(x)$ modulo p, suppose that we find the identical congruence

$$x^p - x \equiv f(x)Q(x) + R(x) \pmod{p}$$

in which $R(x)$ is an integral polynomial of degree less than n. But then every solution of $f(x) \equiv 0 \pmod{p}$ must satisfy $R(x) \equiv 0 \pmod{p}$. Consequently, if $f(x) \equiv 0 \pmod{p}$ has n distinct solutions modulo p, $R(x)$ is identically congruent to zero modulo p.

If, conversely, $R(x)$ is identically congruent to zero for the modulus p, the congruence

$$x^p - x \equiv f(x)Q(x) \pmod{p}$$

is identical and from Theorem 6-3 we infer that $f(x) \equiv 0 \pmod{p}$ has exactly n distinct solutions modulo p.

6-3. Wilson's Theorem

Theorem 6-7. If p is a positive prime, $(p - 1)! + 1 \equiv 0 \pmod{p}$.

Since the integers $1, 2, \ldots, p - 1$ of a reduced residue system modulo p constitute the solutions of the congruence $x^{p-1} \equiv 1 \pmod{p}$, there are exactly $p - 1$ linear factors modulo p of $x^{p-1} - 1$. Hence,

$$x^{p-1} - 1 \equiv (x - 1)(x - 2) \cdots (x - p + 1) \pmod{p}$$

is an identical congruence. It is, therefore, satisfied by $x \equiv 0 \pmod{p}$ with the result that

$$-1 \equiv (-1)^{p-1}(p - 1)! \pmod{p}$$

If p is odd, it follows that $(p - 1)! + 1 \equiv 0 \pmod{p}$, and if $p = 2$, it is evident that the theorem holds.

Corollary. If p is a positive prime and $r = 1, 2, \ldots, p - 2$, the sum of all possible products of distinct integers selected r at a time from the set $1, 2, \ldots, p - 1$ is a multiple of p.

Because $x^{p-1} - 1$ is identically congruent to $(x - 1)(x - 2) \cdots (x - p + 1)$ modulo p, the coefficients of like powers of x in these two polynomials are in the same residue class modulo p. Therefore, the coefficients of all the positive powers of x occurring in the product with the exception of the coefficient of x^{p-1} are congruent to 0 modulo p. But when $p > 2$, except for its sign, the coefficient of x^{p-2} in this product is the sum $1 + 2 + \cdots + p - 1$; the coefficient of x^{p-3} is the sum of products of integers selected two at a time in all possible ways without repetition from 1, 2, . . . , $p - 1$. Likewise, except for sign, the coefficient of x^{p-r-1}, for $r = 1, 2, \ldots, p - 2$, is the sum of products of integers selected r at a time from the same set. All these sums are, therefore, multiples of p. Equating the absolute terms would, of course, give Wilson's theorem.

Theorem 6-8. If $(n - 1)! + 1 \equiv 0(\text{mod } n)$, then n is a prime.

Suppose that $n > 1$ is a composite and that

$$(n - 1)! + 1 \equiv 0(\text{mod } n)$$

Then $n = n_1 n_2$, where $1 < n_1, n_2 < n$, and consequently both n_1 and n_2 are factors of $(n - 1)!$. But neither of these integers can divide 1. Hence, n is a prime.

Theoretically Wilson's theorem and its converse afford a test for a prime, but when n is large, the amount of calculating involved is so great that the test is entirely impracticable.

EXERCISES

1. Use Wilson's theorem to show that 23 is a prime.

2. Show that, for $p > 5$, $(p - 1)! + 1$ has a prime factor different from the prime p.

3. If p is a prime of the form $4n + 1$, prove that $(2n)!$ is a solution of the congruence $x^2 \equiv -1(\text{mod } p)$.

4. If p is a prime of the form $4n - 1$, show that $(2n - 1)!$ is a solution of the congruence $x^2 \equiv 1(\text{mod } p)$.

5. If p is a prime, prove that each of the coefficients of the expansion of $(1 - x)^{p-1}$ is one greater than some multiple of p.

6. If $r_1, r_2, \ldots, r_p$ and $k_1, k_2, \ldots, k_p$ are both complete residue systems for the modulus p, a prime, can $r_1 k_1, r_2 k_2, \ldots, r_p k_p$ form a complete residue system modulo p?

7. Show that if $r_1, r_2, \ldots, r_{p-1}$ is any reduced residue system modulo p, a prime,

$$\prod_{i=1}^{p-1} r_i \equiv -1(\text{mod } p).$$

8. If $r_1, r_2, \ldots, r_{p-1}$ is a reduced residue system modulo p, an odd prime, then p divides any integral rational symmetric function of the r_i, where $i = 1, 2, \ldots, p - 1$, whose degree is less than $p - 1$.

9. Develop another proof of Wilson's theorem by making use of the solutions of $x^2 \equiv 1(\text{mod } p)$ and $ax \equiv 1(\text{mod } p)$, where $(a, p) = 1$ and p is an odd prime. Notice that of the integers 1, 2, 3, . . . , $p - 1$ only 1 and $p - 1$ satisfy the first congruence and that when a is selected from the set 2, 3, . . . , $p - 2$, there is a solution of the second congruence that is in this very set and is distinct from a.

6-4. The Möbius Function.

If the p_i, where $i = 1, 2, \ldots, r$, are distinct positive primes and if $m = \pm p_1^{n_1} p_2^{n_2} \cdots p_r^{n_r}$, we say that $\mu(m) = 0$ if any exponent $n_i > 1$; that $\mu(m) = (-1)^r$ if each $n_i = 1$; and that $\mu(m) = 1$ if each $n_i = 0$, which means that $\mu(\pm 1) = 1$. When it is so defined, $\mu(m)$ is called the *Möbius function*.

*Theorem 6-9. The function $\mu(m)$ is multiplicative.

Take $(a, b) = 1$, and let $a = \pm p_1^{n_1} p_2^{n_2} \cdots p_r^{n_r}$, $b = \pm q_1^{s_1} q_2^{s_2} \cdots q_t^{s_t}$, where the factorizations are into powers of distinct positive primes.

If any n_i, where $i = 1, 2, \ldots, r$, or s_j, where $j = 1, 2, \ldots, t$, is greater than 1, $\mu(a)\mu(b) = 0$. But then $\mu(ab) = 0$.

If all n_i and s_j are 1, then $\mu(a) = (-1)^r$ and $\mu(b) = (-1)^t$, so that $\mu(a)\mu(b) = (-1)^{r+t}$. But $\mu(ab) = (-1)^{r+t}$.

If either $a = \pm 1$, or $a = \pm 1$ and $b = \pm 1$, then $\mu(ab) = \mu(a)\mu(b)$.

*Theorem 6-10. $\sum\limits_{d|m} \mu(d)$ is 0 or 1 according as $|m|$ is greater than or equal to 1.

If $m = 1$, $\sum\limits_{d|1} \mu(d) = \mu(1) = 1$.

If $m = \pm p_1^{n_1} p_2^{n_2} \cdots p_r^{n_r}$, since $\mu(d) = 0$ for any divisor d of m that has a factor p_i^2, where $i = 1, 2, \ldots, r$, we need consider only the divisors of $p_1 p_2 \cdots p_r$. But these divisors are found by combining factors chosen in all possible ways from these r primes. Thus we find

$$_rC_0 = \mu(1)$$

$$_rC_1(-1) = \sum_{i=1}^{r} \mu(p_i)$$

$$_rC_2(-1)^2 = \sum_{\substack{i,j=1 \\ j>i}}^{r} \mu(p_i p_j)$$

$$\cdots \cdots \cdots \cdots \cdots$$

$$_rC_r(-1)^r = \mu(p_1 p_2 \cdots p_r)$$

But $_rC_0 + {}_rC_1(-1) + {}_rC_2(-1)^2 + \cdots + {}_rC_r(-1)^r = (1 - 1)^r = 0$, and hence $\mu(d_1) + \mu(d_2) + \cdots + \mu(d_s) = 0$, where $d_1, d_2, \ldots, d_s$ are the positive divisors of m.

*Theorem 6-11. If m is a positive integer, $\sum\limits_{n=1}^{m} \mu(n) \left[\dfrac{m}{n} \right] = 1$.

The preceding theorem shows that

$$\sum_{d_1|1} \mu(d_1) + \sum_{d_2|2} \mu(d_2) + \cdots + \sum_{d_m|m} \mu(d_m) = 1$$

But 1 will be a divisor of each integer of the set $1, 2, \ldots, m$, so that $\mu(1)$ will occur m times in the above sum; 2 will be a divisor of $\left[\dfrac{m}{2} \right]$ of the integers, so that $\mu(2)$ will occur $\left[\dfrac{m}{2} \right]$ times. Generally, d will be a divisor of $\left[\dfrac{m}{d}\right]$ of the integers from 1 through m, and therefore $\mu(d)$ will occur $\left[\dfrac{m}{d}\right]$ times in the sum.   Hence,

$$\sum_{n=1}^{m}\left(\sum_{d\mid n}\mu(d)\right) = \mu(1)\left[\frac{m}{1}\right] + \mu(2)\left[\frac{m}{2}\right] + \cdots + \mu(m)\left[\frac{m}{m}\right]$$

and

$$\sum_{n=1}^{m}\mu(n)\left[\frac{m}{n}\right] = 1$$

*Theorem 6-12** (The Möbius Inversion Formula).   If, for $m > 0$, $f(m)$ is an arithmetic function and if an arithmetic function $g(m)$ is so defined that

$$g(m) = \sum_{d\mid m} f(d)$$

then

$$f(m) = \sum_{d\mid m} \mu(d)g\left(\frac{m}{d}\right) \tag{4}$$

We shall build up the right-hand member of the equation (4) to be proved by first observing that as d ranges through all the positive divisors of m, the integer m/d does likewise.   According to the hypothesis, it follows that for each positive divisor m/d of m

$$g\left(\frac{m}{d}\right) = \sum_{a\mid m/d} f(a)$$

and

$$\mu(d)g\left(\frac{m}{d}\right) = \mu(d)\sum_{a\mid m/d} f(a)$$

Hence,

$$\sum_{d\mid m}\mu(d)g\left(\frac{m}{d}\right) = \sum_{d\mid m}\mu(d)\sum_{a\mid m/d} f(a)$$

$$= \sum_{d\mid m}\sum_{a\mid m/d}\mu(d)f(a)$$

Reversing the order of summation, we have

$$\sum_{d\mid m} \mu(d)g\left(\frac{m}{d}\right) = \sum_{a\mid m/d}\sum_{d\mid m} \mu(d)f(a)$$

But to say that a ranges through the positive divisors of m/d while d takes on the values of the positive divisors of m is the same as saying that a ranges through the positive divisors of m while d is a positive divisor of m/a. Consequently,

$$\sum_{d\mid m} \mu(d)g\left(\frac{m}{d}\right) = \sum_{a\mid m}\sum_{d\mid m/a} \mu(d)f(a)$$

$$= \sum_{a\mid m} f(a) \sum_{d\mid m/a} \mu(d)$$

But $\displaystyle\sum_{d\mid m/a} \mu(d) = 0$ unless $a = m$, so that

$$\sum_{d\mid m} \mu(d)g\left(\frac{m}{d}\right) = f(m)$$

6-5. An Application of the Möbius Inversion Formula. We have shown that if $m > 0$, $m = \displaystyle\sum_{d\mid m} \phi(d)$. Consequently,

$$\phi(m) = \sum_{d\mid m} \mu(d)\,\frac{m}{d}$$

$$= m \sum_{d\mid m} \frac{\mu(d)}{d}$$

Thus if $m = 1$, then $\phi(m) = 1$, but if $m = p_1^{n_1}p_2^{n_2} \cdots p_r^{n_r}$, then

$$\phi(m) = m\left(1 - \frac{1}{p_1} - \cdots - \frac{1}{p_r} + \frac{1}{p_1p_2} + \cdots + \frac{1}{p_{r-1}p_r} - \frac{1}{p_1p_2p_3}\right.$$
$$\left. - \cdots + (-1)^r \frac{1}{p_1p_2 \cdots p_r}\right)$$

and

$$\phi(m) = m\left(1 - \frac{1}{p_1}\right)\left(1 - \frac{1}{p_2}\right) \cdots \left(1 - \frac{1}{p_r}\right)$$

EXERCISES

1. Is it necessary for the truth of Theorem 6-12 that $f(m)$ and $g(m)$ be arithmetic functions?

2. If $F(n) = \prod_{d|n} f(d)$ and no $f(d)$ is 0, then $f(n) = \prod_{d|n} F(n/d)^{\mu(d)}$. Prove this statement by using a method analogous to that of Sec. 6-5, and then prove it by taking the logarithm of each member of the given equation.

3. Prove that for any positive integer m, $\left| \sum_{n=1}^{m} \mu(n)/n \right| \le 1$. $\Bigg[$ Consider the value of $\sum_{n=1}^{m} \left(\frac{m}{n} - \left[\frac{m}{n} \right] \right)$ together with Theorem 6-11. $\Bigg]$

CHAPTER 7

ON BELONGING TO AN EXPONENT

7-1. The λ Function. We have proved that for any integer a prime to m

$$a^{\phi(m)} \equiv 1 (\text{mod } m)$$

In solving congruences, moreover, we have exhibited some cases in which a positive power, smaller than $\phi(m)$, of a particular integer a is sufficient to produce 1 modulo m even when $a \neq 1$. Take, for example, the congruence $x^2 \equiv 1 (\text{mod } 5)$, which has the solution 4, as well as 1, modulo 5, and the congruence $x^3 \equiv 1 (\text{mod } 14)$, with solutions 9, 11, and 1 modulo 14. It is, therefore, important to ask whether there is a positive integer smaller than $\phi(m)$ and yet such that when any integer prime to m is raised to that integral power, the result is congruent to 1 modulo m. We shall show that when m takes any form except 2^n for $n = 0$, 1, or 2, and p^n or $2p^n$ for p an odd prime and $n > 0$, there is such a positive integer. For example, consider the case where $m = 15$. Here $\phi(m) = 8$, and $x^8 \equiv 1 (\text{mod } 15)$ is, of course, satisfied by all integers prime to 15. But each one of these integers also satisfies the congruence $x^4 \equiv 1 (\text{mod } 15)$.

Now take any integer a prime to 2. Then a is odd and has the form $2k + 1$. Hence,

$$(2k + 1)^2 = 4k(k + 1) + 1$$

or

$$a^2 \equiv 1 (\text{mod } 2^3)$$

But

$$(a^2)^2 = (1 + 2^3 s)^2$$

or

$$a^{2^2} = 1 + 2^4 s + 2^6 s^2$$

so that

$$a^{2^2} \equiv 1 (\text{mod } 2^4)$$

In like manner, if

$$a^{2^k} \equiv 1 (\text{mod } 2^k)$$

it follows that

$$(a^{2^{k-2}})^2 = 1 + 2^{k+1} t + 2^{2k} t^2$$

or

$$a^{2^{k-1}} \equiv 1 (\text{mod } 2^{k+1})$$

98

Hence, we conclude that if $n > 2$,

$$a^{2^{n-2}} \equiv 1 \pmod{2^n}$$

which means that

$$a^{\phi(2^n)/2} \equiv 1 \pmod{2^n}$$

Consequently, for $n > 2$ there is an integer smaller than $\phi(2^n)$ such that this integral power of any integer prime to 2 yields the residue 1 for the modulus 2^n. Accordingly, we proceed to give a name to this number $\phi(2^n)/2$ as well as to other numbers closely related to $\phi(m)$.

It was R. Carmichael who used the symbol $\lambda(m)$ to designate the arithmetic function which E. Lucas had defined as follows:

1. If $m = 2^n$ and $n = 0, 1,$ or $2, \lambda(m) = \phi(m)$.
2. If $m = 2^n$ and $n > 2, \lambda(m) = \phi(m)/2$.
3. If $m = p^n$, p being an odd prime, $\lambda(p^n) = \phi(p^n)$.
4. If $m = 2^n p_1{}^{n_1} p_2{}^{n_2} \cdots p_r{}^{n_r}$, the p_i, where $i = 1, 2, \ldots, r$, being distinct odd primes, then $\lambda(m)$ is the least common multiple of $\lambda(2^n)$, $\lambda(p_1{}^{n_1}), \ldots, \lambda(p_r{}^{n_r})$.

Thus, when m has the form 2^n for $n = 0, 1,$ or 2, the form p^n, or $2p^n$ for $n > 0$ and p an odd prime, the λ function has the same value as the ϕ function, but when m has the factor 2^n with $n > 2$, or 2^2 and an odd prime factor, or two factors that are powers of distinct odd primes, the λ function is at most half of the ϕ function.

When the p_i, where $i = 1, 2, \ldots, r$, are odd primes, if $m = 2^n p_1{}^{n_1} p_2{}^{n_2} \cdots p_r{}^{n_r}$ and $(a, m) = 1$, we know, therefore, that

$$a^{\lambda(2^n)} \equiv 1 \pmod{2^n}$$
$$a^{\lambda(p_i{}^{n_i})} \equiv 1 \pmod{p_i{}^{n_i}}$$

But $\lambda(m)$ is a multiple of each of the functions $\lambda(2^n)$, $\lambda(p_i{}^{n_i})$, and thus $\lambda(m)/\lambda(2^n)$ and $\lambda(m)/\lambda(p_i{}^{n_i})$ are integers. Consequently,

$$(a^{\lambda(2^n)})^{\lambda(m)/\lambda(2^n)} \equiv 1 \pmod{2^n}$$

and

$$(a^{\lambda(p_i{}^{n_i})})^{\lambda(m)/\lambda(p_i{}^{n_i})} \equiv 1 \pmod{p_i{}^{n_i}}$$

Finally, since $2^n, p_1{}^{n_1}, \ldots, p_r{}^{n_r}$ are relatively prime in pairs,

$$a^{\lambda(m)} \equiv 1 \pmod{m}$$

Therefore, if m is not of the form 2^n for $n = 0, 1,$ or 2, and not of the form p^n or $2p^n$ for $n > 0$ and p an odd prime, then the λ function gives a better result than does the ϕ function. It is on this account often advantageous to have:

Theorem 7-1. For $(a, m) = 1$, $a^{\lambda(m)} \equiv 1 \pmod{m}$.

Example. Although $\phi(2800) = \phi(2^4)\phi(5^2)\phi(7) = 960$, $\lambda(2800)$ is the least common multiple of 4, 20, and 6 and is only 60. Hence, for $(a, 2800) = 1$, $a^{60} \equiv 1 \pmod{2800}$.

The new formula is useful in finding the remainder in the division by m of the power of an integer prime to m whenever the exponent of the power lies between $\lambda(m)$ and $\phi(m)$. Thus, to find the remainder when 7^{14} is divided by 180, we start with $7^{12} \equiv 1 (\mod 180)$, for $\lambda(180) = 12$. Then $7^2 \equiv 49 (\mod 180)$, and $7^{14} \equiv 49 \ (\mod 180)$.

7-2. Belonging to an Exponent Modulo m. Since there is always at least one positive power of a particular integer a prime to m that is congruent to 1 modulo m, there must be a least positive integer d such that $a^d \equiv 1 (\mod m)$. We call this integer d *the exponent to which a belongs modulo m*, or we say that a *belongs to d modulo m*. For example, $4^3 \equiv 1 (\mod 7)$, while $4^2 \equiv 2 (\mod 7)$, so that 4 belongs to 3 modulo 7. Again, $3^4 \equiv 1 (\mod 5)$, and there is no smaller positive power of 3 which is congruent to 1 modulo 5. Hence, 3 belongs to $\phi(5)$ modulo 5.

Theorem 7-2. If an integer a, prime to m, belongs to d modulo m, and if $a^k \equiv 1 (\mod m)$, then d divides k.

Suppose that $k = qd + r$, where $0 \leq r < d$, then

$$a^k \equiv (a^d)^q \cdot a^r (\mod m)$$

that is

$$a^r \equiv 1 (\mod m)$$

But d is the least positive exponent such that $a^d \equiv 1 (\mod m)$, and therefore $r = 0$. Consequently, $d \mid k$.

Corollary. The exponent d to which an integer a, prime to m, belongs modulo m is a divisor of $\phi(m)$ and of $\lambda(m)$.

This corollary shows that we need try only divisors of $\lambda(m)$ to find the exponent to which an integer belongs modulo m. For instance, to find the exponent to which 7 belongs modulo 55, we try only the exponents 2, 4, 5, 10, and 20, for $\lambda(55) = 20$. Thus $7^2 \equiv -6 (\mod 55)$, $7^4 \equiv 36 (\mod 55)$, $7^5 \equiv 32 (\mod 55)$, $7^{10} \equiv 34 (\mod 55)$, and $7^{20} \equiv 1 (\mod 55)$. Hence, 7 belongs to $\lambda(55)$ modulo 55.

In 1844 A. L. Crelle gave a device for finding the exponent to which an integer a belongs modulo m. To employ this method, first set up the integers $1, 2, \ldots, m - 1$ in a row, and under 1 put r_1, the least positive residue modulo m of the integer a; under 2 put the least positive residue r_2 of $r_1 + a \equiv 2r_1 (\mod m)$; under 3 put the least positive residue of $r_2 + a \equiv r_2 + r_1 (\mod m)$; . . . . Then the resulting table

$$
\begin{array}{cccccc}
1 & 2 & 3 & 4 & \ldots & m - 1 \\
r_1 & r_2 & r_3 & r_4 & \ldots & r_{m-1}
\end{array}
$$

gives in order in the second row the residues of

$$r_1, \ 2r_1, \ 3r_1, \ \ldots, \ (m - 1)r_1$$

modulo m. According to this scheme the integer r_1 congruent to a modulo m is under 1; the integer congruent to $a^2 \equiv r_1 \cdot r_1 \pmod{m}$ is under r_1; and likewise the integer congruent to $a^s \equiv t \cdot r_1 \pmod{m}$ is under t.

Thus, if $m = 7$ and we wish to find the exponent to which 3 belongs modulo 7, we form the table

$$1 \quad 2 \quad 3 \quad 4 \quad 5 \quad 6$$
$$3 \quad 6 \quad 2 \quad 5 \quad 1 \quad 4$$

Then $3 \equiv 3 \pmod 7$, and so we move to 3 in the first row. We find 2 under 3, and hence $3^2 \equiv 2 \pmod 7$. Moving to 2 in the first row, we find 6 under it, and have $3^3 \equiv 6 \pmod 7$. Continuing in this manner, we find $3^4 \equiv 4$, $3^5 \equiv 5$, and $3^6 \equiv 1 \pmod 7$. The integer 3, therefore, belongs to 6 modulo 7. Moreover, the residues of the first six positive integral powers of 3 are in order 3, 2, 6, 4, 5, 1, and it is evident that this cycle is repeated as the exponent of 3 is increased beyond 6 through the positive integers.

If an integer a prime to m belongs to d modulo m, the least positive residues of the powers a, a^2, a^3, $\ldots$, a^d of a taken in order constitute the *period* of a modulo m. These residues are distinct modulo m, for if $a^s \equiv a^t \pmod{m}$ with $s > t$, then $a^{s-t} \equiv 1 \pmod{m}$. But since s and t have only the values 1, 2, $\ldots$, d, the difference $s - t$ is less than d and cannot be divisible by d. Hence, we have proved:

Theorem 7-3. If an integer a belongs to d modulo m, the integers a, a^2, a^3, $\ldots$, a^d are distinct modulo m.

When $(a, m) = 1$, $s > 0$, and $a^s \equiv b \pmod{m}$, then b is said to be a *power residue* of a modulo m. Thus Theorem 7-3 shows that if a belongs to d modulo m, the first d power residues of a modulo m are incongruent modulo m. Clearly, they constitute the power residues of a modulo m. We say, then, that there are exactly d *incongruent integers that are power residues of a modulo m*, omitting "modulo m" after "incongruent integers," for there can be no confusion about the required modulus.

EXERCISES

1. Find the exponents to which 5 and 7 belong modulo 11.

2. Find the remainder when 7^{182} is divided by 675.

3. Prove that if a and b are prime to 1729, then $a^{36} - b^{36}$ is divisible by 1729.

4. If p is a prime, $(a, p) = 1$, and $a^d \equiv b^d \pmod{p}$, where d is the least positive exponent for which the congruence is true, then d is a divisor of $p - 1$.

5. If a belongs to d modulo p an odd prime, and if d is even, then $a^{d/2} \equiv -1 \pmod{p}$.

6. If p is an odd prime, and if $a^k \equiv -1 \pmod{p}$, where k is the least positive integer for which the congruence is true, then $2k$ is the exponent to which a belongs modulo p.

7. Prove that if the integer a, where $0 < a < p - 2$, belongs to the exponent 3 modulo p, a prime, then $a + 1$ belongs to 6 modulo p.

8. If the integer a belongs to d modulo p, a prime, show that the product of all the distinct residues of the powers of a is congruent to 1 or -1 according as d is odd or even.

9. Show that $x \equiv ba^{\lambda(m)-1}(\mathrm{mod}\ m)$ is a solution of $ax \equiv b(\mathrm{mod}\ m)$ if $(a, m) = 1$.

10. Compare the fact that the powers of 2 will generate all the solutions of $x^4 \equiv 1(\mathrm{mod}\ 5)$ with the corresponding property of the root i of the equation $x^4 - 1 = 0$. What do you notice about the other solutions?

Theorem 7-4. If an integer a prime to p belongs to d modulo p, a prime, there are exactly $\phi(d)$ incongruent integers that belong to d modulo p.

When $p = 2$, d has only the value 1 and then the integer 1 belongs to 1 modulo 2.

When p is an odd prime, consider the congruence

$$x^d \equiv 1(\mathrm{mod}\ p)$$

and suppose that the integer a belongs to d modulo p. Then each integer of the set

$$a, a^2, a^3, \ldots, a^d$$

is prime to p and satisfies the congruence, for

$$(a^s)^d \equiv (a^d)^s \equiv 1(\mathrm{mod}\ p)$$

According to Theorem 7-3, furthermore, no two of these integers are congruent modulo p. Consequently, these powers of a give all the solutions of $x^d \equiv 1(\mathrm{mod}\ p)$, for the modulus is a prime and there are, therefore, no more than d solutions. Hence, any integer that belongs to d is congruent modulo p to an integer of the set $a, a^2, \ldots, a^d$, and none of these integers belongs to an exponent greater than d.

However, if $(s, d) = 1$, a^s belongs to d modulo p, for if we assume that a^s belongs to $k < d$,

$$(a^s)^k \equiv 1(\mathrm{mod}\ p)$$

and

$$a^{sk} \equiv 1(\mathrm{mod}\ p)$$

But since a belongs to d modulo p, $d \mid sk$. Hence, $d \mid k$, and k is not less than d.

On the other hand, if $(s, d) = n \neq 1$, so that $s = ns_0$, $d = nd_0$, then

$$(a^s)^{d_0} \equiv a^{s_0d} \equiv 1(\mathrm{mod}\ p)$$

and a^s does not belong to d modulo p, for d_0 is less than d.

Since there are $\phi(d)$ positive integers less than d and prime to d, exactly $\phi(d)$ of the powers a^s, where $s = 1, 2, \ldots, d$, belong to the exponent d modulo p.

Corollary 1. If d is a divisor of $p - 1$ and an integer a belongs to d modulo p, a prime, the solutions of $x^d \equiv 1(\bmod\ p)$ are congruent to $a, a^2, \ldots, a^d$ modulo p.

Corollary 2. If d is a divisor of $p - 1$ and an integer a belongs to d modulo p, a prime, then a^s belongs to d modulo p if and only if the exponent s is prime to d.

Corollary 3. If d is a divisor of $p - 1$ and an integer a belongs to d modulo p, a prime, then a^s, where $(s, d) = n \neq 1$, belongs to the exponent d/n modulo p.

To prove Corollary 3, notice that if $p = 2$, d can be only 1, for a is odd. In the case of an odd prime, if $d = d_0 n$, we saw that

$$(a^s)^{d_0} \equiv 1(\bmod\ p)$$

Now suppose that

$$(a^s)^t \equiv 1(\bmod\ p)$$

with $0 < t \leq d_0$. Then $d \mid st$. But if $s = s_0 n$, then $(s_0, d_0) = 1$, and it follows that $d_0 \mid t$. This is impossible when $t < d_0$. Therefore, $t = d_0$, and a^s belongs to d_0 modulo p.

Theorem 7-5. When $(s, t) = 1$, if a belongs to s, and b belongs to t modulo m, then ab belongs to st modulo m.

We know that $a^s \equiv 1(\bmod\ m)$ and $b^t \equiv 1(\bmod\ m)$, so that

$$(ab)^{st} \equiv (a^s)^t (b^t)^s \equiv 1(\bmod\ m)$$

But if ab belongs to k modulo m, so that

$$(ab)^k \equiv 1(\bmod\ m)$$

then $k \mid st$ and $k \leq st$. Moreover,

$$(ab)^{ks} \equiv b^{ks} \equiv 1(\bmod\ m)$$

and therefore $t \mid ks$, so that $t \mid k$. In like manner,

$$(ab)^{kt} \equiv a^{kt} \equiv 1(\bmod\ m)$$

and $s \mid kt$, so that $s \mid k$. Since $(s, t) = 1$, it follows that $st \mid k$ and $st \leq k$. Consequently, $k = st$.

Theorem 7-6 (H. G. Erlerus, 1841). When p_1 and p_2 are odd primes, if $m \equiv a_1(\bmod\ p_1)$ and $m \equiv a_2(\bmod\ p_2)$, and if in addition a_1 belongs to d_1 modulo p_1 and a_2 belongs to d_2 modulo p_2, then m belongs to the least common multiple of d_1 and d_2 for the modulus $p_1 p_2$.

Since $m^{d_1} \equiv 1(\bmod\ p_1)$ and $m^{d_2} \equiv 1(\bmod\ p_2)$, if L is the least common multiple of d_1 and d_2, then

$$(m^{d_1})^{L/d_1} \equiv 1(\bmod\ p_1)$$

and

$$(m^{d_2})^{L/d_2} \equiv 1(\bmod\ p_2)$$

Therefore,

$$m^L \equiv 1(\text{mod } p_1 p_2)$$

But if m belongs to k modulo $p_1 p_2$, the last congruence implies that $k \mid L$. Again, from

$$m^k \equiv 1(\text{mod } p_1 p_2)$$

we infer that

$$m^k \equiv 1(\text{mod } p_i) \qquad i = 1, 2$$

Therefore, $d_1 \mid k$, $d_2 \mid k$, and $L \mid k$. Hence, $k = L$.

Examples. Because 3 belongs to 5 modulo 11 and 10 belongs to 2 for the same modulus, and since the exponents 5 and 2 are relatively prime, it is evident from Theorem 7-5 that 30, and hence 8, belongs to the exponent 10 modulo 11.

Again, 7 belongs to 10 for the modulus 11, and 5 belongs to 4 modulo 13. Thus, according to Theorem 7-6, the integer 18 belongs to 20 modulo 143.

EXERCISES

1. Find an integer that belongs to 2 modulo 19 and one that belongs to 3 modulo 19. Using these results, find an integer that belongs to 6 modulo 19.

2. Set up the least positive residues of the powers of 2, 3, and 6 modulo 17.

3. Find all the integers that belong to 16 modulo 17.

4. Solve the congruences $x^3 \equiv 1(\text{mod } 7)$ and $x^{10} \equiv 1(\text{mod } 31)$.

5. Show that 2 belongs to 12 modulo 13, and thus find the exponent to which 8 belongs modulo 13. Do any other integers belong to this exponent modulo 13?

6. Find the integer to which 7 belongs modulo 5 and modulo 11. Then determine the integer to which 7 belongs modulo 55.

7. When p is a prime, if a and b are prime to p, and if $a \equiv b(\text{mod } p^n)$, show that $a^p \equiv b^p(\text{mod } p^{n+1})$, and hence by induction that $a^{p^r} \equiv b^{p^r}(\text{mod } p^{n+r})$.

8. When the modulus m is composite, prove theorems analogous to Corollaries 2 and 3 of Theorem 7-4.

9. If $p_1 = 2$ and p_2 is an odd prime, does Theorem 7-6 hold? Generalize the theorem.

7-3. Another Test for a Prime. If we can find one integer a prime to the integer m and satisfying the condition

$$a^{m-1} \equiv 1(\text{mod } m)$$

is it true that m is a prime? This question is easily answered, for $\lambda(21) = 6$, and so $a^6 \equiv 1(\text{mod } 21)$ for all integers a that are prime to 21. Thus $2^6 \equiv 1(\text{mod } 21)$, and $8^2 \equiv 1(\text{mod } 21)$. Hence, $8^{20} \equiv 1(\text{mod } 21)$, and yet 21 is not a prime.

Is it even true that m is a prime if, for all a that are prime to m,

$$a^{m-1} \equiv 1(\text{mod } m)$$

Again we can answer negatively by showing a case in which the hypothesis is fulfilled but where m is a composite. Any integer a prime to $561 = 3(11)(17)$ satisfies the congruence

$$a^{80} \equiv 1 (\text{mod } 561)$$

because $\lambda(561) = 80$. Consequently,

$$a^{560} \equiv 1 (\text{mod } 561)$$

Thus the exact converse of Fermat's theorem is not true.

An important test for a prime can, nevertheless, be derived from these ideas. The following theorem was first proved by Lucas* in 1876, and from it powerful methods for deciding the primality of integers having certain forms have been developed:

Theorem 7-7. If an integer a is prime to an integer m greater than 1, and if $a^{m-1} \equiv 1 (\text{mod } m)$ although there is no positive integer k less than $m - 1$ and such that $a^k \equiv 1 (\text{mod } m)$, then m is a prime.

Assuming that $m > 1$ is composite, since $(a, m) = 1$,

$$a^{\phi(m)} \equiv 1 (\text{mod } m)$$

But $\phi(m) < m - 1$ because m has a factor between 1 and m. Therefore, m is a prime.

Actually, by virtue of Theorem 7-2, in applying this test for a prime we need evaluate only those powers a^k for which k is a divisor of $m - 1$.

Example. To test 47 for a prime, we can make use of the fact that 2 belongs to 23 and 46 belongs to 2 modulo 47 and determine by Theorem 7-5 that $2 \cdot 46 \equiv 45 (\text{mod } 47)$ belongs to $23 \cdot 2 = 46$ for the modulus 47. Or we may reason that since the divisors of 46 are only 1, 2, 23, and 46, and because $45^{23} \equiv (47 - 2)^{23} \equiv (-2)^{23} \equiv -1 (\text{mod } 47)$, so that 45 does not belong to 1, 2, or 23, then the integer 45 belongs to 46 modulo 47. Hence, by virtue of Theorem 7-7, 47 is a prime.

7-4. Primitive Roots. Is there a positive integer k smaller than $\lambda(m)$ and satisfying the condition that, for any integer a prime to m, $a^k \equiv 1 (\text{mod } m)$? The answer has been completely determined because Gauss showed that exactly $\phi(\phi(m))$ integers belong to $\phi(m)$ if m is 2^n, with $n = 0$, 1, or 2, or if m is p^n or $2p^n$, where $n > 0$ and p is an odd prime, and R. Carmichael showed that for all other moduli there is at least one integer that belongs to $\lambda(m)$. Consequently, there is no positive integer k smaller than $\lambda(m)$ and such that, for all integers prime to m, $a^k \equiv 1 (\text{mod } m)$. We shall proceed to develop these ideas.

We call an integer that belongs to $\phi(m)$ modulo m a *primitive root of m* or a *primitive root modulo m*. It is evident that 1 is a primitive root of 1 and 2 and that 3 is a primitive root of 2^2. There are no other primitive roots of these moduli.

---

* E. Lucas, *Am. J. Math.*, Vol. 1, p. 301, 1878.

Theorem 7-8. There are exactly $\phi(p-1)$ incongruent integers that are primitive roots modulo p, an odd prime.

Of course when d is a divisor of $p-1$, as far as we have proved, no integer need belong to d modulo p, but we have shown that if one integer does belong to d for the modulus p, exactly $\phi(d)$ incongruent integers modulo p belong to d. Therefore, if we let $\psi(d)$ represent the number of integers from 1 through $p-1$ that belong to d modulo p,

$$\psi(d) \leq \phi(d)$$

Besides, each integer from 1 through p that is prime to p belongs to one and only one exponent for the modulus p, and this exponent must be a divisor of $p-1$. It is thus evident that

$$\psi(d_1) + \psi(d_2) + \cdots + \psi(d_r) = p - 1$$

where the d_i, with $i = 1, 2, \ldots, r$, are the distinct positive divisors of $p-1$. But we have also shown that

$$\phi(d_1) + \phi(d_2) + \cdots + \phi(d_r) = p - 1$$

Because no $\psi(d_i)$ can exceed the corresponding $\phi(d_i)$, if any $\psi(d_i)$ were less than the corresponding $\phi(d_i)$, these statements could not both be true. Therefore, for all i,

$$\psi(d_i) = \phi(d_i)$$

In particular when the divisor d is $p-1$ itself, there are exactly $\phi(p-1) = \phi(\phi(p))$ incongruent integers that belong to $p-1$ modulo p.

Corollary. If p is an odd prime and d is a divisor of $p-1$, $\phi(d)$ of the integers from 1 through $p-1$ belong to d modulo p.

Example. We shall find the primitive roots of 17 and the integers that belong to the divisors of $\phi(17) = 16$. Using Crelle's method, we see that for the modulus 17 the powers of 3 give the residues

$$3, 9, 10, 13, 5, 15, 11, 16, 14, 8, 7, 4, 12, 2, 6, 1$$

It is clear, then, that the primitive roots of 17 determined by the powers of 3 having exponents prime to 16 are 3, 3^3, 3^5, 3^7, 3^9, 3^{11}, 3^{13}, 3^{15} and reduce to 3, 10, 5, 11, 14, 7, 12, and 6, respectively, for the modulus 17. Notice that $3^2 \equiv 9 \pmod{17}$ belongs to the exponent 8 modulo 17, for $(2, 16) = 2$ and $\frac{16}{2} = 8$. Moreover, the other integers that belong to 8 modulo 17 are of the form 3^s, where $(s, 16) = 2$. Hence, $s = 6, 10,$ and 14. The integers are, therefore, 3^6, 3^{10}, and 3^{14}, and they reduce to 15, 8, and 2 modulo 17. In like manner we can find the integers that belong to 4 modulo 17, for in this case $(s, 16) = 4$. Thus 3^4 and 3^{12} belong to 4 modulo 17. There is just one integer that belongs to 2, and it is $3^8 \equiv 16 \pmod{17}$.

EXERCISES

1. Find all primitive roots of $p = 5, 7, 11$, and 13.

2. Prove that the product of all the integers that belong to a particular exponent $d > 2$ modulo p, an odd prime, is congruent to 1 modulo p.

3. Show that $2^{341} - 2$ is divisible by 341 even though 341 is not a prime.

4. Find by trial composites m other than 561 such that $a^{m-1} \equiv 1 \pmod{m}$ for all integers prime to m.

7-5. Gauss' Method for Finding a Primitive Root Modulo p.

To find a primitive root of a prime p, first choose any integer a_1 prime to p, and find the exponent d_1 to which a_1 belongs modulo p. If d_1 is not $p - 1$, find the least positive residues of

$$a_1, a_1^2, a_1^3, \ldots, a_1^{d_1}$$

modulo p. None of these integers is a primitive root of p since each one satisfies the congruence

$$x^{d_1} \equiv 1 \pmod{p}$$

Now select any positive integer a_2 less than p and not one of the residues of the powers of a_1. Then if a_2 is not a primitive root of p, a_2 belongs to some d_2 modulo p.

The exponent d_2 cannot be a divisor of d_1, for if $d_1 = kd_2$,

$$a_2^{kd_2} \equiv 1 \pmod{p}$$

and $x \equiv a_2 \pmod{p}$ would be a solution of $x^{d_1} \equiv 1 \pmod{p}$, which is impossible because the powers of a_1 determine all the solutions of this congruence.

If d_2 is a multiple of d_1, but not $p - 1$, we have found an integer that belongs to an exponent modulo p that is greater than d_1.

If $(d_1, d_2) = 1$, then $a_1 a_2$ belongs to $d_1 d_2$ modulo p.

If $b = (d_1, d_2)$ and b is neither 1 nor d_1, factor b into powers of distinct primes so that $b = p_1^{n_1} p_2^{n_2} \cdots p_r^{n_r}$. Then separate b into two relatively prime factors b_1 and b_2 by taking $p_i^{n_i}$ as a factor of b_1 or b_2 according as d_1 or d_2 contains the lower power of p_i. If the power of p_i is the same in both d_1 and d_2, take $p_i^{n_i}$ as a factor of either b_1 or b_2.

Then according to Corollary 3 of Theorem 7-4, $a_1^{b_1}$ belongs to d_1/b_1, and $a_2^{b_2}$ belongs to d_2/b_2 modulo p. However, $((d_1/b_1), (d_2/b_2)) = 1$, for if $d_1 = bd_{01}$ and $d_2 = bd_{02}$, then $(d_{01}, d_{02}) = 1$. Moreover, $d_1/b_1 = b_2 d_{01}$, and $d_2/b_2 = b_1 d_{02}$, and we know that $(b_1, b_2) = 1$. But $(b_1, d_{01}) = 1$ also, for if p^s is the highest power of any prime in b_1, it is the highest power of p that is a factor of d_1 and thus p does not divide d_{01}. In like manner, $(b_2, d_{02}) = 1$. Consequently, the product $a_1^{b_1} a_2^{b_2}$ belongs to $d_1 d_2/b_1 b_2 = d_1 d_2/b$, modulo p, and this exponent is the least common multiple of d_1 and d_2.

Thus under any circumstances we have found an integer that belongs to an exponent modulo p larger than d_1. After setting up the power residues of this integer, we continue as before by choosing a positive integer less than p but not among any of the power residues thus far determined. After proceeding for a finite number of steps, we must find an integer that belongs to $p - 1$ modulo p.

Example. To find a primitive root of 41, first find the power residues of 2 modulo 41. These residues of 2, 2^2, . . . , 2^{10} are in order 2, 4, 8, 16, 32, 23, 5, 10, 20, 40. Since $2^{10} \equiv -1 \pmod{41}$, the remaining residues are the negatives of these integers, and 2, therefore, belongs to 20 modulo 41.

Because the integer 3 does not occur among the power residues of 2, we determine the power residues of 3 modulo 41. They are 3, 9, 27, 40, -3, -9, -27, -40. Consequently, 3 belongs to 8 modulo 41.

Since $(20, 8) = 4$, we use the factors 4 and 1 as b_1 and b_2. We know that 2^4 belongs to 5 and 3 belongs to 8 modulo 41. Consequently, $16 \cdot 3 \equiv 7 \pmod{41}$ belongs to the least common multiple of 5 and 8 and is, therefore, a primitive root of 41.

The power residues of 7 modulo 41 are

$$7, \quad 8, \ 15, \ 23, \ 38, \ 20, \ 17, \ 37, \ 13, \quad 9$$
$$22, \ 31, \ 12, \quad 2, \ 14, \ 16, \ 30, \quad 5, \ 35, \ 40$$

and the negatives of the above integers taken in order.

7-6. Primitive Roots Modulo p^n and $2p^n$

Theorem 7-9. If p is an odd prime, there are just $\phi(\phi(p^n))$ incongruent primitive roots modulo p^n.

Suppose that the integer a is a primitive root modulo p. This statement means, of course, that every integer in the class with a belongs to the exponent $p - 1$ for the modulus p. We shall show that we can choose an integer in this residue class that is a primitive root of p^n. Specifically, if

$$a^{p-1} \not\equiv 1 \pmod{p^2}$$

we shall prove that a is a primitive root modulo p^n, but if

$$a^{p-1} \equiv 1 \pmod{p^2}$$

we shall prove that k can be so chosen that the integer $a + kp$ satisfies the condition

$$(a + kp)^{p-1} \not\equiv 1 \pmod{p^2}$$

and that this integer is a primitive root of p^n.

First, let us suppose that when a belongs to $p - 1$ modulo p, $a^{p-1} \equiv 1 \pmod{p^2}$. Then

$$(a + kp)^{p-1} \equiv a^{p-1} + (p-1)a^{p-2}kp + \cdots + (kp)^{p-1}(\bmod\ p^2)$$
$$\equiv 1 - a^{p-2}kp(\bmod\ p^2)$$

and consequently $(a + kp)^{p-1}$ is congruent to 1 modulo p^2 if and only if k is divisible by p. If we, therefore, choose k prime to p, then $a + kp$ will not only belong to $p - 1$ modulo p but

$$(a + kp)^{p-1} \not\equiv 1(\bmod\ p^2)$$

that is, there is always a primitive root $r = a + kp$ of p such that $r^{p-1} \not\equiv 1(\bmod\ p^2)$.

It is true that since $(r, p) = 1$, $r^{\phi(p^n)} \equiv 1(\bmod\ p^n)$. But does r belong to an exponent t modulo p^n smaller than $\phi(p^n)$? If so, t is a divisor of $\phi(p^n) = p^{n-1}(p-1)$. More than that, since it is necessarily true that $r^t \equiv 1(\bmod\ p)$ and r belongs to $p - 1$ modulo p, it is clear that $p - 1$ divides t. Hence, t has the form $p^s(p-1)$ with $s = 0, 1, 2, \ldots$, or $n - 1$. But if s did not exceed $n - 2$, we could raise each member of the congruence $r^t \equiv 1(\bmod\ p^n)$ to the p^{n-2-s} power and obtain

$$r^{p^{n-2}(p-1)} \equiv 1(\bmod\ p^n)$$

We shall show, however, that the last congruence cannot be true and hence that r cannot belong to an exponent less than $\phi(p^n)$ modulo p^n. To do so, use the fact that

$$r^{p-1} \equiv 1(\bmod\ p)$$

in the form $r^{p-1} = 1 + cp$, where $(c, p) = 1$. Then

$$(r^{p-1})^{p^{n-2}} \equiv (1 + cp)^{p^{n-2}}(\bmod\ p^n)$$
$$\equiv 1 + p^{n-2}cp + \frac{p^{n-2}(p^{n-2} - 1)}{2!}(cp)^2 + \cdots$$
$$+ (cp)^{p^{n-2}}(\bmod\ p^n)$$

The $(m + 1)$st term of this expansion is

$$\frac{p^{n-2}(p^{n-2} - 1) \cdots (p^{n-2} - m + 1)}{m!} c^m p^m$$

and it is obviously a multiple of p^n if $m \geq 2$ and if $(m, p) = 1$, for $\frac{(p^{n-2} - 1) \cdots (p^{n-2} - m + 1)}{(m - 1)!}$ is an integer. But if $m = kp^t$ with $(k, p) = 1$, the expression will not be a multiple of p^n unless $p^{n-2-t} \cdot p^{kp^t} \geq p^n$, that is, unless $n - 2 - t + kp^t \geq n$. But $kp^t \geq t + 2$. Each term after the second of the expansion is, therefore, a multiple of p^n.

Hence, for $n \geq 3$

$$r^{p^{n-2}(p-1)} \equiv 1 + p^{n-1}c(\bmod\ p^n)$$

and because $(c, p) = 1$,

$$r^{p^{n-2}(p-1)} \not\equiv 1 (\bmod\ p^n)$$

If $n = 2$, we know that

$$r^{p-1} \not\equiv 1 (\bmod\ p^2)$$

whereas

$$r^{p(p-1)} \equiv 1 (\bmod\ p^2)$$

Consequently, r is a primitive root modulo p^n, where $n \geq 1$.
Now consider the congruence

$$x^{p^{n-1}(p-1)} \equiv 1 (\bmod\ p^n)$$

Each of the integers

$$r, r^2, \ldots, r^{p^{n-1}(p-1)}$$

satisfies this congruence, and each of them is prime to p. They are, moreover, incongruent modulo p^n, for if

$$r^u \equiv r^v (\bmod\ p^n) \qquad u, v = 1, 2, \ldots, p^{n-1}(p - 1)$$

assuming $u > v$, we conclude that $r^{u-v} \equiv 1 (\bmod\ p^n)$. This result is impossible because $u - v$ is less than $p^{n-1}(p - 1)$. Hence, these $\phi(p^n)$ integers are distinct solutions modulo p^n of the conditional congruence. But only integers prime to p can be solutions of this congruence, and since there are exactly $\phi(p^n)$ integers from 1 through p^n that are prime to p, we have found all the solutions.

Furthermore, the integers that belong to $\phi(p^n)$ modulo p^n must be among the solutions of the given congruence. By arguing just as we did in Theorem 7-4, we can show that r^s belongs to $\phi(p^n)$ modulo p^n if and only if s is prime to $p^{n-1}(p - 1)$. There are, then, exactly $\phi(\phi(p^n))$ incongruent integers that are primitive roots modulo p^n.

Example. We have already shown that 3 is a primitive root of 17. But $3^{16} \equiv 171 (\bmod\ 289)$. Accordingly, 3 is a primitive root of 17^2 since $3^{16} \not\equiv 1 (\bmod\ 289)$. Furthermore, the powers of 3 having exponents prime to $\phi(17^2) = (17)(16)$ constitute the complete set of distinct primitive roots of 17^2. There are exactly $\phi(272) = 128$ of them.

The theorem shows, moreover, that because $3^{16} \not\equiv 1 (\bmod\ 289)$, 3 is a primitive root of 17^3, 17^4, ...

EXERCISES

1. Find all the primitive roots of 5^2 and 5^3.

2. Find the primitive roots of 49. Find also all the integers that belong to the exponent 6 modulo 49. Find a primitive root of 343.

3. If p is an odd prime, prove that any primitive root of p^n is a primitive root of p.

4. Prove that if p is a prime and an integer a prime to p belongs to the exponent d modulo p, and if p^h is the highest power of p that divides $a^d - 1$, then a belongs to the exponent dp^{n-h} modulo p^n for $n \geq h$.

5. If p is an odd prime, prove that the product of two primitive roots modulo p^n is not a primitive root modulo p^n.

6. If r belongs to $\phi(p^n)$ modulo p^n and $(s, \phi(p^n)) = d \neq 1$, does r^s belong to $\phi(p^n)/d$ modulo p^n?

Theorem 7-10. There are exactly $\phi(\phi(2p^n))$ incongruent primitive roots modulo $2p^n$.

Any integer that satisfies the congruence

$$x^{\phi(2p^n)} \equiv 1 \pmod{2p^n}$$

is necessarily odd, and so a primitive root of $2p^n$ must be odd. But if an odd integer a belongs to $\phi(2p^n) = p^{n-1}(p - 1)$ modulo $2p^n$, it is a primitive root of p^n, for

$$a^{p^{n-1}(p-1)} \equiv 1 \pmod{2p^n}$$

implies that

$$a^{p^{n-1}(p-1)} \equiv 1 \pmod{p^n}$$

and if a belonged to $d < p^{n-1}(p - 1)$ modulo p^n, then since a is odd, $a^d \equiv 1 \pmod{2p^n}$. The last congruence is, of course, impossible, for a is a primitive root of $2p^n$. We must, therefore, look for the primitive roots of $2p^n$ among the primitive roots of p^n.

But if r is an odd primitive root of p^n, it is a primitive root of $2p^n$, for $r^{\phi(p^n)} - 1$ is divisible by 2 as well as by p^n, and if r belonged to an exponent smaller than $\phi(2p^n)$ modulo $2p^n$, it would belong to that exponent modulo p^n.

Moreover, if r is an even primitive root of p^n, the integer $r + p^n$, which is also a primitive root of p^n because it is in the same residue class as r modulo p^n, is odd and is of necessity a primitive root of $2p^n$.

We have shown, therefore, that a primitive root of p^n is a primitive root of $2p^n$ if and only if it is an odd integer.

It is evident, furthermore, that two odd primitive roots of p^n that are in the same residue class modulo p^n are congruent modulo $2p^n$. On the other hand, if two of the $\phi(\phi(p^n))$ odd primitive roots modulo p^n selected one from each of the residue classes modulo p^n were congruent modulo $2p^n$, they would be congruent modulo p^n. There are, therefore, exactly $\phi(\phi(2p^n))$ incongruent primitive roots of $2p^n$.

Example. We have shown that 3 is a primitive root of 17^2. It is also a primitive root of $2(17^2) = 578$, for it is odd.

In like manner 3^3 and 3^5 are primitive roots of 578. But $3^7 \equiv 166 \pmod{289}$ and is, therefore, an even primitive root of 289. It is not a primitive root of 578, but the odd number $166 + 289 = 455$, which is in the same class as 166 modulo 289, is a primitive root of 578. Again, $3^9 \equiv$

49(mod 289) is a primitive root of 578, and although $3^{11} \equiv 152$(mod 289) is not a primitive root of 578, it yields $152 + 289 = 441$, which is. There are in all $\phi(272) = 128$ incongruent primitive roots of 578.

EXERCISES

1. Find all the primitive roots of 50 and 250.

2. Find the primitive roots of 98. Determine the integers that belong to the exponent 3 modulo 98. Find a primitive root of 686.

3. Prove that the congruence $x^{\phi(2p^n)} \equiv 1$(mod $2p^n$) has exactly $\phi(2p^n)$ solutions modulo $2p^n$ if p is an odd prime.

4. If r is a primitive root of $2p^n$, p being an odd prime, show that r^s belongs to $\phi(2p^n)$ if and only if $(s,\phi(2p^n)) = 1$. Prove, furthermore, that if $(s,\phi(2p^n)) = d$, then r^s belongs to $\phi(2p^n)/d$ modulo $2p^n$.

5. Show that if p is an odd prime, the product of two primitive roots modulo $2p^n$ is not a primitive root of $2p^n$.

7-7. Primitive λ Roots. R. Carmichael called integers that belong to $\lambda(m)$ for the modulus m *primitive λ roots of m.**

When $m = 2^n$, where $n > 2$, the integer 3 always belongs to $\lambda(2^n) = 2^{n-2}$ modulo 2^n, for if 3 belonged to a smaller exponent, $3^{2^{n-3}}$ would have to be congruent to 1 modulo 2^n. That this relation is not true is evident from the following argument: According to the binomial expansion,

$$(2^2 - 1)^{2^{n-3}} \equiv 1 - 2^{n-3} \cdot 2^2 + 2^{n-4}(2^{n-3} - 1)2^4 - \cdots + 2^{2^{n-2}}(\text{mod } 2^n)$$

so that, for $n > 3$,

$$3^{2^{n-3}} \equiv 1 - 2^{n-1}(\text{mod } 2^n)$$

and hence in this case $3^{2^{n-3}} \not\equiv 1$(mod 2^n). When $n = 3$, $\lambda(2^3) = 2$ and it is obvious that 3 belongs to 2 modulo 2^3.

Because a primitive root is necessarily a primitive λ root, we have now shown that there is a primitive λ root for every modulus of the form p^n with p a prime. On this basis R. Carmichael proved by induction that there is always a primitive λ root of m. He showed that if r_1 is a primitive λ root of $m_1 = p_1{}^{n_1}p_2{}^{n_2} \cdots p_{k-1}{}^{n_{k-1}}$ and r_2 is a primitive λ root of $p_k{}^{n_k}$, where the p_i, with $i = 1, 2, \ldots, k$, are distinct primes, then an integer r that satisfies both the congruences

$$x \equiv r_1(\text{mod } m_1)$$

and

$$x \equiv r_2(\text{mod } p_k{}^{n_k})$$

is a primitive λ root of $m = m_1p_k{}^{n_k}$. To show that this statement is true, suppose that r belongs to s for the modulus m. Then

$$r^s \equiv 1(\text{mod } m_1)$$

---

* R. Carmichael, *Bull. Am. Math. Soc.*, Vol. 16, No. 2, pp. 232–238, 1909–1910.

and
$$r^s \equiv 1 (\mathrm{mod}\ p_k{}^{n_k})$$

But r belongs to $\lambda(m_1)$ modulo m_1 and to $\lambda(p_k{}^{n_k})$ for the modulus $p_k{}^{n_k}$. Therefore, both $\lambda(m_1)$ and $\lambda(p_k{}^{n_k})$ divide s. This means that the smallest s can be is the least common multiple of $\lambda(m_1)$ and $\lambda(p_k{}^{n_k})$. This integer is exactly $\lambda(m)$. It is true, moreover, that $r^{\lambda(m)} \equiv 1 (\mathrm{mod}\ m)$ since $(r, m) = 1$. Therefore, r is a primitive λ root modulo m.

Carmichael also showed that when r is a primitive λ root of m, the powers of r whose exponents are prime to $\lambda(m)$ give $\phi(\lambda(m))$ incongruent primitive λ roots of m, and the product of these λ roots is congruent to 1 modulo m. These powers of r do not necessarily yield all the primitive λ roots of m, but the same powers of another primitive λ root will either repeat in some order the results obtained from r or give $\phi(\lambda(m))$ different primitive λ roots of m distinct from those generated by r.

Although the theory of numbers is a branch of mathematics that we evaluate on the basis of the profundity of its truths and the variety and simplicity of its methods rather than on its applicability to practical problems, yet it is interesting to observe that in 1935 H. P. Lawther showed how the theory of primitive roots and primitive λ roots can be applied to the problem of splicing telephone cables.*

Example. To find a primitive λ root of 21, we first find a primitive root of 7 and also of 3. It can be easily verified that 3 belongs to 6 modulo 7 and that 2 belongs to 2 modulo 3. We then find the common solution of the congruences

$$x \equiv 3 (\mathrm{mod}\ 7)$$
$$x \equiv 2 (\mathrm{mod}\ 3)$$

The solution is $x \equiv 17 (\mathrm{mod}\ 21)$, and this integer is a primitive λ root of 21.

If we now find the powers of 17 that have exponents prime to $\lambda(21) = 6$, we have a set of $\phi(6) = 2$ primitive λ roots of 21. They are 17 and $17^5 \equiv 5 (\mathrm{mod}\ 21)$.

There are but two incongruent primitive roots of 7, and they are 3 and 5. When we use the integer 5 with the only primitive root of 3 to form the set of congruences

$$x \equiv 5 (\mathrm{mod}\ 7)$$
$$x \equiv 2 (\mathrm{mod}\ 3)$$

we find that the solution is $x \equiv 5 (\mathrm{mod}\ 21)$. But the set of powers, 5 and 5^5, repeat the two primitive λ roots of 21 already found. This situation, however, does not mean that there are no other primitive λ roots of 21, for the number 2 belongs to 6 modulo 21. Moreover, 2 and $2^5 \equiv 11 (\mathrm{mod}\ 21)$ form a new set of two primitive λ roots of 21.

* H. P. Lawther, Jr., *Am. Math. Monthly*, Vol. 42, No. 2, pp. 81–91, 1935.

EXERCISES

1. Prove that if r is a primitive λ root of m, the powers of r having exponents prime to $\lambda(m)$ are primitive λ roots of m.

2. Prove that if $\lambda(m) > 2$, the product of all the incongruent primitive λ roots of m is congruent to 1 modulo m.

7-8. Integers Belonging to a Divisor of $\lambda(2^n)$ Modulo 2^n

*Theorem 7-11.** If $n \geq 3$ and d, not 2, divides 2^{n-2}, then there are exactly d incongruent integers that belong to d modulo 2^n, but if $d = 2$, there are just three incongruent integers that belong to d modulo 2^n.

We have shown that the integer 3 is a primitive λ root of 2^n if $n \geq 3$. On this basis we shall show that for the modulus 2^n any integer having the form $8k \pm 3$ cannot belong to an exponent smaller than 2^{n-2}. If $n > 3$,

$$(8k \pm 3)^{2^{n-3}} \equiv (3 \pm 8k)^{2^{n-3}} \equiv 3^{2^{n-3}} \pm 2^{n-3}(3)^{2^{n-3}-1}(2^3k) + \cdots$$
$$\pm 2^{n-3} \cdot 3(2^3k)^{2^{n-3}-1} + (2^3k)^{2^{n-3}}(\mod 2^n)$$

Hence,

$$(8k \pm 3)^{2^{n-3}} \equiv 3^{2^{n-3}}(\mod 2^n)$$

But since $3^{2^{n-3}} \not\equiv 1(\mod 2^n)$, $8k \pm 3$ belongs to 2^{n-2} modulo 2^n if $n > 3$. Consequently, in this case there are at least 2^{n-2} integers belonging to $\lambda(2^n)$ modulo 2^n, for, in the expression $8k + 3$, k can have the values $0, 1, 2, \ldots, 2^{n-3} - 1$ and, in $8k - 3$, k can be $1, 2, \ldots, 2^{n-3}$, thereby yielding all positive integers of the required form that are less than 2^n.

If $n = 3$, it is obvious that 3 and 5 belong to $\lambda(2^3) = 2$ modulo 2^3. But besides these two integers the integer $7 = 2^3 - 1$ is a primitive λ root of 2^3. Consequently, three incongruent integers belong to $\lambda(2^3)$ modulo 2^3.

Again, if $n > 3$, we can prove that for the modulus 2^n all integers having the form $8k \pm 1$, in which k is prime to 2, belong to the exponent 2^{n-3}, for

$$(8k \pm 1)^{2^{n-3}} \equiv 1 \pm 2^{n-3}(2^3k) + \cdots + (2^3k)^{2^{n-3}}(\mod 2^n)$$
$$\equiv 1(\mod 2^n)$$

On the other hand, if $n > 4$,

$$(8k \pm 1)^{2^{n-4}} \equiv 1 \pm 2^{n-4}(2^3k) + 2^{n-5}(2^{n-4} - 1)(2^3k)^2 \pm \cdots$$
$$+ (2^3k)^{2^{n-4}}(\mod 2^n)$$
$$\equiv 1 \pm 2^{n-1}k(\mod 2^n)$$

Hence, if $(k, 2) = 1$ and $n > 4$, the integers $8k \pm 1$ belong to the exponent 2^{n-3} modulo 2^n. Moreover, in this case values of k that are prime to 2 can be chosen from the integers $1, 2, 3, \ldots, 2^{n-3}$ in $\phi(2^{n-3})$ ways, and thus the form $8k \pm 1$ yields $2\phi(2^{n-3}) = 2^{n-3}$ integers from 1 through 2^n that belong to 2^{n-3} modulo 2^n. But if $n = 4$, not only the integers 9 and 7 belong to 2 modulo 2^4, but also $2^4 - 1 = 15$ belongs to 2 modulo 2^4.

We observe, moreover, that if $k = 2r$ with $(r, 2) = 1$,

$$(8k \pm 1)^{2^{n-4}} \equiv 1 (\mathrm{mod}\ 2^n)$$

and that $2^4 r \pm 1$ must, therefore, belong to an exponent which is a divisor of 2^{n-4} for this modulus.

Similarly, we find that, for $n > s \geq 3$,

$$(2^s r \pm 1)^{2^{n-s}} \equiv 1 \pm 2^{n-s}(2^s r) + \cdots + (2^s r)^{2^{n-s}} (\mathrm{mod}\ 2^n)$$
$$\equiv 1 (\mathrm{mod}\ 2^n)$$

If, in addition, $(r, 2) = 1$ and $n > s + 1$,

$$(2^s r \pm 1)^{2^{n-s-1}} \equiv 1 \pm 2^{n-s-1}(2^s r) + 2^{n-s-2}(2^{n-s-1} - 1)(2^s r)^2 \pm \cdots$$
$$+ (2^s r)^{2^{n-s-1}} (\mathrm{mod}\ 2^n)$$
$$\equiv 1 \pm 2^{n-1} r (\mathrm{mod}\ 2^n)$$

so that in this case $2^s r \pm 1$ belongs to 2^{n-s} modulo 2^n. There are then $\phi(2^{n-s})$ ways of choosing r prime to 2 so that the integers $2^s r \pm 1$ are between 1 and 2^n. Thus at least $2\phi(2^{n-s}) = 2^{n-s}$ incongruent integers belong to 2^{n-s} modulo 2^n for $n > s + 1 \geq 4$.

But if $n = s + 1 \geq 4$, the integers $2^{n-1} \pm 1$ belong to 2 modulo 2^n, and it is also evident that $2^n - 1$ belongs to 2 modulo 2^n. Consequently, for $n \geq 4$, $2\phi(2) + 1 = 3$ incongruent integers belong to 2 modulo 2^n.

It is, furthermore, apparent that 1 belongs to 1 modulo 2^n for $n \geq 3$.

Consequently, if $n > 3$, we have shown that, of the 2^{n-1} integers 1 through 2^n that are prime to 2,

2^{n-2} of them belong to 2^{n-2} modulo 2^n

$2\phi(2^{n-3}) = 2^{n-3}$ belong to 2^{n-3}

$2\phi(2^{n-4}) = 2^{n-4}$ belong to 2^{n-4}

. . . .

$2\phi(2^{n-s}) = 2^{n-s}$ belong to 2^{n-s}

. . . .

$2\phi(2) + 1 = 3$ belong to 2

1 belongs to 1 modulo 2^n

But $1 + 3 + 2^2 + 2^3 + \cdots + 2^{n-2} = 2^{n-1}$, and we have thereby accounted for all the 2^{n-1} positive integers less than 2^n and prime to 2. Therefore, the number of integers given in each case is exactly the number of incongruent integers that belong to the specified exponent modulo 2^n when $n > 3$.

When $n = 3$, three incongruent integers belong to 2 and one belongs to 1 modulo 2^3.

Corollary. The congruence $x^{2^k} \equiv 1 \pmod{2^n}$, where $0 < k \leq n - 2$, has 2^{k+1} solutions if $n > 2$.

Theorem 7-11 shows that the congruence $x^2 \equiv 1 \pmod{2^n}$, for $n > 2$, has 2^2 solutions modulo 2^n since the solutions must be prime to 2 and belong to the divisors of 2. For a like reason $x^{2^k} \equiv 1 \pmod{2^n}$, with $1 < k \leq n - 2$, has $1 + 3 + 2^2 + 2^3 + \cdots + 2^k = 2^{k+1}$ solutions modulo 2^n if $n > 2$.

*Theorem 7-12. If d is a divisor of $\lambda(2^n)$ and $n = 0, 1,$ or 2, there is exactly one positive integer less than 2^n that belongs to d modulo 2^n.

7-9. Integers Belonging to a Divisor of $\phi(p^n)$ Modulo p^n

*Theorem 7-13. If p is an odd prime and d is a divisor of $\phi(p^n)$, where $n > 1$, there is an integer that belongs to d modulo p^n.

If $d \mid \phi(p^n)$, $d = kp^u$, where k is a divisor of $p - 1$ and $0 \leq u \leq n - 1$.

Take an integer a that belongs to k modulo p. Then $a^k \equiv 1 \pmod{p}$. If $a^k \equiv 1 \pmod{p^2}$, there is an integer r that is congruent to a modulo p and is such that $r^k \not\equiv 1 \pmod{p^2}$, for

$$(a + mp)^k \equiv a^k + ka^{k-1}mp + \cdots + (mp)^k \pmod{p^2}$$
$$\equiv 1 + ka^{k-1}mp \pmod{p^2}$$

Hence, if $(m, p) = 1$,

$$(a + mp)^k \not\equiv 1 \pmod{p^2}$$

Therefore, let $r = a + mp$. Then r belongs to k modulo p, and $r^k = 1 + cp$ with $(c, p) = 1$. Keeping in mind that the exponent to which r belongs modulo p^n has the factor k, we see that for $n \geq 2$ and $(w, p) = 1$,

$$(r^k)^{wp^{n-2}} \equiv (1 + cp)^{wp^{n-2}} \pmod{p^n}$$

and

$$(r^k)^{wp^{n-2}} \equiv 1 + wcp^{n-1} \pmod{p^n}$$
$$\not\equiv 1 \pmod{p^n}$$

But

$$(r^k)^{p^{n-1}} \equiv 1 \pmod{p^n}$$

Therefore, r belongs to kp^{n-1} modulo p^n when $n > 1$.

Furthermore, if a belongs to k modulo p and

$$a^k \equiv 1 \pmod{p^{s-1}}$$

but

$$a^k \not\equiv 1 \pmod{p^s}$$

there is an $r \equiv a \pmod{p^i}$, where $i = 1, 2, \ldots, s - 1$, such that

$$r^k \equiv 1 \pmod{p^s},$$

for since $a^k = 1 - tp^{s-1}$ with $(t, p) = 1$,

$$(a + mp^{s-1})^k \equiv a^k + ka^{k-1}mp^{s-1} \pmod{p^s}$$
$$\equiv 1 - tp^{s-1} + ka^{k-1}mp^{s-1} \pmod{p^s}$$

But an integer m prime to p can be so chosen that

$$ka^{k-1}mp^{s-1} \equiv tp^{s-1}(\bmod\ p^s)$$

for this congruence is equivalent to

$$ka^{k-1}m \equiv t(\bmod\ p)$$

Hence,

$$(a + mp^{s-1})^k \equiv 1(\bmod\ p^s)$$

Let $r = a + mp^{s-1}$. Then r belongs to the exponent k for each p^i, where $i = 1, 2, \ldots, s$.

In like manner if $r^k \equiv 1(\bmod\ p^{s+1})$, we can find an integer $v = r + gp^s$ with $(g, p) = 1$ such that

$$(r + gp^s)^k \not\equiv 1(\bmod\ p^{s+1})$$

This v is in the class with r for each of the moduli p^i, where $i = 1, 2, \ldots, s$, and hence v belongs to k for each of these moduli. Furthermore, since $v^k = 1 + cp^s$ with $(c, p) = 1$, if $(w, p) = 1$ and $n > s$,

$$(v^k)^{wp^{n-s-1}} \equiv (1 + cp^s)^{wp^{n-s-1}}(\bmod\ p^n)$$
$$\equiv 1 + wcp^{n-1}(\bmod\ p^n)$$
$$\not\equiv 1(\bmod\ p^n)$$

but

$$(v^k)^{p^{n-s}} \equiv 1(\bmod\ p^n)$$

Therefore, v belongs to kp^{n-s} modulo p^n for $n > s > 0$. This result implies that there is always an integer that belongs to a divisor of $\phi(p^n)$ modulo p^n.

*Theorem 7-14. If d is a divisor of $\phi(p^n)$, there are exactly $\phi(d)$ incongruent integers that belong to d modulo p^n.

We have proved that there is an integer a that belongs to d modulo p^n. As a result it is clear that the integers $a, a^2, \ldots, a^d$ satisfy

$$x^d \equiv 1(\bmod\ p^n)$$

Moreover, a^s, where $s = 1, 2, \ldots, d$, belongs to d modulo p^n if and only if $(s, d) = 1$. Therefore, $\phi(d)$ of the above powers of a belong to d modulo p^n. Consequently, if $\psi(d)$ is the number of incongruent integers that belong to d modulo p^n, $\psi(d) \geq \phi(d)$. However, every integer from 1 through p^n that is prime to p belongs to just one divisor of $\phi(p^n)$ modulo p^n, and so

$$\psi(d_1) + \psi(d_2) + \cdots + \psi(d_m) = p^{n-1}(p - 1)$$

where the d_i, with $i = 1, 2, \ldots, m$, are the divisors of $\phi(p^n)$. Moreover,

$$\phi(d_1) + \phi(d_2) + \cdots + \phi(d_m) = p^{n-1}(p - 1)$$

and hence each $\psi(d_i) = \phi(d_i)$.

7-10. Integers Belonging to a Divisor of $\phi(2p^n)$ modulo $2p^n$

*Theorem 7-15. There are exactly $\phi(d)$ incongruent integers modulo $2p^n$ that belong to any divisor d of $\phi(2p^n)$ modulo $2p^n$.

If r belongs to $\phi(2p^n)$ modulo $2p^n$, the incongruent integers modulo $2p^n$ that satisfy the congruence

$$x^{\phi(2p^n)} \equiv 1 \pmod{2p^n}$$

are $r, r^2, \ldots, r^{\phi(2p^n)}$. These are all the integers from 1 through $2p^n$ that are prime to $2p^n$. In the manner previously employed we can show that r^s is a primitive root of $2p^n$ if and only if $(s, \phi(2p^n)) = 1$, and that if $(s, \phi(2p^n)) = d \neq 1$, r^s belongs to $\phi(2p^n)/d$ modulo $2p^n$. There is, then, always at least one integer r^s that belongs to any divisor of $\phi(2p^n)$ modulo $2p^n$, for as s takes the values $1, 2, \ldots, \phi(2p^n)$, the integer $d = (s, \phi(2p^n))$ ranges over all divisors of $\phi(2p^n)$ and so does $\phi(2p^n)/d$.

But if b belongs to d, a divisor of $\phi(2p^n)$, modulo $2p^n$, then

$$(b^d)^{\phi(2p^n)/d} \equiv b^{\phi(2p^n)} \equiv 1 \pmod{2p^n}$$

and b satisfies the congruence $x^{\phi(2p^n)} \equiv 1 \pmod{2p^n}$ and is, therefore, congruent to a power of r modulo $2p^n$. Consequently, all integers that belong to d modulo $2p^n$ are congruent modulo $2p^n$ to just one integer of the set $r, r^2, r^3, \ldots, r^{\phi(2p^n)}$. By choosing s so that $(s, \phi(2p^n)) = \phi(2p^n)/d$, r^s will belong to d modulo $2p^n$. But there are exactly $\phi(d)$ integers s in the set $1, 2, 3, \ldots, \phi(2p^n)$ that have with $\phi(2p^n)$ the greatest common divisor $\phi(2p^n)/d$. Hence, exactly $\phi(d)$ incongruent integers belong to d modulo $2p^n$.

7-11. Integers Belonging to a Divisor of $\lambda(m)$ Modulo m.

One of the author's students, Bernard Sussman, and the author have developed the following proof of a method for finding not only all the primitive λ roots of m but also all the integers that belong to any divisor of $\lambda(m)$ modulo m.*

It has been shown thus far that if $m = \prod_{j=0}^{r} p_j^{n_j}$, a primitive λ root α_j can be determined for each of the moduli $p_j^{n_j}$ and the common solution of the set of congruences

$$x \equiv \alpha_j \pmod{p_j^{n_j}} \qquad j = 0, 1, \ldots, r \tag{1}$$

is a primitive λ root of m. We have seen, moreover, that this common solution X generates by means of its powers X^v, with v prime to $\lambda(m)$, exactly $\phi(\lambda(m))$ incongruent primitive λ roots of m. If there is a primitive λ root of m distinct from those already found, that too will generate $\phi(\lambda(m))$ incongruent primitive λ roots of m none of which is in a pre-

* R. Carmichael, *Quart. J. Math.*, Vol. 44, pp. 94–104, 1913.

ceding set. Thus the number of incongruent primitive λ roots of m is a multiple of $\phi(\lambda(m))$, but it is our problem to find this multiple and to show how to determine all the primitive λ roots modulo m.

Let $\psi(d)(\bmod 2^n)$ be the number of incongruent integers that belong to d, a divisor of $\lambda(2^n)$, for the modulus 2^n. Then if we understand that $p_0 = 2$, the number of α_0 that can be used in the congruences (1) is $\psi(\lambda(2^{n_0}))(\bmod 2^{n_0})$ and the number of α_j, where $j = 1, 2, \ldots, r$, is $\phi(\lambda(p_j^{n_j}))$. Consequently, there are

$$\psi(\lambda(2^{n_0}))(\bmod 2^{n_0}) \prod_{j=1}^{r} \phi(\lambda(p_j^{n_j}))$$

sets of congruences (1), each set having a single solution modulo m, and each of these solutions is a distinct primitive λ root modulo m.

But the primitive λ roots so determined are not necessarily all that exist. Let d_{ij}, where $i = 1, 2, \ldots, q_j$, represent the q_j divisors of $\lambda(p_j^{n_j})$. Choose any set of $r + 1$ divisors d_{ij} of the $\lambda(p_j^{n_j})$, where $j = 0, 1, 2, \ldots, r$, that contains exactly one divisor of each $\lambda(p_j^{n_j})$ and such that the least common multiple of the d_{ij} is the number $\lambda(m)$. Then find integers t_{ij} that belong to the d_{ij} modulo $p_j^{n_j}$, and find the common solution Y modulo m of the set of congruences

$$y \equiv t_{ij}(\bmod p_j^{n_j}) \qquad j = 0, 1, 2, \ldots, r \qquad (2)$$

This integer Y is a primitive λ root modulo m, for it is evident that

$$Y^{\lambda(m)} \equiv 1(\bmod p_j^{n_j})$$

and that

$$Y^{\lambda(m)} \equiv 1(\bmod m)$$

But if Y belonged to an exponent $u < \lambda(m)$ modulo m, then $Y^u \equiv 1(\bmod m)$ and $Y^u \equiv 1(\bmod p_j^{n_j})$, where $j = 0, 1, 2, \ldots, r$. Thus u would be divisible by each d_{ij}, and hence by their least common multiple, which is $\lambda(m)$. Therefore, u is not less than $\lambda(m)$, and Y belongs to $\lambda(m)$ modulo m. It is evident also that if there are k_{ij} integers t_{ij} that belong to d_{ij} modulo $p_j^{n_j}$, there will be $\prod_{j=1}^{r} k_{ij}$ congruences (2) for one choice of the d_{ij}. Consequently, there are exactly $\psi(d_{i0})(\bmod 2^{n_0}) \prod_{j=1}^{r} \phi(d_{ij})$ incongruent primitive λ roots of m determined by one choice of the d_{ij}, where $j = 0, 1, \ldots, r$, having least common multiple $\lambda(m)$, and this number is obviously a multiple of $\phi(\lambda(m))$.

Each set of $\psi(d_{i0})(\bmod 2^{n_0}) \prod_{j=1}^{r} \phi(d_{ij})$ incongruent primitive λ roots of m

separates without repetition of an element into subsets of $\phi(\lambda(m))$ integers. Each such subset is generated by the powers, with exponents prime to $\lambda(m)$, of any member of the subset, for if g_1 and g_2 are primitive λ roots of m determined by one selection of the d_{ij}, and if $g_2 \not\equiv g_1{}^t(\mathrm{mod}\ m)$, where t is prime to $\lambda(m)$ and $0 < t < \lambda(m)$, and if

$$g_1{}^{s_1} \equiv g_2{}^{s_2}\ (\mathrm{mod}\ m)$$

where s_1 and s_2 are prime to $\lambda(m)$, then

$$g_1{}^{s_1 t} \equiv g_2{}^{s_2 t}(\mathrm{mod}\ m)$$

But because the powers of $g_2{}^{s_2}$ repeat the original $\phi(\lambda(m))$ roots generated by g_2, for a certain t, say t_1,

$$g_1{}^{s_1 t_1} \equiv g_2{}^{s_2 t_1} \equiv g_2(\mathrm{mod}\ m)$$

This conclusion implies that our assumption is false. There will, therefore, be exactly

$$\frac{\psi(d_{i0})(\mathrm{mod}\ 2^{n_0}) \prod\limits_{j=1}^{r} \phi(d_{ij})}{\phi(\lambda(m))}$$

such sets developed from each of q distinct choices of $r + 1$ divisors d_{ij}, where $i = 1, 2, \ldots, q_j$, $j = 1, 2, \ldots, r$, having the least common multiple $\lambda(m)$. No primitive λ root of m generated by the powers of a primitive λ root β that has been determined by one choice d_{ij} of the d_{ij} can be found among the primitive λ roots of m determined by a distinct set of divisors d_{izj}, for the sets $d_{i_1 j}$ and $d_{i_2 j}$ differ by at least one divisor corresponding to a λ function of a power of a particular prime. Furthermore, assuming that $d_{i_1 h}$ is distinct from $d_{i_2 h}$ and that β belongs to $d_{i_1 h}$ modulo $p_h{}^{n_h}$ and γ belongs to $d_{i_2 h}$ modulo $p_h{}^{n_h}$, let us suppose that $\beta^v \equiv \gamma^w(\mathrm{mod}\ m)$ with v and w prime to $\lambda(m)$. Then $\beta^v \equiv \gamma^w(\mathrm{mod}\ p_h{}^{n_h})$. But v and w are prime to $\lambda(p_h{}^{n_h})$ and hence to the divisors of $\lambda(p_h{}^{n_h})$. However,

$$(\beta^v)^{d_{i_1 h}} \equiv (\beta^{d_{i_1 h}})^v \equiv 1(\mathrm{mod}\ p_h{}^{n_h})$$

Hence,

$$(\gamma^w)^{d_{i_1 h}} \equiv 1(\mathrm{mod}\ p_h{}^{n_h})$$

and thus $d_{i_2 h}$ divides $w d_{i_1 h}$. Therefore, $d_{i_2 h}$ divides $d_{i_1 h}$. In like manner, $d_{i_1 h}$ divides $d_{i_2 h}$, and finally $d_{i_1 h} = d_{i_2 h}$, which is contrary to our assumption. If there are q sets of divisors d_{ij}, the primitive λ roots of m determined by them are, therefore, distinct modulo m.

But each integer which belongs to $\lambda(m)$ modulo m and which is, therefore, prime to each of the $p_j{}^{n_j}$ belongs to exactly one exponent that is a divisor of $\lambda(p_j{}^{n_j})$ modulo $p_j{}^{n_j}$. Hence, from all possible choices of sets of $r + 1$ positive integers d_{ij}, where $i = 1, 2, \ldots, q_j$, $j = 0, 1, 2, \ldots, r$, for which the least common multiple of the d_{ij} in a set is $\lambda(m)$, we find all the incongruent primitive λ roots modulo m, for if α belongs to $\lambda(m)$ modulo m, then

$$\alpha^{\lambda(p_j{}^{n_j})} \equiv 1 (\bmod \ p_j{}^{n_j}) \qquad j = 0, 1, \ldots, r$$

and hence α belongs to an exponent d_{ij} modulo $p_j{}^{n_j}$ that divides $\lambda(p_j{}^{n_j})$. If, however, the least common multiple of these d_{ij} were $u < \lambda(m)$, α would belong to u modulo m. Thus when $\psi(\lambda(m))(\bmod \ m)$ is the number of incongruent integers that belong to $\lambda(m)$ for the modulus m, we have:

Theorem 7-16. If the p_j, where $j = 0, 1, 2, \ldots, r$, are distinct primes, there are exactly

$$\psi(\lambda(m))(\bmod \ m) = \sum_q \psi(d_{i0})(\bmod \ 2^{n_0}) \prod_{j=1}^{r} \phi(d_{ij})$$

incongruent primitive λ roots modulo $m = \prod_{j=0}^{r} p_j{}^{n_j}$, where the summation is taken over the number q of distinct sets of $r+1$ divisors d_{ij}, with $i = 1, 2, \ldots, q_j$, of the $\lambda(p_j{}^{n_j})$ whose least common multiple is $\lambda(m)$ and where each of the q sets contains just one divisor of each of the $\lambda(p_j{}^{n_j})$. These primitive λ roots of m can be separated into subsets₁ of $\phi(\lambda(m))$ integers generated by any member of the subset.

It is, furthermore, obvious that the method with an analogous proof holds for finding the integers that belong to any divisor of $\lambda(m)$ for the modulus m.

Examples. At the end of Sec. 7-7 we showed that the primitive roots of 7 and 3 yield exactly two distinct primitive λ roots of 21. But it is evident that $\lambda(21) = 6$ can be built up, not only as the least common multiple of $\phi(7) = 6$ and $\phi(3) = 2$, but also as the least common multiple of the factors 6 of $\phi(7)$ and 1 of $\phi(3)$, and again as the least common multiple of the factors 3 of $\phi(7)$ and 2 of $\phi(3)$, and in no other way from factors of $\phi(7)$ and $\phi(3)$.

Using the fact that 3 and 5 belong to 6 modulo 7 and that 1 belongs to 1 modulo 3, the sets of congruences

$$x \equiv 3(\bmod \ 7) \qquad x \equiv 5(\bmod \ 7)$$
$$x \equiv 1(\bmod \ 3) \qquad x \equiv 1(\bmod \ 3)$$

show that 10 and 19 are primitive λ roots of 21. Notice that the powers of 10 yield $\phi(\lambda(21)) = 2$ primitive λ roots of 21, and they are 10 and $10^5 \equiv 19(\bmod \ 21)$.

The integers 2 and 4 belong to 3 modulo 7, and 2 belongs to 2 modulo 3. Therefore, the sets of congruences to be solved are

$$x \equiv 2(\bmod \ 7) \qquad x \equiv 4(\bmod \ 7)$$
$$x \equiv 2(\bmod \ 3) \qquad x \equiv 2(\bmod \ 3)$$

Their solutions are $x \equiv 2$, $x \equiv 11 \pmod{21}$, respectively, and again we observe that $2^5 \equiv 11 \pmod{21}$. There are then but three sets of two primitive λ roots of 21, and therefore exactly six incongruent integers that belong to 6 modulo 21.

As a second example consider the problem of finding the primitive λ roots of $168 = 2^3 \cdot 3 \cdot 7$. Since $\lambda(2^3) = 2$, $\lambda(3) = 2$, and $\lambda(7) = 6$, we must determine all possible ways in which $\lambda(168) = 6$ can be set up as the least common multiple of one factor of $\lambda(2^3)$, one factor of $\lambda(3)$, and one factor of $\lambda(7)$. These sets of factors are listed in the following table.

Case	Factors of $\lambda(2^3)$	Factors of $\lambda(3)$	Factors of $\lambda(7)$	Number of incongruent primitive λ roots of 168 determined
(1)	2	2	6	6
(2)	1	1	6	2
(3)	1	2	6	2
(4)	2	1	6	6
(5)	1	2	3	2
(6)	2	1	3	6
(7)	2	2	3	6

Case 1. The sets of congruences to be satisfied are

$$x \equiv 3 \pmod 8 \qquad x \equiv 3 \pmod 8$$
$$x \equiv 2 \pmod 3 \qquad x \equiv 2 \pmod 3$$
$$x \equiv 3 \pmod 7 \qquad x \equiv 5 \pmod 7$$

$$x \equiv 5 \pmod 8 \qquad x \equiv 5 \pmod 8$$
$$x \equiv 2 \pmod 3 \qquad x \equiv 2 \pmod 3$$
$$x \equiv 3 \pmod 7 \qquad x \equiv 5 \pmod 7$$

$$x \equiv 7 \pmod 8 \qquad x \equiv 7 \pmod 8$$
$$x \equiv 2 \pmod 3 \qquad x \equiv 2 \pmod 3$$
$$x \equiv 3 \pmod 7 \qquad x \equiv 5 \pmod 7$$

The primitive λ roots of 168 so determined are 59, 131, 101, 5, 143, and 47, respectively, and they occur in sets of $\phi(6) = 2$, which are 5 and $5^5 \equiv 101 \pmod{168}$; 47 and $47^5 \equiv 143 \pmod{168}$; and 59 and $59^5 \equiv 131 \pmod{168}$.

Case 2. The congruences are

$$x \equiv 1 \pmod 8 \qquad x \equiv 1 \pmod 8$$
$$x \equiv 1 \pmod 3 \qquad x \equiv 1 \pmod 3$$
$$x \equiv 3 \pmod 7 \qquad x \equiv 5 \pmod 7$$

The solutions are $x \equiv 73$ and $x \equiv 73^5 \equiv 145 \pmod{168}$.

Case 3. The congruences are

$$x \equiv 1 (\mathrm{mod}\ 8) \qquad x \equiv 1 (\mathrm{mod}\ 8)$$
$$x \equiv 2 (\mathrm{mod}\ 3) \qquad x \equiv 2 (\mathrm{mod}\ 3)$$
$$x \equiv 3 (\mathrm{mod}\ 7) \qquad x \equiv 5 (\mathrm{mod}\ 7)$$

The solutions are $x \equiv 17$ and $x \equiv 17^5 \equiv 89 (\mathrm{mod}\ 168)$.

Case 4. The congruences are

$$x \equiv 3 (\mathrm{mod}\ 8) \qquad x \equiv 3 (\mathrm{mod}\ 8)$$
$$x \equiv 1 (\mathrm{mod}\ 3) \qquad x \equiv 1 (\mathrm{mod}\ 3)$$
$$x \equiv 3 (\mathrm{mod}\ 7) \qquad x \equiv 5 (\mathrm{mod}\ 7)$$

$$x \equiv 5 (\mathrm{mod}\ 8) \qquad x \equiv 5 (\mathrm{mod}\ 8)$$
$$x \equiv 1 (\mathrm{mod}\ 3) \qquad x \equiv 1 (\mathrm{mod}\ 3)$$
$$x \equiv 3 (\mathrm{mod}\ 7) \qquad x \equiv 5 (\mathrm{mod}\ 7)$$

$$x \equiv 7 (\mathrm{mod}\ 8) \qquad x \equiv 7 (\mathrm{mod}\ 8)$$
$$x \equiv 1 (\mathrm{mod}\ 3) \qquad x \equiv 1 (\mathrm{mod}\ 3)$$
$$x \equiv 3 (\mathrm{mod}\ 7) \qquad x \equiv 5 (\mathrm{mod}\ 7)$$

The solutions modulo 168 are 115, 19, 157, 61, 31, and 103, respectively, and they form the sets 19 and $19^5 \equiv 115 (\mathrm{mod}\ 168)$; 31 and $31^5 \equiv 103 (\mathrm{mod}\ 168)$; 61 and $61^5 \equiv 157 (\mathrm{mod}\ 168)$.

Case 5. The congruences are

$$x \equiv 1 (\mathrm{mod}\ 8) \qquad x \equiv 1 (\mathrm{mod}\ 8)$$
$$x \equiv 2 (\mathrm{mod}\ 3) \qquad x \equiv 2 (\mathrm{mod}\ 3)$$
$$x \equiv 2 (\mathrm{mod}\ 7) \qquad x \equiv 4 (\mathrm{mod}\ 7)$$

The solutions are $x \equiv 65$ and $x \equiv 65^5 \equiv 137 (\mathrm{mod}\ 168)$.

Case 6. The congruences are

$$x \equiv 3 (\mathrm{mod}\ 8) \qquad x \equiv 3 (\mathrm{mod}\ 8)$$
$$x \equiv 1 (\mathrm{mod}\ 3) \qquad x \equiv 1 (\mathrm{mod}\ 3)$$
$$x \equiv 2 (\mathrm{mod}\ 7) \qquad x \equiv 4 (\mathrm{mod}\ 7)$$

$$x \equiv 5 (\mathrm{mod}\ 8) \qquad x \equiv 5 (\mathrm{mod}\ 8)$$
$$x \equiv 1 (\mathrm{mod}\ 3) \qquad x \equiv 1 (\mathrm{mod}\ 3)$$
$$x \equiv 2 (\mathrm{mod}\ 7) \qquad x \equiv 4 (\mathrm{mod}\ 7)$$

$$x \equiv 7 (\mathrm{mod}\ 8) \qquad x \equiv 7 (\mathrm{mod}\ 8)$$
$$x \equiv 1 (\mathrm{mod}\ 3) \qquad x \equiv 1 (\mathrm{mod}\ 3)$$
$$x \equiv 2 (\mathrm{mod}\ 7) \qquad x \equiv 4 (\mathrm{mod}\ 7)$$

The solutions modulo 168 are 163, 67, 37, 109, 79, and 151. They form the sets 37 and $37^5 \equiv 109 (\mathrm{mod}\ 168)$; 67 and $67^5 \equiv 163 (\mathrm{mod}\ 168)$; 79 and $79^5 \equiv 151 (\mathrm{mod}\ 168)$.

Case 7. The congruences are

$$x \equiv 3(\text{mod } 8) \qquad x \equiv 3(\text{mod } 8)$$
$$x \equiv 2(\text{mod } 3) \qquad x \equiv 2(\text{mod } 3)$$
$$x \equiv 2(\text{mod } 7) \qquad x \equiv 4(\text{mod } 7)$$

$$x \equiv 5(\text{mod } 8) \qquad x \equiv 5(\text{mod } 8)$$
$$x \equiv 2(\text{mod } 3) \qquad x \equiv 2(\text{mod } 3)$$
$$x \equiv 2(\text{mod } 7) \qquad x \equiv 4(\text{mod } 7)$$

$$x \equiv 7(\text{mod } 8) \qquad x \equiv 7(\text{mod } 8)$$
$$x \equiv 2(\text{mod } 3) \qquad x \equiv 2(\text{mod } 3)$$
$$x \equiv 2(\text{mod } 7) \qquad x \equiv 4(\text{mod } 7)$$

The solutions modulo 168 are 107, 11, 149, 53, 23, and 95, and they form the sets 11 and $11^5 \equiv 107(\text{mod } 168)$; 23 and $23^5 \equiv 95(\text{mod } 168)$; 53 and $53^5 \equiv 149(\text{mod } 168)$.

EXERCISES

1. Find the primitive λ roots of 32.
2. Find the integers that belong to 4 modulo 32.
3. Find the integers that belong to 6 and to 9 modulo 27.
4. Find the integers that belong to 6 and to 9 modulo 54.
5. Find the primitive λ roots of 72.

CHAPTER 8

INDICES

8-1. Indices for a Prime Modulus. When p is a prime and r is a primitive root of p, we have shown that $r, r^2, \ldots, r^{p-1}$ are incongruent modulo p. Hence, the power residues of r modulo p are in some order the integers $1, 2, \ldots, p - 1$ and form a reduced residue system modulo p. It is evident, then, that any integer n that is prime to p is congruent to one of the above powers of r for the modulus p. Thus

$$n \equiv r^s (\text{mod } p)$$

Gauss called the exponent s of r the *index of n modulo p relative to the base r*. To express this idea, we write $s = \text{ind}_r n$, but we usually omit the base r when there is no danger of confusion as is true in the case of the congruence $r^{\text{ind } n} \equiv n(\text{mod } p)$.

As thus defined, the index of n modulo p is unique for the modulus $p - 1$, for if

$$n \equiv r^s \equiv r^t (\text{mod } p)$$

and if $s > t$, then

$$r^{s-t} \equiv 1 (\text{mod } p)$$

and

$$s \equiv t (\text{mod } p - 1)$$

It is, therefore, convenient to use the least positive exponent s such that $n \equiv r^s (\text{mod } p)$ as the index of n modulo p. Obviously the index of n modulo 2 is useless.

Of course, the index of n determined by the primitive root r may be different from that determined by another primitive root of p. For instance, for the modulus 7, $\text{ind}_3 2 \equiv 2(\text{mod } 6)$ but $\text{ind}_5 2 \equiv 4(\text{mod } 6)$.

Theorem 8-1. If $m \equiv n(\text{mod } p)$, their indices relative to a particular primitive root of a prime p are the same modulo $p - 1$, and conversely.

The proof follows immediately from the fact that if r is a primitive root of p, the congruences $r^{\text{ind } m} \equiv r^{\text{ind } n}(\text{mod } p)$, and $\text{ind}_r m \equiv \text{ind}_r n(\text{mod } p - 1)$ imply each other.

Theorem 8-2. If p is a prime, and m and n are prime to p, then $\text{ind}_r mn \equiv \text{ind}_r m + \text{ind}_r n(\text{mod } p - 1)$.

125

Since

$$n \equiv r^{\text{ind } n}(\text{mod } p)$$

and

$$m \equiv r^{\text{ind } m}(\text{mod } p)$$

it follows that

$$mn \equiv r^{\text{ind } m + \text{ind } n}(\text{mod } p)$$

But

$$mn \equiv r^{\text{ind } mn}(\text{mod } p)$$

Therefore,

$$\text{ind}_r mn \equiv \text{ind}_r m + \text{ind}_r n(\text{mod } p - 1)$$

Theorem 8-3. If p is a prime and n is prime to p, then $\text{ind}_r n^k \equiv k \, \text{ind}_r n(\text{mod } p - 1)$.

If

$$n \equiv r^{\text{ind } n}(\text{mod } p)$$

then

$$n^k \equiv r^{k \, \text{ind } n}(\text{mod } p)$$

Also

$$n^k \equiv r^{\text{ind } n^k}(\text{mod } p)$$

Hence,

$$\text{ind}_r n^k \equiv k \, \text{ind}_r n(\text{mod } p - 1)$$

It is evident from these laws that the index of an integer plays a role which is analogous to that played by the logarithm of a number. This analogy is further emphasized by the following formula for changing the base of a system of indices from one primitive root of p to another:

Theorem 8-4. If p is a prime and n is prime to p, then $\text{ind}_{r_1} n \equiv \text{ind}_{r_2} n \, \text{ind}_{r_1} r_2(\text{mod } p - 1)$.

Let r_1 and r_2 be distinct primitive roots modulo p. Then

$$r_1^{\text{ind}_{r_1} n} \equiv r_2^{\text{ind}_{r_2} n}(\text{mod } p)$$

Hence, taking indices to the base r_1,

$$\text{ind}_{r_1} n \, \text{ind}_{r_1} r_1 \equiv \text{ind}_{r_2} n \, \text{ind}_{r_1} r_2(\text{mod } p - 1)$$

or

$$\text{ind}_{r_1} n \equiv \text{ind}_{r_2} n \, \text{ind}_{r_1} r_2(\text{mod } p - 1)$$

Theorem 8-5. If r_1 and r_2 are primitive roots of p, a prime, then $\text{ind}_{r_1} r_2 \, \text{ind}_{r_2} r_1 \equiv 1(\text{mod } p - 1)$.

$$r_1^{\text{ind}_{r_1} r_2} \equiv r_2(\text{mod } p)$$
$$\text{ind}_{r_1} r_2 \, \text{ind}_{r_2} r_1 \equiv \text{ind}_{r_2} r_2(\text{mod } p - 1)$$

and

$$\text{ind}_{r_1} r_2 \, \text{ind}_{r_2} r_1 \equiv 1(\text{mod } p - 1)$$

If we construct a table of power residues of a primitive root r of p, we can use indices in the solution of any congruences of the form $ax^n \equiv b(\mathrm{mod}\ p)$, with $(a, p) = 1$, for the theorems given above show that

$$\mathrm{ind}\ a + n\ \mathrm{ind}\ x \equiv \mathrm{ind}\ b(\mathrm{mod}\ p - 1)$$

Therefore,

$$n\ \mathrm{ind}\ x \equiv \mathrm{ind}\ b - \mathrm{ind}\ a(\mathrm{mod}\ p - 1)$$

and unless $d = (n,\ p - 1)$ divides $\mathrm{ind}\ b - \mathrm{ind}\ a$, no value of $\mathrm{ind}\ x$ satisfies the last congruence, and consequently there is no solution of $ax^n \equiv b(\mathrm{mod}\ p)$. But if $d\ |\ (\mathrm{ind}\ b - \mathrm{ind}\ a)$, there are exactly d incongruent values modulo $p - 1$ of $\mathrm{ind}\ x$ that satisfy $n\ \mathrm{ind}\ x \equiv \mathrm{ind}\ b - \mathrm{ind}\ a(\mathrm{mod}\ p - 1)$. By letting $(p - 1)/d = m_0$ we can express these incongruent solutions modulo $p - 1$ as

$$i,\ i + m_0,\ i + 2m_0,\ \ldots,\ i + (d - 1)m_0$$

Therefore,

$$x \equiv r^{i+km_0}(\mathrm{mod}\ p) \qquad k = 0, 1, \ldots, d - 1$$

gives exactly d incongruent solutions modulo p of the given congruence. By referring to a table of power residues of r, the d values of x are easily determined.

Of course, this method of solving a congruence requires that we have a table of indices for each prime that is used as a modulus. In 1839 Jacobi* constructed such tables of power residues for each prime and power of a prime less than 1000. Since then men like Goldberg, Wertheim, and Cunningham have contributed to the task of finding the power residues of the least positive primitive root of every prime less than 10,160. M. Kraitchik† has listed a primitive root of each prime less than 25,000, but many errors have been found in his tables.

It is quite evident that, instead of defining the index of an integer only in the case of a prime modulus, we might have used any other modulus m for which primitive roots exist, for in these cases the residues of the powers of a primitive root likewise form a reduced residue system modulo m. However, tables for such indices are less frequently available than are those with modulus p, a prime. They are, moreover, not essential because, as we have shown in Chap. 5, we can reduce the solution of any congruence to the problem of solving congruences with prime moduli.

Examples. 1. Solve: $5x \equiv 7(\mathrm{mod}\ 11)$.

Using the primitive root 2 of 11, we set up the following table of indices:

ind	1	2	3	4	5	6	7	8	9	10
n	2	4	8	5	10	9	7	3	6	1

* L. E. Dickson, "History of the Theory of Numbers," Vol. 1, p. 185.
† *Ibid.*, Vol. 1, p. 202.

Then
$$\text{ind } 5 + \text{ind } x \equiv \text{ind } 7 (\text{mod } 10)$$
or
$$4 + \text{ind } x \equiv 7 (\text{mod } 10)$$
and
$$\text{ind } x \equiv 3 (\text{mod } 10)$$
Therefore,
$$x \equiv 8 (\text{mod } 11)$$

2. Solve: $7x^3 \equiv 3 (\text{mod } 11)$.
$$\text{ind } 7 + 3 \text{ ind } x \equiv \text{ind } 3 (\text{mod } 10)$$
$$3 \text{ ind } x \equiv 8 - 7 (\text{mod } 10)$$
Hence,
$$\text{ind } x \equiv 7 (\text{mod } 10)$$
and
$$x \equiv 7 (\text{mod } 11)$$

3. Solve: $3x^4 \equiv 2 (\text{mod } 11)$.
$$\text{ind } 3 + 4 \text{ ind } x \equiv \text{ind } 2 (\text{mod } 10)$$
$$4 \text{ ind } x \equiv 3 (\text{mod } 10)$$

But $(4, 10) = 2$, and $2 \nmid 3$, so that there is no solution of the given congruence.

4. Solve: $5x^2 \equiv 3 (\text{mod } 11)$.
$$\text{ind } 5 + 2 \text{ ind } x \equiv \text{ind } 3 (\text{mod } 10)$$
$$2 \text{ ind } x \equiv 4 (\text{mod } 10)$$

There are two solutions since $(2, 10) = 2$ and $2 \mid 4$.
$$\text{ind } x \equiv 2 (\text{mod } 10) \qquad x \equiv 4 (\text{mod } 11)$$
and
$$\text{ind } x \equiv 7 (\text{mod } 10) \qquad x \equiv 7 (\text{mod } 11)$$

5. Solve: $7x \equiv 4 (\text{mod } 121)$.

Any solution of this congruence must satisfy $7x \equiv 4 (\text{mod } 11)$. But
$$\text{ind } 7 + \text{ind } x \equiv \text{ind } 4 (\text{mod } 10)$$
$$\text{ind } x \equiv 5 (\text{mod } 10)$$

Hence, $x \equiv 10 (\text{mod } 11)$, and all solutions of the original congruence have the form $x = 10 + 11k$. Therefore,
$$7(10 + 11k) \equiv 4 (\text{mod } 121)$$
or
$$77k \equiv 55 (\text{mod } 121)$$
Hence,
$$7k \equiv 5 (\text{mod } 11)$$

and
$$\text{ind } 7 + \text{ind } k \equiv \text{ind } 5 (\text{mod } 10)$$
so that
$$\text{ind } k \equiv 7 (\text{mod } 10)$$
and
$$k \equiv 7 (\text{mod } 11)$$
Therefore,
$$x \equiv 87 (\text{mod } 121)$$

8-2. Euler's Criterion for the Solvability of $x^n \equiv c(mod\ m)$. For moduli m that have primitive roots we can determine a convenient test for the solvability of a congruence of the form $x^n \equiv c(\text{mod } m)$ with $(c, m) = 1$. Because any binomial congruence $ax^n \equiv b(\text{mod } m)$ with a and b prime to m can be reduced to this form by multiplying each member of the congruence by the solution of $ax \equiv 1(\text{mod } m)$, the problem is also solved in the latter case.

Theorem 8-6. If m is any modulus for which there is a primitive root and $(c, m) = 1$, the congruence $x^n \equiv c(\text{mod } m)$ has a solution if and only if $c^{\phi(m)/d} \equiv 1(\text{mod } m)$, where $d = (n, \phi(m))$. Furthermore, when there is one solution, there are exactly d solutions modulo m of the given congruence.

Suppose that r is a primitive root of m and that $c \equiv r^s(\text{mod } m)$. If $x^n \equiv c(\text{mod } m)$ has a solution $x \equiv r^k(\text{mod } m)$, it follows that $r^{kn} \equiv r^s(\text{mod } m)$ and $kn \equiv s(\text{mod } \phi(m))$. Since k satisfies this linear congruence, $d = (n, \phi(m))$ must divide s. Hence,

$$c^{\phi(m)/d} \equiv r^{s\phi(m)/d} \equiv (r^{\phi(m)})^{s/d} \equiv 1(\text{mod } m)$$

Conversely, if
$$c^{\phi(m)/d} \equiv 1(\text{mod } m)$$
then
$$r^{s\phi(m)/d} \equiv 1(\text{mod } m)$$

Therefore, $s\phi(m)/d$ is a multiple of $\phi(m)$, and s/d is an integer. As a result, the congruence $nk \equiv s(\text{mod } \phi(m))$ is satisfied by just d incongruent values modulo $\phi(m)$ of k. Corresponding to these integers, there are exactly d incongruent values modulo m of x that form the complete set of solutions of $x^n \equiv c(\text{mod } m)$.

Theorem 8-7. If p is a prime and $d = (n, p - 1)$, there are $(p - 1)/d$ incongruent values modulo p of c, prime to p, such that $x^n \equiv c(\text{mod } p)$ has a solution.

According to Theorem 8-6, the congruence $x^n \equiv c(\text{mod } p)$ has a solution if and only if $c^{(p-1)/d} \equiv 1(\text{mod } p)$ where $d = (n, p - 1)$. But the congruence $x^{(p-1)/d} \equiv 1(\text{mod } p)$ has a solution. There are, thus, exactly

$(p - 1)/d$ incongruent solutions modulo p of this congruence, and these are the values of c for which the first one is solvable.

It is evident also that if an integer c is a residue of the nth power of an integer for a modulus m having a primitive root, and if $d = (n, \phi(m))$, the same c is a residue of the dth power of an integer for that modulus, for if $c^{\phi(m)/d} \equiv 1 \pmod{m}$, the congruence $x^d \equiv c \pmod{m}$ has a solution. Hence, if $d \neq n$, a residue of an nth power modulo m is always a residue of a power that is smaller than n and is a divisor of both n and $\phi(m)$. It is thus clear that when p is a prime of the form $5k + 2$, $5k + 3$, or $5k + 4$, the test for a solution of $x^5 \equiv c \pmod{p}$ is the same as the test for a solution of $x \equiv c \pmod{p}$. Since the last congruence is always solvable, an integer c, prime to p, is always a residue of a fifth power for prime moduli of the form $5k + 2$, $5k + 3$, and $5k + 4$. But if $p = 5k + 1$, c is a residue of a fifth power modulo p if and only if $c^k \equiv 1 \pmod{p}$. If p is a prime of the form $4k - 1$, the very test for a residue of a fourth power modulo p, $c^{2k-1} \equiv 1 \pmod{p}$, is the same as that for a second power and hence in this case the set of residues of fourth powers modulo p is identical with the set of residues of second powers. If $p = 4k + 1$, then $4 = (4, 4k)$ and no such statement can be made. Again, if p is of the form $3k + 2$, every integer not a multiple of 3 is a cubic residue modulo p, but if p is of the form $3k + 1$, c is a cubic residue if and only if $c^k \equiv 1 \pmod{p}$. Finally, if the modulus is an odd prime $p = 2k + 1$, c is a residue of a second power if and only if $c^k \equiv 1 \pmod{p}$. It is to the study of these quadratic residues that we turn in the next chapter.

EXERCISES

1. Prove that the least positive residues of $1^2, 2^2, \ldots, (p - 1)^2$ modulo p, where p is an odd prime, repeat themselves exactly twice.

2. If p is a prime and n is prime to $p - 1$, prove that the integers $1^n, 2^n, 3^n, \ldots, (p - 1)^n$ form a reduced residue system modulo p. Thus show that if p is a prime of the form $3n + 2$, the integers $1^3, 2^3, 3^3, \ldots, (p - 1)^3$ form a reduced residue system modulo p.

3. Prove that the odd prime divisors of $x^4 + 1$ are of the form $8n + 1$.

4. If p is a prime, determine when the existence of a solution of $x^6 \equiv c \pmod{p}$ is dependent upon the existence of a solution of $x^n \equiv c \pmod{p}$ with $n < 6$.

5. Determine whether or not there is a solution and, if so, solve the congruences:

a. $$x^3 \equiv 5 \pmod{13}$$
b. $$x^4 \equiv 7 \pmod{13}$$

6. Show that if r is a primitive root of p, then $r^{(p-1)/2} \equiv -1 \pmod{p}$, and thus that if $(a, p) = 1$, ind $(p - a) \equiv$ ind $a \pm [(p - 1)/2] \pmod{p - 1}$.

7. Set up a table of indices for the prime 13, and solve the following congruences:

a. $$5x \equiv 4 \pmod{13}$$
b. $$5x^2 \equiv 6 \pmod{13}$$

8. Find the index of 5 for each of the primitive roots of 13.

9. Find the index of 5 modulo 13 relative to the base 6 by using a table to the base 2.

10. Use the following table of power residues of the primitive root 5 of 193 to solve the congruences:

a.	$3x \equiv 2 \pmod{193}$
b.	$3x \equiv 191 \pmod{193}$
c.	$7x \equiv 157 \pmod{193}$
d.	$x^3 \equiv 64 \pmod{193}$

TABLE OF INDICES FOR THE PRIME 193

n	1	2	3	4	5	6	7	8	9	10
ind	192	34	84	68	1	118	104	102	168	35
n	11	12	13	14	15	16	17	18	19	20
ind	183	152	141	138	85	136	31	10	145	69
n	21	22	23	24	25	26	27	28	29	30
ind	188	25	162	186	2	175	60	172	123	119
n	31	32	33	34	35	36	37	38	39	40
ind	82	170	75	65	105	44	5	179	33	103
n	41	42	43	44	45	46	47	48	49	50
ind	151	30	24	59	169	4	29	28	16	36
n	51	52	53	54	55	56	57	58	59	60
ind	115	17	77	94	184	14	37	157	148	153
n	61	62	63	64	65	66	67	68	69	70
ind	47	116	80	12	142	109	18	99	54	139
n	71	72	73	74	75	76	77	78	79	80
ind	177	78	91	39	86	21	95	67	167	137
n	81	82	83	84	85	86	87	88	89	90
ind	144	185	122	64	32	58	15	93	147	11
n	91	92	93	94	95	96	97	98	99	100
ind	53	38	166	63	146	62	158	50	159	70
n	101	102	103	104	105	106	107	108	109	110
ind	134	149	107	51	189	111	154	128	160	26
n	111	112	113	114	115	116	117	118	119	120
ind	89	48	41	71	163	191	117	182	135	187
n	121	122	123	124	125	126	127	128	129	130
ind	174	81	43	150	3	114	13	46	108	176
n	131	132	133	134	135	136	137	138	139	140
ind	20	143	57	52	61	133	110	88	190	173
n	141	142	143	144	145	146	147	148	149	150
ind	113	19	132	112	124	125	100	73	155	120
n	151	152	153	154	155	156	157	158	159	160
ind	126	55	7	129	83	101	140	9	161	171
n	161	162	163	164	165	166	167	168	169	170
ind	74	178	23	27	76	156	79	98	90	66
n	171	172	173	174	175	176	177	178	179	180
ind	121	92	165	49	106	127	40	181	42	45
n	181	182	183	184	185	186	187	188	189	190
ind	56	87	131	72	6	8	22	97	164	180
n	191	192								
ind	130	96								

TABLE OF INDICES FOR THE PRIME 193—*(Continued)*

ind	1	2	3	4	5	6	7	8	9	10
n	5	25	125	46	37	185	153	186	158	18
ind	11	12	13	14	15	16	17	18	19	20
n	90	64	127	56	87	49	52	67	142	131
ind	21	22	23	24	25	26	27	28	29	30
n	76	187	163	43	22	110	164	48	47	42
ind	31	32	33	34	35	36	37	38	39	40
n	17	85	39	2	10	50	57	92	74	177
ind	41	42	43	44	45	46	47	48	49	50
n	113	179	123	36	180	128	61	112	174	98
ind	51	52	53	54	55	56	57	58	59	60
n	104	134	91	69	152	181	133	86	44	27
ind	61	62	63	64	65	66	67	68	69	70
n	135	96	94	84	34	170	78	4	20	100
ind	71	72	73	74	75	76	77	78	79	80
n	114	184	148	161	33	165	53	72	167	63
ind	81	82	83	84	85	86	87	88	89	90
n	122	31	155	3	15	75	182	138	111	169
ind	91	92	93	94	95	96	97	98	99	100
n	73	172	88	54	77	192	188	168	68	147
ind	101	102	103	104	105	106	107	108	109	110
n	156	8	40	7	35	175	103	129	66	137
ind	111	112	113	114	115	116	117	118	119	120
n	106	144	141	126	51	62	117	6	30	150
ind	121	122	123	124	125	126	127	128	129	130
n	171	83	29	145	146	151	176	108	154	191
ind	131	132	133	134	135	136	137	138	139	140
n	183	143	136	101	119	16	80	14	70	157
ind	141	142	143	144	145	146	147	148	149	150
n	13	65	132	81	19	95	89	59	102	124
ind	151	152	153	154	155	156	157	158	159	160
n	41	12	60	107	149	166	58	97	99	109
ind	161	162	163	164	165	166	167	168	169	170
n	159	23	115	189	173	93	79	9	45	32
ind	171	172	173	174	175	176	177	178	179	180
n	160	28	140	121	26	130	71	162	38	190
ind	181	182	183	184	185	186	187	188	189	190
n	178	118	11	55	82	24	120	21	105	139
ind	191	192								
n	116	1								

CHAPTER 9

QUADRATIC RESIDUES

9-1. The General Quadratic Congruence

Theorem 9-1. A solvable quadratic congruence $a_0y^2 + a_1y + a_2 \equiv 0 \pmod{n}$, where $a_0 \not\equiv 0 \pmod{n}$, can be reduced to the form $x^2 \equiv a \pmod{m}$ in which $(a, m) = 1$.

By multiplying the modulus and each member of the congruence

$$a_0y^2 + a_1y + a_2 \equiv 0 \pmod{n}$$

by $4a_0$, we obtain the equivalent congruence

$$4a_0^2y^2 + 4a_0a_1y + 4a_0a_2 \equiv 0 \pmod{4a_0n}$$

which, upon completing the square, becomes

$$(2a_0y + a_1)^2 \equiv a_1^2 - 4a_0a_2 \pmod{4a_0n}$$

Now let

$$4a_0n = m$$
$$2a_0y + a_1 \equiv z \pmod{m}$$

and

$$a_1^2 - 4a_0a_2 \equiv b \pmod{m}$$

The original congruence is thereby reduced to the form

$$z^2 \equiv b \pmod{m}$$

Suppose that $(b, m) = d = e^2k$, where e^2 is the largest square contained in d, and that $m = m_0d$, $b = b_0d$. Then ek divides z. Therefore, let

$$z \equiv ekw \pmod{m}$$

and the congruence takes the form

$$e^2k^2w^2 \equiv b \pmod{m}$$

or

$$kw^2 \equiv b_0 \pmod{m_0}$$

If $(k, m_0) = s$, unless $s \mid b_0$ there is no solution. But $(b_0, m_0) = 1$. Consequently, there is no solution unless $s = 1$. If $s = 1$, multiply each member of the last congruence by k, and let

$$x \equiv kw \pmod{m_0}$$

134

Then
$$x^2 \equiv b_0 k (\mathrm{mod}\ m_0)$$
and if we set
$$b_0 k \equiv a (\mathrm{mod}\ m_0)$$

we have attained the required form $x^2 \equiv a (\mathrm{mod}\ m_0)$ with $(a, m_0) = 1$.

The problem of solving any quadratic congruence is, therefore, reduced to that of solving binomial quadratic congruences and linear congruences.

Examples. 1. Solve: $x^2 \equiv 6 (\mathrm{mod}\ 15)$.

Let $x \equiv 3z (\mathrm{mod}\ 15)$. Then $3z^2 \equiv 2 (\mathrm{mod}\ 5)$. Multiplying by 3, which is prime to 5, and letting $z \equiv 3w (\mathrm{mod}\ 5)$, we have $w^2 \equiv 6 (\mathrm{mod}\ 5)$, or $w^2 \equiv 1 (\mathrm{mod}\ 5)$. Hence, $w \equiv 1, 4 (\mathrm{mod}\ 5)$, $z \equiv 3, 2 (\mathrm{mod}\ 5)$, and finally, $x \equiv 9, 6 (\mathrm{mod}\ 15)$.

2. Solve: $x^2 \equiv 24 (\mathrm{mod}\ 60)$.

Since $(24, 60) = 12$, let $x \equiv 6z (\mathrm{mod}\ 60)$. Then $3z^2 \equiv 2 (\mathrm{mod}\ 5)$. Let $z \equiv 3w (\mathrm{mod}\ 5)$, so that $w^2 \equiv 1 (\mathrm{mod}\ 5)$. Therefore, $w \equiv 1, 4 (\mathrm{mod}\ 5)$, $z \equiv 3, 2 (\mathrm{mod}\ 5)$, and finally, $x \equiv 18, 48, 12, 42 (\mathrm{mod}\ 60)$.

EXERCISES

Solve the congruences:

a. $\qquad\qquad x^2 \equiv 28 (\mathrm{mod}\ 84)$

b. $\qquad\qquad x^2 \equiv 64 (\mathrm{mod}\ 420)$

9-2. Quadratic Residues. When $(a, m) = 1$ and the congruence $x^2 \equiv a (\mathrm{mod}\ m)$ has a solution, the integer a is a *quadratic residue modulo m*, or a *quadratic residue of m*, but if the congruence has no solution, a is a *quadratic nonresidue modulo m*, or a *quadratic nonresidue of m*. For example, 2 is a quadratic residue of 7 because 3 satisfies $x^2 \equiv 2 (\mathrm{mod}\ 7)$, but 2 is a quadratic nonresidue modulo 5 because there is no solution of $x^2 \equiv 2 (\mathrm{mod}\ 5)$. Can you find a number whose square gives the remainder 4 when it is divided by 15?

If an integer a is prime to $m > 0$, its quality of being a quadratic residue or nonresidue modulo m is called its *quadratic character with respect to m*. Obviously all integers in the class with a modulo m have the same quadratic character with respect to m.

The problem of determining the quadratic character of a is, therefore, equivalent to that of testing the solvability of the congruence $x^2 \equiv a (\mathrm{mod}\ m)$. We have already shown that by factoring m into powers of primes we can reduce the discussion to the question of solving the congruence $x^2 \equiv a (\mathrm{mod}\ p^n)$ with p a prime, and finally to the case $x^2 \equiv a (\mathrm{mod}\ p)$. Theorem 5-13 shows that when p is an odd prime, these last two congruences either are both insolvable or have the same number of solutions, and therefore in this case it will be necessary to study in detail only the quadratic residues of p.

In the case of the prime 2, any odd integer is a quadratic residue of 2, and the even integers are excluded from the discussion.   But for $f(x) = x^2 - a$, $f'(x) = 2x$, and thus $d = (2x',2)$ is always 2.   Hence, Theorem 5-13 shows that either a solution of $x^2 \equiv a(\bmod\ 2^{n-1})$ satisfies $x^2 \equiv a(\bmod\ 2^n)$ and yields two solutions of the second congruence or no solution of the second congruence can be developed from the particular solution x' of the first.   The problem of determining quadratic residues of powers of the even prime must, therefore, be considered separately from that of powers of odd primes.

Euler (1707–1783), Lagrange (1736–1813), and Legendre (1752–1833) were all very much interested in the theory of quadratic residues, but Gauss (1777–1855) was the one who contributed most to this subject. The fact is that Gauss was one of the greatest mathematicians of all time.   It is really no wonder that his name is connected with so much that has been produced in the theory of numbers, for it was his favorite study.   He considered it the "queen of mathematics."   His "Disquisitiones arithmeticae," published in 1801, is the classic of the theory of numbers and exhibits very well the elegance of form and rigor of presentation for which he is noted.   Some of the topics to which he made great contributions are quadratic forms, biquadratic residues, and the theory of congruences.

Theorem 9-2   (Euler's Criterion).   If p is an odd prime, the integer a is a quadratic residue of p if and only if $a^{(p-1)/2} \equiv 1(\bmod\ p)$.

This theorem is included in Theorem 8-6.   Nevertheless, we shall give an independent proof for the case when $n = 2$.

Let $a_1, a_2, \ldots, a_{p-1}$ be a reduced residue system modulo p, and suppose that a is a quadratic nonresidue modulo p.   Then each congruence

$$a_i x \equiv a(\bmod\ p)   \qquad i = 1, 2, \ldots, p - 1$$

has just one solution $x \equiv a_j(\bmod\ p)$ distinct from a_i and prime to p. Moreover, no two of these congruences have the same solution, for if

$$a_i a_j \equiv a(\bmod\ p)$$

and

$$a_k a_j \equiv a(\bmod\ p)   \qquad i \neq k \neq j$$

then

$$a_i \equiv a_k(\bmod\ p)$$

whereas these integers are distinct modulo p.   The integers a_i are thereby separated into $(p - 1)/2$ pairs, and the product of these pairs implies that

$$a_1 a_2 \cdots a_{p-1} \equiv a^{(p-1)/2}(\bmod\ p)$$

But from Wilson's theorem

$$a_1 a_2 \cdots a_{p-1} \equiv (p - 1)! \equiv -1(\bmod\ p)$$

Therefore,

$$a^{(p-1)/2} \equiv -1(\mathrm{mod}\ p)$$

If a is a quadratic residue modulo p and $x \equiv r(\mathrm{mod}\ p)$ is one solution of $x^2 \equiv a(\mathrm{mod}\ p)$, then $x \equiv p - r(\mathrm{mod}\ p)$ is the other solution, for $(p - r)^2 \equiv r^2(\mathrm{mod}\ p)$. Hence, the congruence

$$a_i x \equiv a(\mathrm{mod}\ p)$$

has $x \equiv a_i(\mathrm{mod}\ p)$ as a solution if and only if $a_i \equiv r(\mathrm{mod}\ p)$ or $a_i \equiv p - r(\mathrm{mod}\ p)$. The remaining $p - 3$ values of a_i set up $(p - 3)/2$ pairs of distinct integers such that the product of each pair is congruent to a modulo p. Consequently,

$$\frac{a_1 a_2 \cdot \cdot \cdot a_{p-1}}{r(p - r)} \equiv a^{(p-3)/2}(\mathrm{mod}\ p)$$

But

$$r(p - r) \equiv -r^2 \equiv -a(\mathrm{mod}\ p)$$

Therefore,

$$(p - 1)! \equiv -a^{(p-1)/2}(\mathrm{mod}\ p)$$

and

$$a^{(p-1)/2} \equiv 1(\mathrm{mod}\ p)$$

Furthermore, if $a^{(p-1)/2} \equiv 1(\mathrm{mod}\ p)$, a must be a quadratic residue of p, for if it were not, $a^{(p-1)/2} \equiv -1(\mathrm{mod}\ p)$. This condition is, therefore, a test for a quadratic residue of p if p is an odd prime and a is prime to p.

Examples. Since $5^3 \equiv 6(\mathrm{mod}\ 7)$, 5 is a quadratic nonresidue modulo 7, and because $2^3 \equiv 1(\mathrm{mod}\ 7)$, 2 is a quadratic residue modulo 7.

It is interesting to observe that if the modulus is a composite m, the following theorem gives a necessary condition for a quadratic residue of m:

Theorem 9-3. If a is a quadratic residue modulo $m > 2$, then $a^{\phi(m)/2} \equiv 1(\mathrm{mod}\ m)$ and $a^{\lambda(m)/2} \equiv 1(\mathrm{mod}\ m)$.

Suppose that r, prime to m, satisfies the congruence $x^2 \equiv a(\mathrm{mod}\ m)$. Then because $\phi(m)$ is even if $m > 2$,

$$(r^2)^{\phi(m)/2} \equiv a^{\phi(m)/2}(\mathrm{mod}\ m)$$

But

$$r^{\phi(m)} \equiv 1(\mathrm{mod}\ m)$$

Hence,

$$a^{\phi(m)/2} \equiv 1(\mathrm{mod}\ m)$$

It is obvious that if $m > 2$, $\phi(m)$ may be replaced by $\lambda(m)$ in the above proof.

This result, however, does not provide a sufficient condition for a quadratic residue of m, for although $(7, 48) = 1$, $\lambda(48)/2 = 2$, and $7^2 \equiv 1(\mathrm{mod}\ 48)$, still $x^2 \equiv 7(\mathrm{mod}\ 48)$ has no solution.

Theorem 9-4. The quadratic residues of an odd prime p coincide with the even powers of any primitive root of p.

Consider the congruence $x^2 \equiv a(\bmod p)$ with $(a, p) = 1$. Then if r is a primitive root of p, because the powers $r, r^2, \ldots, r^{p-1}$ form a reduced residue system modulo p, either

$$a \equiv r^{2k}(\bmod p)$$

or

$$a \equiv r^{2k+1}(\bmod p)$$

In the first case, it is evident that a is a quadratic residue of p, for $(r^k)^2 \equiv a(\bmod p)$. Applying Euler's criterion to the second case, if

$$(r^{2k+1})^{(p-1)/2} \equiv 1(\bmod p),$$

the exponent of r must be a multiple of $p - 1$. But then $(2k + 1)/2$ would have to be an integer, and that is impossible. Hence, in the second case a is a quadratic nonresidue of p. Thus the set of quadratic residues of p consists of the even powers of a primitive root of p.

Corollary 1. The odd powers of any primitive root of an odd prime p coincide with the quadratic nonresidues of an odd prime p.

Corollary 2. There are exactly $(p - 1)/2$ incongruent quadratic residues and the same number of incongruent quadratic nonresidues of an odd prime p.

Corollary 3. The product of two quadratic residues or two quadratic nonresidues of an odd prime p is a quadratic residue of p, but the product of a quadratic residue and a quadratic nonresidue of p is a quadratic nonresidue of p.

When a table of indices is at hand, it is convenient to use the even powers of a primitive root of p to set up the quadratic residues of p, but if a primitive root of p must be computed, the method implied by the following theorem is usually the more expeditious one for finding quadratic residues:

Theorem 9-5. The integers $1^2, 2^2, \ldots, \left(\dfrac{p-1}{2}\right)^2$ are the incongruent quadratic residues of the odd prime p.

Because $a^2 \equiv (p - a)^2(\bmod p)$, we need use only the integers $1^2, 2^2,$ $\ldots, \left(\dfrac{p-1}{2}\right)^2$ to determine the quadratic residues modulo p. Each of these integers is evidently a quadratic residue of p, but, more than that, no two of them are congruent modulo p, for if

$$a_1{}^2 \equiv a_2{}^2(\bmod p)$$

then

$$(a_1 - a_2)(a_1 + a_2) \equiv 0(\bmod p)$$

and p divides at least one of $a_1 - a_2$ and $a_1 + a_2$.   But since both a_1 and a_2 are positive and less than $p/2$, neither $a_1 - a_2$ nor $a_1 + a_2$ is divisible by p.   These $(p-1)/2$ integers, therefore, yield all the quadratic residues of p.

Examples.   Because 2 is a primitive root of 13, the quadratic residues of 13 are $2^2 \equiv 4$, $2^4 \equiv 3$, $2^6 \equiv 12$, $2^8 \equiv 9$, $2^{10} \equiv 10$, and $2^{12} \equiv 1 \pmod{13}$. Using the method of Theorem 9-5, they are $1^2 \equiv 1$, $2^2 \equiv 4$, $3^2 \equiv 9$, $4^2 \equiv 3$, $5^2 \equiv 12$, $6^2 \equiv 10 \pmod{13}$.

EXERCISES

1. Is 15 a quadratic residue of 17?

2. Find all quadratic residues of 29 and 31.

3. Prove that the product of the distinct quadratic residues of a prime $p = 4n - 1$ is congruent to 1 modulo p, whereas if $p = 4n + 1$, this product is congruent to -1 modulo p.

4. If p is a prime, prove that the congruence $x^6 + 7x^4 - 36 \equiv 0 \pmod{p}$ has a solution.

5. If p is a prime of the form $4n + 1$, prove that there is always an x such that $x^2 + 1$ is divisible by p.

6. If b is a quadratic residue of 7, find all solutions of $x^2 \equiv b \pmod{7}$ for each b.

7. If b is a quadratic residue of 7, find all solutions of $x^2 \equiv b \pmod{7^2}$ for each b.

8. Determine whether or not there are solutions, and if so, solve the congruences $x^2 \equiv 9 \pmod{13^2}$ and $x^2 \equiv 5 \pmod{13^2}$.

9. Prove that if the prime $p = 2^n + 1$, every quadratic nonresidue of p is a primitive root modulo p.

10. Make use of Fermat's theorem to show that if a is a quadratic residue of a prime p, then $a^{(p-1)/2} \equiv 1 \pmod{p}$.

11. If p is a prime greater than 3, prove that the sum of the quadratic residues of p is divisible by p.

9-3. The Legendre Symbol.   Legendre was chiefly interested in elliptic functions and the theory of numbers, but he also wrote a book on geometry which was so well received that at the time it rivaled Euclid's "Elements" in popularity.   In 1830 he published two volumes on the theory of numbers that organized his own researches and those of his predecessors in this subject.   In this work he partly proved the remarkable law of quadratic reciprocity.

If p is an odd prime and $(a, p) = 1$, by letting $\left(\dfrac{a}{p}\right) = +1$ or -1 according as a is a quadratic residue or a quadratic nonresidue of p, Legendre introduced a symbol well fitted for expressing the quadratic character of a with respect to p.   This symbol enables us to express succinctly some important facts with which we are already familiar.

1. It is evident that if p is an odd prime and $(a, p) = 1$, then $\left(\dfrac{a^2}{p}\right) = +1$.

2. If $a_1 \equiv a_2 \pmod{p}$, a_1 and a_2 being prime to the odd prime p, then $\left(\dfrac{a_1}{p}\right) = \left(\dfrac{a_2}{p}\right)$.

3. Euler's criterion shows that if p is an odd prime and $(a, p) = 1$, then $\left(\dfrac{a}{p}\right) \equiv a^{(p-1)/2} \pmod{p}$.

4. Corollary 3 of Theorem 9-4 implies that if p is an odd prime and $(a_i, p) = 1$, where $i = 1, 2, \ldots, n$, then $\left(\dfrac{a_1 a_2 \cdots a_n}{p}\right) = \left(\dfrac{a_1}{p}\right)\left(\dfrac{a_2}{p}\right) \cdots \left(\dfrac{a_n}{p}\right)$.

5. If a_1 and a_2 are prime to p, $\left(\dfrac{a_1}{p}\right)\left(\dfrac{a_2}{p}\right) = +1$, as well as $\left(\dfrac{a_1}{p}\right) = \left(\dfrac{a_2}{p}\right)$, expresses the fact that a_1 and a_2 have the same quadratic character with respect to the odd prime p. Furthermore, $\left(\dfrac{a_1}{p}\right)\left(\dfrac{a_2}{p}\right) = -1$ and $\left(\dfrac{a_1}{p}\right) = -\left(\dfrac{a_2}{p}\right)$ indicate that a_1 and a_2 have opposite quadratic characters with respect to p.

9-4. The Prime Moduli of Which an Integer Is a Quadratic Residue. Having solved the problem of determining the quadratic residues of a prime, we now ask if we can find the prime moduli of which a given integer is a quadratic residue. If the integer is odd, it is, of course, a quadratic residue of the prime 2 and so the question must be settled only for odd primes.

Suppose that $a = \pm k^2 b$, with k^2 the largest square in a and $b > 0$. Then because $\left(\dfrac{a}{p}\right) = \left(\dfrac{\pm 1}{p}\right)\left(\dfrac{b}{p}\right)$, the quadratic character of a with respect to an odd prime p is determined by the quadratic character of ± 1 and the positive prime factors of a that occur in it to an odd power. Let these primes be $q_1, q_2, \ldots, q_n$. Then

$$\left(\frac{a}{p}\right) = \left(\frac{\pm 1}{p}\right)\left(\frac{q_1}{p}\right)\left(\frac{q_2}{p}\right) \cdots \left(\frac{q_n}{p}\right)$$

and therefore our question about the prime moduli of which a is a quadratic residue can be answered by studying the symbols $\left(\dfrac{\pm 1}{p}\right)$, $\left(\dfrac{2}{p}\right)$, and $\left(\dfrac{q}{p}\right)$, where q is an odd prime.

Taking these symbols in order, it is first of all evident that $\left(\dfrac{1}{p}\right) = +1$ for every prime p.

Theorem 9-6. The integer -1 is a quadratic residue of all primes of the form $4n + 1$ and a quadratic nonresidue of all primes of the form $4n + 3$.

The congruence $x^2 \equiv -1 \pmod{p}$ has a solution if and only if $(-1)^{(p-1)/2} \equiv 1 \pmod{p}$. If $p = 4n + 1$, then $(p - 1)/2 = 2n$, but if $p = 4n + 3$, it is clear that $(p - 1)/2 = 2n + 1$. Hence, -1 is a quadratic residue of the first set of primes, and it is a quadratic nonresidue of the second set.

Example. There is no solution of $x^2 \equiv -1 \pmod{31}$, but there are two solutions of $x^2 \equiv -1 \pmod{29}$, and they are $x \equiv 12$ and $x \equiv -12 \pmod{29}$.

Theorem 9-7 (The Lemma of Gauss). Take p an odd prime and q prime to p. Find the least positive residues modulo p of the integers $q, 2q, \ldots, [(p - 1)/2]q$. If u is the number of these residues that are greater than $p/2$, then $\left(\dfrac{q}{p}\right) = (-1)^u$.

The integers

$$q, 2q, 3q, \ldots, \frac{p - 1}{2} q \tag{1}$$

are prime to p and incongruent modulo p. Their least positive residues modulo p are, therefore, distinct integers of the set

$$1, 2, \ldots, p - 1 \tag{2}$$

Let

$$a_1, a_2, \ldots, a_u$$

represent the least positive residues greater than $p/2$ of the integers in (1), while

$$b_1, b_2, \ldots, b_v$$

denote those least positive residues which are less than $p/2$. Then $u + v = (p - 1)/2$.

The integers of the set

$$p - a_1, p - a_2, \ldots, p - a_u$$

are prime to p, less than $p/2$, and are incongruent modulo p. Moreover, these integers are distinct from the b_i, for if

$$b_i \equiv p - a_j \pmod{p} \qquad i = 1, 2, \ldots, v; j = 1, 2, \ldots, u$$

then

$$b_i + a_j \equiv 0 \pmod{p}$$

However, both b_i and a_j are congruent modulo p to integers of (1), and therefore $sq + tq \equiv 0 \pmod{p}$, where s and t are distinct integers of the set $1, 2, \ldots, (p - 1)/2$. Hence, $s + t \equiv 0 \pmod{p}$. But since both

s and t are positive and less than $p/2$, the sum $s + t$ cannot be divisible by p. Thus $b_i + a_j$ cannot be divisible by p. Consequently, the integers

$$b_1, b_2, \ldots, b_v, p - a_1, p - a_2, \ldots, p - a_u$$

form a set of $(p - 1)/2$ incongruent integers modulo p all of which are positive and less than $p/2$. They are, therefore, in some order the integers $1, 2, \ldots, (p - 1)/2$. As a result,

$$b_1 b_2 \cdots b_v (p - a_1)(p - a_2) \cdots (p - a_u) \equiv \frac{p - 1}{2}! \pmod{p}$$

and

$$(-1)^u b_1 b_2 \cdots b_v a_1 a_2 \cdots a_u \equiv \frac{p - 1}{2}! \pmod{p}$$

But the b_i and the a_j are the residues of the products in (1). Therefore,

$$b_1 b_2 \cdots b_v a_1 a_2 \cdots a_u \equiv q \cdot 2q \cdot \ \cdots \ \cdot \frac{p - 1}{2} q \pmod{p}$$

$$\equiv \frac{p - 1}{2}! \, q^{(p-1)/2} \pmod{p}$$

and

$$(-1)^u \frac{p - 1}{2}! \, q^{(p-1)/2} \equiv \frac{p - 1}{2}! \pmod{p}$$

By multiplying by $(-1)^u$ and dividing by $[(p - 1)/2]!$, we have

$$q^{(p-1)/2} \equiv (-1)^u \pmod{p}$$

But

$$\left(\frac{q}{p}\right) \equiv q^{(p-1)/2} \pmod{p}$$

according to Euler's criterion. Hence,

$$\left(\frac{q}{p}\right) \equiv (-1)^u \pmod{p}$$

but since both $\left(\frac{q}{p}\right)$ and $(-1)^u$ have only the values $+1$ and -1, it follows that $\left(\frac{q}{p}\right) = (-1)^u$.

Theorem 9-8. If p is an odd prime and q is odd and prime to p, and if $M = \left[\frac{q}{p}\right] + \left[\frac{2q}{p}\right] + \cdots + \left[\frac{p - 1}{2}\frac{q}{p}\right]$, then $\left(\frac{q}{p}\right) = (-1)^M$.

Let $(p - 1)/2 = s$. Also let the least positive residues modulo p of $q, 2q, \ldots, sq$ be in order $r_1, r_2, \ldots, r_s$. Then

$$q = p\left[\frac{q}{p}\right] + r_1$$

$$2q = p\left[\frac{2q}{p}\right] + r_2$$

$$\cdots \cdots \cdots \cdots$$

$$sq = p\left[\frac{sq}{p}\right] + r_s$$

Adding these equations and using the fact that $1 + 2 + \cdots + [(p - 1)/2] = (p^2 - 1)/8$, we have

$$\frac{p^2 - 1}{8}q = pM + r_1 + r_2 + \cdots + r_s$$

But these integers r_k, where $k = 1, 2, \ldots, (p - 1)/2$, are the a_i, where $i = 1, 2, \ldots, u$, and the b_j, where $j = 1, 2, \ldots, v$, of Theorem 9-7.

Let $\displaystyle\sum_{i=1}^{u} a_i = A$ and $\displaystyle\sum_{j=1}^{v} b_j = B$. Then

$$\frac{p^2 - 1}{8}q = pM + A + B \tag{3}$$

But in Theorem 9-7 we also showed that the $p - a_i$ together with the b_j are in some order the integers $1, 2, \ldots, (p - 1)/2$. Hence,

$$\frac{p^2 - 1}{8} = pu - A + B \tag{4}$$

By subtracting Eq. (4) from (3), we find

$$\frac{p^2 - 1}{8}(q - 1) = p(M - u) + 2A \tag{5}$$

Consequently, if both p and q are odd, $M - u$ is even; that is, $M \equiv u \pmod 2$. Hence, when q is odd and prime to the odd prime p, by applying Theorem 9-7 we have

$$\left(\frac{q}{p}\right) = (-1)^u = (-1)^M$$

On the other hand, if $q = 2$, then $\left[\dfrac{q}{p}\right] = 0$, $\left[\dfrac{2q}{p}\right] = 0, \ldots,$ $\left[\dfrac{(p - 1)q/2}{p}\right] = \left[\dfrac{p - 1}{p}\right] = 0$. Hence, $M = 0$, and Eq. (5) shows that since $p = 2k + 1$,

$$\frac{p^2 - 1}{8} \equiv -(2k + 1)u \pmod 2$$

$$\equiv -u \equiv u \pmod 2$$

Therefore, by Theorem 9-7,

$$\left(\frac{2}{p}\right) = (-1)^u = (-1)^{(p^2-1)/8}$$

Corollary. The integer 2 is a quadratic residue of all primes of the form $8n \pm 1$ and a quadratic nonresidue of all primes of the form $8n \pm 3$.

When $p = 8n \pm 1$, then $(p^2 - 1)/8 = 8n^2 \pm 2n$, and $\left(\frac{2}{p}\right) = +1$, but

when $p = 8n \pm 3$, $(p^2 - 1)/8 = 8n^2 \pm 6n + 1$, and $\left(\frac{2}{p}\right) = -1$.

Examples. $\left(\frac{2}{23}\right) = (-1)^{(22)(24)/8} = +1$,   but $\left(\frac{2}{29}\right) = (-1)^{(28)(30)/8}$
$= -1$.

Theorem 9-9 (The Quadratic Reciprocity Law). If p and q are distinct odd primes, $\left(\frac{q}{p}\right)\left(\frac{p}{q}\right) = (-1)^{\frac{p-1}{2}\cdot\frac{q-1}{2}}$.

We shall present a proof of this theorem that is based upon a geometric demonstration given by F. G. Eisenstein (1823–1852).

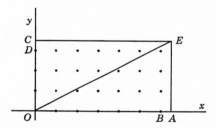

Taking rectangular coördinate axes and a convenient unit, mark off units from O along the x axis to represent the integers 1, 2, . . . , $(p - 1)/2$, and in like manner along the y axis to represent 1, 2, . . . , $(q - 1)/2$. Then $OB = (p - 1)/2$, and $OD = (q - 1)/2$. Let $OA = p/2$ and $OC = q/2$. We then call all points both of whose coördinates are integers *lattice points*. Within the rectangle $OAEC$, but not on its boundary, there are, therefore, $\frac{p - 1}{2} \cdot \frac{q - 1}{2}$ lattice points.

The equation of the line OE is $py = qx$, and it intersects any line $x = k$ parallel to the y axis in the point $\left(k, \frac{kq}{p}\right)$. Therefore, if k is a positive integer, $\left[\frac{kq}{p}\right]$ is the number of lattice points on $x = k$ above the x axis and on or below OE. However, when k takes the values 1, 2, . . . ,

$(p - 1)/2$, since $(q,p) = 1$, kq/p is not an integer and so there will be no lattice points on OE and within the rectangle $OAEC$. Consequently, the number of lattice points within the triangle OAE is

$$\left[\frac{q}{p}\right] + \left[\frac{2q}{p}\right] + \cdots + \left[\frac{p-1}{2}\frac{q}{p}\right] = M$$

In like manner by taking $py = qx$ and the lines $y = t$, for $t = 1, 2,$ $\ldots$, $(q - 1)/2$, we find that the number of lattice points within the triangle OEC is

$$\left[\frac{p}{q}\right] + \left[\frac{2p}{q}\right] + \cdots + \left[\frac{q-1}{2}\frac{p}{q}\right] = N$$

Hence, the number of lattice points within the rectangle $OAEC$ is $M + N = \dfrac{p-1}{2} \cdot \dfrac{q-1}{2}$.

We have shown that $\left(\dfrac{q}{p}\right) = (-1)^M$ and that $\left(\dfrac{p}{q}\right) = (-1)^N$. Therefore,

$$\left(\frac{p}{q}\right)\left(\frac{q}{p}\right) = (-1)^{M+N}$$

and consequently when p and q are distinct odd primes,

$$\left(\frac{p}{q}\right)\left(\frac{q}{p}\right) = (-1)^{\frac{p-1}{2} \cdot \frac{q-1}{2}}$$

This famous theorem was discovered at different times by Euler, Legendre, and Gauss, but Gauss was the first one to prove it. He accomplished this feat in 1796, when he was but eighteen years of age. He appraised the theorem so highly as to call it the "gem of higher arithmetic" and developed six different proofs of it. Among the leading mathematicians who have also proved the theorem are Cauchy, Eisenstein, Jacobi, Kronecker, Kummer, Liouville, and Zeller. Indeed, the interest that it has continued to arouse is evidenced by the fact that it was proved in about fifty ways* during the nineteenth century. More than that, the number of proofs keeps growing, but, of course, not all of them are essentially different.

Because of the importance of the quadratic reciprocity law, it is worth while giving a second proof of it that does not depend upon the geometric meaning of M. The following proof is a modification of one of Gauss' proofs:

* P. Bachmann, "Grundlehren der neueren Zahlentheorie."

Taking p and q as odd primes with $q < p$ and

$$M = \left[\frac{q}{p}\right] + \left[\frac{2q}{p}\right] + \cdots + \left[\frac{p-1}{2}\frac{q}{p}\right]$$

$$N = \left[\frac{p}{q}\right] + \left[\frac{2p}{q}\right] + \cdots + \left[\frac{q-1}{2}\frac{p}{q}\right]$$

we wish to prove that $M + N = \frac{p-1}{2} \cdot \frac{q-1}{2}$. We observe that if $k = 1, 2, \ldots, (p-1)/2$, no kq/p is an integer, for both k and q are less than the prime p. Moreover, $\left[\frac{q}{p}\right] = 0$, and $\left[\frac{2q}{p}\right]$ is at most 1. Of course, if $\left[\frac{kq}{p}\right] = s$, so that $kq = sp + r$ with $0 < r < p$, then $(k+1)q = sp + r + q$. But $\left[\frac{r+q}{p}\right]$ is at most 1. Therefore, $\left[\frac{(k+1)q}{p}\right]$ is at most $s + 1$.

Furthermore, the value of the last term of M which is $\left[\frac{(p-1)q}{2p}\right] = \left[\frac{pq-p+p-q}{2p}\right]$, can be written $\left[\frac{q-1}{2} + \frac{p-q}{2p}\right] = (q-1)/2$, because $p - q < 2p$.

Assuming that for $k < (p-1)/2$ the integer $\left[\frac{kq}{p}\right]$ is the last term of the expression for M whose value is s, we shall find the number k of this term of the series in terms of p, q, and s. Since $\left[\frac{(k+1)q}{p}\right] = s + 1$,

$$\frac{kq}{p} < s + 1 < \frac{(k+1)q}{p}$$

Hence,

$$k < \frac{(s+1)p}{q} < k + 1$$

and therefore

$$k = \left[\frac{(s+1)p}{q}\right]$$

is the number of the last term of the expression for M having the value s, where $0 \le s < (q-1)/2$. It follows then that the number of the last term of this series that has the value $s - 1$ is $\left[\frac{sp}{q}\right]$. Consequently, for all nonnegative $s < (q-1)/2$, the number of terms of M that have the value s is $\left[\dfrac{(s+1)p}{q}\right] - \left[\dfrac{sp}{q}\right]$. Moreover, the number of terms of M that have the value $(q-1)/2$ is $(p-1)/2 - \left[\dfrac{q-1}{2}\dfrac{p}{q}\right]$. Therefore,

$$
\begin{aligned}
M &= \left[\frac{q}{p}\right] + \left[\frac{2q}{p}\right] + \cdots + \left[\frac{p-1}{2}\frac{q}{p}\right] \\
&= 0 \cdot \left\{ \left[\frac{p}{q}\right] - \left[\frac{0 \cdot p}{q}\right] \right\} + 1 \left\{ \left[\frac{2p}{q}\right] - \left[\frac{p}{q}\right] \right\} + 2 \left\{ \left[\frac{3p}{q}\right] - \left[\frac{2p}{q}\right] \right\} \\
&\quad + \cdots + s \left\{ \left[\frac{(s+1)p}{q}\right] - \left[\frac{sp}{q}\right] \right\} + \cdots \\
&\qquad\qquad\qquad + \frac{q-1}{2} \left\{ \frac{p-1}{2} - \left[\frac{q-1}{2}\frac{p}{q}\right] \right\} \\
&= -\left[\frac{p}{q}\right] - \left[\frac{2p}{q}\right] - \cdots - \left[\frac{q-1}{2}\frac{p}{q}\right] + \frac{p-1}{2} \cdot \frac{q-1}{2} \\
&= -N + \frac{p-1}{2} \cdot \frac{q-1}{2}
\end{aligned}
$$

Hence, $M + N = \dfrac{p-1}{2} \cdot \dfrac{q-1}{2}$, and the quadratic reciprocity law follows.

Corollary 1. If at least one of the primes p and q is of the form $4n + 1$, then $\left(\dfrac{p}{q}\right)\left(\dfrac{q}{p}\right) = +1$, so that $\left(\dfrac{p}{q}\right) = \left(\dfrac{q}{p}\right)$.

Corollary 2. If both the primes p and q are of the form $4n + 3$, then $\left(\dfrac{p}{q}\right)\left(\dfrac{q}{p}\right) = -1$ and $\left(\dfrac{p}{q}\right) = -\left(\dfrac{q}{p}\right)$.

Examples. 1. Test $x^2 \equiv 15 \pmod{17}$ for a solution.

Since $15 \equiv -2 \pmod{17}$, we factor -2 and have $\left(\dfrac{-2}{17}\right) = \left(\dfrac{-1}{17}\right)\left(\dfrac{2}{17}\right)$. Also $\left(\dfrac{-1}{17}\right) = (-1)^8 = +1$, and $\left(\dfrac{2}{17}\right) = (-1)^{(16)(18)/8} = +1$. Hence, $\left(\dfrac{-2}{17}\right) = +1$, and there is a solution of the congruence.

2. Is 67 a quadratic residue of 89?

Since $67 \equiv -22 \pmod{89}$, we find $\left(\dfrac{-22}{89}\right) = \left(\dfrac{-1}{89}\right)\left(\dfrac{2}{89}\right)\left(\dfrac{11}{89}\right)$. Furthermore, $\left(\dfrac{-1}{89}\right) = +1$, for 89 is of the form $4n + 1$; $\left(\dfrac{2}{89}\right) = +1$, for 89 is of the form $8n + 1$; and $\left(\dfrac{11}{89}\right)\left(\dfrac{89}{11}\right) = +1$, according to Corollary 1 above. Thus $\left(\dfrac{11}{89}\right) = \left(\dfrac{89}{11}\right)$. However, $\left(\dfrac{89}{11}\right) = \left(\dfrac{1}{11}\right) = +1$. Therefore, there is a solution of $x^2 \equiv 67 \pmod{89}$.

3. Is 33 a quadratic residue of 89?

Factoring immediately we have $\left(\dfrac{33}{89}\right) = \left(\dfrac{3}{89}\right)\left(\dfrac{11}{89}\right)$. But $\left(\dfrac{3}{89}\right)\left(\dfrac{89}{3}\right)$ $= +1$, and $\left(\dfrac{89}{3}\right) = \left(\dfrac{2}{3}\right) = -1$. Therefore, $\left(\dfrac{3}{89}\right) = -1$, and, from above, $\left(\dfrac{11}{89}\right) = +1$. Consequently, $\left(\dfrac{33}{89}\right) = -1$, and the congruence $x^2 \equiv 33 \pmod{89}$ has no solution.

The quadratic reciprocity law also enables us to solve the problem previously stated of determining the odd primes of which a given integer is a quadratic residue or nonresidue. It is apparent that if we wish to find the primes of which a composite is a quadratic residue or nonresidue, the composite must be factored into primes and the conclusions drawn by means of Corollary 3 of Theorem 9-4. We shall, therefore, consider first the case where the given number is an odd prime q.

If q is of the form $4n + 1$, then $\left(\dfrac{q}{p}\right) = \left(\dfrac{p}{q}\right)$. Hence, if $\left(\dfrac{q}{p}\right)$ is to be $+1$, p must be a quadratic residue of q as well as being odd, and if $\left(\dfrac{q}{p}\right)$ is to be -1, p must be an odd quadratic nonresidue of q. For example, if $q = 5$, the prime p must satisfy the congruence

$$x \equiv 1 \pmod 2$$

and one of

$$x \equiv 1, 4 \pmod 5$$

in order that $\left(\dfrac{5}{p}\right) = +1$. Hence, $p \equiv 1, 9 \pmod{10}$; that is, 5 is a quadratic residue of all primes of the form $10k \pm 1$. On the other hand, if $\left(\dfrac{5}{p}\right)$ is to be -1, then p must satisfy

$$x \equiv 1 \pmod 2$$

and one of the congruences

$$x \equiv 2, 3 \pmod 5$$

Thus $p \equiv 3, 7 \pmod{10}$, and 5 is a quadratic nonresidue of all primes of the form $10k + 3$ and $10k + 7$.

If the given prime q is of the form $4n + 3$, then $\left(\dfrac{q}{p}\right)\left(\dfrac{p}{q}\right) = (-1)^{(p-1)/2}$

and so $\left(\dfrac{q}{p}\right) = (-1)^{(p-1)/2}\left(\dfrac{p}{q}\right)$. In this case if $\left(\dfrac{q}{p}\right)$ is to be $+1$, either

$$p \equiv 1(\text{mod } 4) \qquad \text{and} \qquad \left(\dfrac{p}{q}\right) = +1$$

or

$$p \equiv 3(\text{mod } 4) \qquad \text{and} \qquad \left(\dfrac{p}{q}\right) = -1$$

If $\left(\dfrac{q}{p}\right)$ is to be -1, then either

$$p \equiv 3(\text{mod } 4) \qquad \text{and} \qquad \left(\dfrac{p}{q}\right) = +1$$

or

$$p \equiv 1(\text{mod } 4) \qquad \text{and} \qquad \left(\dfrac{p}{q}\right) = -1$$

Accordingly, if $q = 7$ and $\left(\dfrac{7}{p}\right)$ is to be $+1$, then p must satisfy

$$x \equiv 1(\text{mod } 4)$$

and one of the congruences

$$x \equiv 1,\ 2,\ 4(\text{mod } 7)$$

giving $p \equiv 1,\ 9,\ 25(\text{mod } 28)$, or p satisfies the congruence

$$x \equiv 3(\text{mod } 4)$$

and one of

$$x \equiv 3,\ 5,\ 6(\text{mod } 7)$$

with the result that $p \equiv 3,\ 19,\ 27(\text{mod } 28)$. Hence, 7 is a quadratic residue of all primes of the form $28k + 1$, $28k + 3$, $28k + 9$, $28k + 19$, $28k + 25$, and $28k + 27$. In like manner we find that 7 is a quadratic nonresidue of all primes of the form $28k + 5$, $28k + 11$, $28k + 13$, $28k + 15$, $28k + 17$, and $28k + 23$.

Now suppose that the given integer is of the form $2q$ with the prime $q = 4n + 1$. Then $\left(\dfrac{2q}{p}\right) = \left(\dfrac{2}{p}\right)\left(\dfrac{q}{p}\right) = (-1)^{(p^2-1)/8}\left(\dfrac{p}{q}\right)$. If $2q$ is to be a quadratic residue of p, it follows that either

$$p \equiv \pm 1(\text{mod } 8) \qquad \text{and} \qquad \left(\dfrac{p}{q}\right) = +1$$

or

$$p \equiv \pm 3(\text{mod } 8) \qquad \text{and} \qquad \left(\dfrac{p}{q}\right) = -1$$

If either

$$p \equiv \pm 1 (\text{mod } 8) \quad \text{and} \quad \left(\frac{p}{q}\right) = -1$$

or

$$p \equiv \pm 3 (\text{mod } 8) \quad \text{and} \quad \left(\frac{p}{q}\right) = +1$$

then $2q$ is a quadratic nonresidue of p.

When the given integer is of the form $2q$ with the prime $q = 4n + 3$, it is evident that $\left(\frac{2q}{p}\right) = (-1)^{(p^2-1)/8} \left(\frac{q}{p}\right)$. But $\left(\frac{q}{p}\right) = (-1)^{(p-1)/2} \left(\frac{p}{q}\right)$, so that $\left(\frac{2q}{p}\right) = (-1)^{(p^2+4p-5)/8} \left(\frac{p}{q}\right)$. The exponent $(p^2 + 4p - 5)/8$ is even if and only if $p \equiv 1, 3 (\text{mod } 8)$. Hence, $\left(\frac{2q}{p}\right)$ will be $+1$ when either

$$p \equiv 1, 3 (\text{mod } 8) \quad \text{and} \quad \left(\frac{p}{q}\right) = +1$$

or when

$$p \equiv 5, 7 (\text{mod } 8) \quad \text{and} \quad \left(\frac{p}{q}\right) = -1$$

The conditions for $\left(\frac{2q}{p}\right)$ to be -1 are now obvious.

Finally, let us suppose that the given integer is the product of two odd primes q_1 and q_2 with $q_1 = 4n + 1$ and $q_2 = 4s + 3$. Then $\left(\frac{q_1 q_2}{p}\right) = \left(\frac{q_1}{p}\right)\left(\frac{q_2}{p}\right)$. By combining the first two cases it is clear that the primes p determined by those of which both q_1 and q_2 are quadratic residues are characterized by the following statements:

1. They satisfy $x \equiv 1 (\text{mod } 2)$.
2. They are quadratic residues of q_1.
3. They satisfy $x \equiv 1 (\text{mod } 4)$ and are quadratic residues of q_2, or they satisfy $x \equiv 3 (\text{mod } 4)$ and are quadratic nonresidues of q_2.

There are also primes p described by the conditions:

1. They satisfy $x \equiv 1 (\text{mod } 2)$.
2. They are quadratic nonresidues of q_1.
3. They satisfy $x \equiv 3 (\text{mod } 4)$ and are quadratic residues of q_2, or they satisfy $x \equiv 1 (\text{mod } 4)$ and are quadratic nonresidues of q_2.

Examples. 1. Find the odd primes of which 14 is a quadratic residue.

If 14 is to be a quadratic residue of the odd prime p, then p must satisfy two congruences selected in the manner already exhibited from each one of the following sets:

$$x \equiv 1, 3 (\mod 8)$$
$$x \equiv 1, 2, 4 (\mod 7)$$

and

$$x \equiv 5, 7 (\mod 8)$$
$$x \equiv 3, 5, 6 (\mod 7)$$

From the first set we find that $p \equiv 1, 9, 11, 25, 43, 51 (\mod 56)$, and from the second, $p \equiv 5, 13, 31, 45, 47, 55 (\mod 56)$.

2. Find the odd primes of which 35 is a quadratic residue.

$\left(\frac{35}{p}\right) = \left(\frac{5}{p}\right)\left(\frac{7}{p}\right)$, and both symbols must be $+1$ or both -1 for $\left(\frac{35}{p}\right)$ to be $+1$. Hence, p satisfies one of the congruences

$$x \equiv \pm 1 (\mod 10)$$

and one of

$$x \equiv 1, 3, 9, 19, 25, 27 (\mod 28)$$

giving $p \equiv 1, 9, 19, 29, 31, 59, 81, 109, 111, 121, 131, 139 (\mod 140)$, or p satisfies one of the congruences

$$x \equiv 3, 7 (\mod 10)$$

and one of

$$x \equiv 5, 11, 13, 15, 17, 23 (\mod 28)$$

with the result that $p \equiv 13, 17, 23, 33, 43, 67, 73, 97, 107, 117, 123, 127 (\mod 140)$.

EXERCISES

1. Evaluate: $\left(\frac{-1}{179}\right), \left(\frac{2}{101}\right), \left(\frac{45}{73}\right), \left(\frac{51}{73}\right)$.

2. Is there a solution of $x^2 \equiv 21 (\mod 41)$?

3. Find the values of q for which $\left(\frac{q}{19}\right) = +1$.

4. Find the primes of which 11 is a quadratic residue.

5. Find the primes of which 6 is a quadratic nonresidue.

6. Prove that 10 is a quadratic residue of all primes $p \equiv 1, 3, 9, 13, 27, 31, 37, 39 (\mod 40)$.

7. Prove that -3 is a quadratic residue of all primes of the form $6n + 1$ and a quadratic nonresidue of primes of the form $6n - 1$.

8. Find the primes of which 15 is a quadratic residue.

9. Show that a quadratic residue of an odd prime p is also a quadratic residue of p^n.

10. Prove that there are infinitely many primes of the form $4n + 1$. (Assume the number of these primes is finite and use them to construct an integer $4k^2 + 1$. Consider the form of the prime factors of this integer.)

11. Show that there is an infinite number of primes of the form $8n + 1$.

12. Prove that 3 is a primitive root of every prime of the form $2^{2^n} + 1$ by considering the quadratic character of 3 with respect to such a prime.

9-5. The Jacobi Symbol.   Let $P = p_1 p_2 \ldots p_r$, where the p_i, with $i = 1, 2, \ldots, r$, are positive odd primes, not necessarily distinct.   Then if m is any integer prime to P, the Jacobi symbol $\left(\dfrac{m}{P}\right)$ is defined in the following manner:

$$\left(\frac{m}{P}\right) = \left(\frac{m}{p_1}\right)\left(\frac{m}{p_2}\right) \cdots \left(\frac{m}{p_r}\right)$$

where the symbols to the right of the equality sign are Legendre symbols.

When $P = p_1 p_2 \cdots p_r$ and $Q = q_1 q_2 \cdots q_s$, with the p_i and q_j, where $j = 1, 2, \cdots, s$, positive odd primes, the properties of the Jacobi symbol are expressed by the following theorems:

Theorem 9-10.   If m is prime to both the positive odd integers P and Q, $\left(\dfrac{m}{P}\right)\left(\dfrac{m}{Q}\right) = \left(\dfrac{m}{PQ}\right)$.

Applying the definition given above, $\left(\dfrac{m}{P}\right) = \left(\dfrac{m}{p_1}\right)\left(\dfrac{m}{p_2}\right) \cdots \left(\dfrac{m}{p_r}\right)$, and $\left(\dfrac{m}{Q}\right) = \left(\dfrac{m}{q_1}\right)\left(\dfrac{m}{q_2}\right) \cdots \left(\dfrac{m}{q_s}\right)$.   Hence, $\left(\dfrac{m}{P}\right)\left(\dfrac{m}{Q}\right) = \left(\dfrac{m}{p_1}\right) \cdots \left(\dfrac{m}{p_r}\right)$ $\left(\dfrac{m}{q_1}\right) \cdots \left(\dfrac{m}{q_s}\right)$, and therefore $\left(\dfrac{m}{P}\right)\left(\dfrac{m}{Q}\right) = \left(\dfrac{m}{PQ}\right)$.

Theorem 9-11.   If m and n are prime to the positive odd integer P, $\left(\dfrac{mn}{P}\right) = \left(\dfrac{m}{P}\right)\left(\dfrac{n}{P}\right)$.

$\left(\dfrac{mn}{P}\right) = \left(\dfrac{mn}{p_1}\right)\left(\dfrac{mn}{p_2}\right) \cdots \left(\dfrac{mn}{p_r}\right)$.   But the Legendre symbol $\left(\dfrac{mn}{p_i}\right)$ $= \left(\dfrac{m}{p_i}\right)\left(\dfrac{n}{p_i}\right)$.   Hence, $\left(\dfrac{mn}{P}\right) = \left(\dfrac{m}{p_1}\right)\left(\dfrac{n}{p_1}\right)\left(\dfrac{m}{p_2}\right)\left(\dfrac{n}{p_2}\right) \cdots \left(\dfrac{m}{p_r}\right)\left(\dfrac{n}{p_r}\right)$ $= \left(\dfrac{m}{P}\right)\left(\dfrac{n}{P}\right)$.

Theorem 9-12.   If m and n are prime to the positive odd integer P and if $m \equiv n (\bmod P)$, then $\left(\dfrac{m}{P}\right) = \left(\dfrac{n}{P}\right)$.

Because $m \equiv n (\bmod P)$ implies that $m \equiv n (\bmod p_i)$, where $i = 1, 2, \ldots, r$, the theorem follows immediately from the definition of the Jacobi symbol.

Theorem 9-13.   If P is a positive odd integer, $\left(\dfrac{-1}{P}\right) = (-1)^{(P-1)/2}$.

According to the definition $\left(\dfrac{-1}{P}\right) = \left(\dfrac{-1}{p_1}\right)\left(\dfrac{-1}{p_2}\right) \cdots \left(\dfrac{-1}{p_r}\right) =$ $(-1)^{\sum [(p_i-1)/2]}$, where $i = 1, 2, \ldots, r$.   But $P = p_1 p_2 \cdots p_r =$

$\{1 + (p_1 - 1)\}\{1 + (p_2 - 1)\} \cdots \{1 + (p_r - 1)\}$, and thus $P = 1 +$

$$\sum_{i=1}^{r} (p_i - 1) + \sum_{\substack{i,k=1 \\ i<k}}^{r} (p_i - 1)(p_k - 1) + \cdots + \prod_{i=1}^{r} (p_i - 1). \quad \text{But } p_i - 1$$

$\equiv 0 (\bmod\ 2)$, so that $P \equiv 1 + \sum_{i=1}^{r} (p_i - 1)(\bmod\ 4)$. Hence, $\dfrac{P-1}{2} \equiv$

$\sum_{i=1}^{r} \dfrac{p_i - 1}{2}$ (mod 2). Therefore, $\left(\dfrac{-1}{P}\right) = (-1)^{(P-1)/2}$.

Theorem 9-14. If P is a positive odd integer, $\left(\dfrac{2}{P}\right) = (-1)^{(P^2-1)/8}$.

$$\left(\frac{2}{P}\right) = \left(\frac{2}{p_1}\right)\left(\frac{2}{p_2}\right) \cdots \left(\frac{2}{p_r}\right) = (-1)^{\sum_i [(p_i^2-1)/8]}, \text{ and } P^2 = \{1 + (p_1^2}$$

$$- 1)\}\{1 + (p_2^2 - 1)\} \cdots \{1 + (p_r^2 - 1)\} = 1 + \sum_{i=1}^{r} (p_i^2 - 1) +$$

$$\sum_{\substack{i,k=1 \\ i<k}}^{r} (p_i^2 - 1)(p_k^2 - 1) + \cdots + \prod_{i=1}^{r} (p_i^2 - 1). \quad \text{But since } p_i^2 - 1 \equiv$$

$0 (\bmod\ 8)$, it follows that $P^2 \equiv 1 + \sum_{i=1}^{r} (p_i^2 - 1)(\bmod\ 64)$, and $\dfrac{P^2-1}{8} \equiv$

$\sum_{i=1}^{r} \dfrac{p_i^2 - 1}{8}$ (mod 8). Hence, $\left(\dfrac{2}{P}\right) = (-1)^{(P^2-1)/8}$.

Theorem 9-15. If P and Q are positive, relatively prime odd integers,

$$\left(\frac{P}{Q}\right)\left(\frac{Q}{P}\right) = (-1)^{\frac{P-1}{2}\cdot\frac{Q-1}{2}}.$$

$\left(\dfrac{P}{Q}\right) = \left(\dfrac{P}{q_1}\right)\left(\dfrac{P}{q_2}\right) \cdots \left(\dfrac{P}{q_s}\right)$ and $\left(\dfrac{P}{q_j}\right) = \left(\dfrac{p_1}{q_j}\right)\left(\dfrac{p_2}{q_j}\right) \cdots \left(\dfrac{p_r}{q_j}\right)$. After

factoring $\left(\dfrac{Q}{P}\right)$ in like manner and forming the pairs $\left(\dfrac{p_i}{q_j}\right)\left(\dfrac{q_j}{p_i}\right)$, we find

$$\left(\frac{P}{Q}\right)\left(\frac{Q}{P}\right) = \prod_{i,j} \left(\frac{p_i}{q_j}\right)\left(\frac{q_j}{p_i}\right) = (-1)^{\sum_{i,j} \frac{p_i-1}{2}\cdot\frac{q_j-1}{2}}, \text{ where } i = 1, 2, \ldots, r \text{ and}$$

$j = 1, 2, \ldots, s$.

For a fixed j, $\sum_{i=1}^{r} (p_i - 1)(q_j - 1) = (q_j - 1) \sum_{i=1}^{r} (p_i - 1)$. But we

saw that $\sum_{i=1}^{r} (p_i - 1) \equiv P - 1(\bmod\ 4)$, and because $q_j - 1$ is even, it is evident that

$$(q_j - 1) \sum_{i=1}^{r} (p_i - 1) \equiv (P - 1)(q_j - 1)(\text{mod } 8)$$

Therefore,

$$\sum_{i,j} (p_i - 1)(q_j - 1) = \sum_{j} \left\{ (q_j - 1) \sum_{i} (p_i - 1) \right\}$$

$$\equiv \sum_{j} (P - 1)(q_j - 1)(\text{mod } 8)$$

$$\equiv (P - 1) \sum_{j} (q_j - 1)(\text{mod } 8)$$

Because $P - 1$ is even, $(P - 1) \sum_{j} (q_j - 1) \equiv (P - 1)(Q - 1)(\text{mod } 8)$.

Hence,

$$\sum_{i,j} \left(\frac{p_i - 1}{2} \cdot \frac{q_j - 1}{2} \right) \equiv \frac{P - 1}{2} \cdot \frac{Q - 1}{2} \ (\text{mod } 2)$$

Therefore,

$$\left(\frac{P}{Q} \right) \left(\frac{Q}{P} \right) = (-1)^{\frac{P-1}{2} \cdot \frac{Q-1}{2}}$$

According to the definition of the Jacobi symbol, $\left(\dfrac{m}{P} \right)$ is $+1$ when all $\left(\dfrac{m}{p_i} \right) = +1$ or when an even number are -1. In the first case the congruences

$$x^2 \equiv m(\text{mod } p_i) \qquad i = 1, 2, \ldots, r \tag{6}$$

have a solution for each p_i, and consequently there is a solution of

$$x^2 \equiv m(\text{mod } P) \tag{7}$$

But in the second case the congruences (6) fail to have a solution for certain p_i, and therefore (7) has no solution. Hence, if the Jacobi symbol $\left(\dfrac{m}{P} \right) = +1$, we have a necessary but not a sufficient condition that m be a quadratic residue of P. However, if $\left(\dfrac{m}{P} \right) = -1$, it is evident that congruence (7) has no solution.

Let us take some examples to illustrate the differences in the use of the Jacobi and the Legendre symbols. Consider the congruence $x^2 \equiv 135(\text{mod } 173)$ in which 135 and 173 are odd and relatively prime. Using

Jacobi symbols, we find $\left(\dfrac{135}{173}\right)\left(\dfrac{173}{135}\right) = +1$ and $\left(\dfrac{173}{135}\right) = \left(\dfrac{38}{135}\right) =$ $\left(\dfrac{2}{135}\right)\left(\dfrac{19}{135}\right)$. But $\left(\dfrac{2}{135}\right) = +1$. Also $\left(\dfrac{19}{135}\right)\left(\dfrac{135}{19}\right) = -1$. However, $\left(\dfrac{135}{19}\right) = \left(\dfrac{2}{19}\right) = -1$, so that $\left(\dfrac{19}{135}\right) = +1$, and $\left(\dfrac{173}{135}\right) = +1$. Therefore, $\left(\dfrac{135}{173}\right) = +1$. Since 173 is a prime, this is a Legendre symbol and we can conclude that there is a solution of the congruence.

Since 173 is a prime, we can, moreover, solve the problem by using only Legendre symbols. Thus $\left(\dfrac{135}{173}\right) = \left(\dfrac{5}{173}\right)\left(\dfrac{9}{173}\right)\left(\dfrac{3}{173}\right)$. But

$$\left(\dfrac{5}{173}\right)\left(\dfrac{173}{5}\right) = +1,$$

and $\left(\dfrac{173}{5}\right) = \left(\dfrac{3}{5}\right) = -1$. Hence, $\left(\dfrac{5}{173}\right) = -1$. Furthermore,

$$\left(\dfrac{3}{173}\right)\left(\dfrac{173}{3}\right) = +1.$$

But $\left(\dfrac{173}{3}\right) = \left(\dfrac{2}{3}\right) = -1$, and so $\left(\dfrac{3}{173}\right) = -1$. Hence, $\left(\dfrac{135}{173}\right) = +1$, and therefore the given congruence has a solution.

Now consider the congruence $x^2 \equiv 21 \pmod{253}$, where 253 is not a prime. In this case $\left(\dfrac{21}{253}\right)\left(\dfrac{253}{21}\right) = +1$, and $\left(\dfrac{253}{21}\right) = \left(\dfrac{1}{21}\right) = +1$. Hence, $\left(\dfrac{21}{253}\right) = +1$, but this is a Jacobi symbol, and we can reach no conclusion as to the existence of a solution of the congruence. However, $\left(\dfrac{21}{253}\right) = \left(\dfrac{21}{11}\right)\left(\dfrac{21}{23}\right)$, and since $\left(\dfrac{21}{11}\right) = \left(\dfrac{-1}{11}\right) = -1$, there is no solution of $x^2 \equiv 21 \pmod{11}$. Hence, there is no solution of the given congruence.

EXERCISES

1. Apply both Jacobi and Legendre symbols to determine whether or not the congruence $x^2 \equiv 35 \pmod{71}$ has a solution.

2. Evaluate the following symbols and interpret the results: $\left(\dfrac{51}{97}\right)$, $\left(\dfrac{365}{991}\right)$, $\left(\dfrac{105}{221}\right)$.

3. Use Legendre symbols to determine all the quadratic residues of 41.

9-6. The Solution of $x^2 \equiv a(\bmod 2^n)$. It is evident that if $(a, 2) = 1$, the congruence $x^2 \equiv a(\bmod 2)$ has the solution $x \equiv 1(\bmod 2)$, but if $(a, 2) = 1$, the congruence $x^2 \equiv a(\bmod 4)$ has a solution if and only if $a \equiv 1(\bmod 4)$, in which case there are two solutions 1 and 3 modulo 4.

Theorem 9-16. If $n \geq 3$ and $x^2 \equiv a(\bmod 2^n)$ has a solution, then $a \equiv 1(\bmod 8)$.

Suppose x_0 satisfies the congruence. Then $x_0^2 \equiv a(\bmod 2^n)$, and therefore $x_0^2 \equiv a(\bmod 8)$. But x_0 is odd, and its square is, therefore, congruent to 1 modulo 8. Hence, $a \equiv 1(\bmod 8)$.

Theorem 9-17. If $a \equiv 1(\bmod 8)$, there are exactly four distinct solutions modulo 2^n, where $n \geq 3$, of the congruence $x^2 \equiv a(\bmod 2^n)$.

We shall first show by induction that the congruence $x^2 \equiv a(\bmod 2^n)$ with $a \equiv 1(\bmod 8)$ has a solution. We know that under the given condition $x^2 \equiv a(\bmod 8)$ has a solution. Assuming that, for a given k, $x^2 \equiv a(\bmod 2^k)$ is satisfied by x_0, we infer that $x_0^2 - a = 2^k h$. We, therefore, wish to determine t so that $x_0 + 2^{k-1}t$ satisfies $x^2 \equiv a(\bmod 2^{k+1})$, that is, so that

$$(x_0 + 2^{k-1}t)^2 \equiv a(\bmod 2^{k+1})$$
$$x_0^2 - a + 2^k x_0 t + 2^{2k-2}t^2 \equiv 0(\bmod 2^{k+1})$$
$$2^k(h + x_0 t) \equiv 0(\bmod 2^{k+1})$$

and finally

$$h + x_0 t \equiv 0(\bmod 2)$$

Because this congruence always has a solution, there is a value of t for which $x_0 + 2^{k-1}t$ satisfies $x^2 \equiv a(\bmod 2^{k+1})$. Thus the congruence $x^2 \equiv a(\bmod 2^n)$ has a solution if $a \equiv 1(\bmod 8)$.

But whenever $x^2 \equiv a(\bmod 2^n)$, where $n \geq 3$, has one solution $x \equiv x_1(\bmod 2^n)$, it has exactly four solutions, for suppose that x_1 and x_2 satisfy the congruence. Then

$$x_1^2 \equiv x_2^2(\bmod 2^n)$$

and

$$(x_1 - x_2)(x_1 + x_2) \equiv 0(\bmod 2^n)$$

and because both x_1 and x_2 are odd,

$$\frac{x_1 - x_2}{2} \cdot \frac{x_1 + x_2}{2} \equiv 0(\bmod 2^{n-2})$$

However, $[(x_1 - x_2)/2] + [(x_1 + x_2)/2] = x_1$, and therefore one of $(x_1 - x_2)/2$ and $(x_1 + x_2)/2$ is odd. As a result, the other is divisible by 2^{n-2}. Hence, one of the congruences $(x_1 \pm x_2)/2 \equiv 0(\bmod 2^{n-2})$ holds. Therefore, $x_2 \equiv x_1(\bmod 2^{n-1})$, or $x_2 \equiv -x_1(\bmod 2^{n-1})$. But when x_1 satisfies $x^2 \equiv a(\bmod 2^n)$, $-x_1$ does also. Consequently, all four integers $\pm x_1$, $\pm x_1 + 2^{n-1}$ satisfy $x^2 \equiv a(\bmod 2^n)$, and they are incongruent modulo 2^n.

But there are exactly four solutions of $x^2 \equiv a(\mathrm{mod}\ 2^n)$, for a must be congruent to 1 modulo 2^3, and thus a has just 2^{n-3} distinct values modulo 2^n. Therefore, the 2^{n-1} odd positive integers less than 2^n separate into 2^{n-3} sets of four such that all four integers in a set satisfy one and only one of the 2^{n-3} congruences $x^2 \equiv a(\mathrm{mod}\ 2^n)$ determined by the permissible values of a.

Example. In the case of $x^2 \equiv a(\mathrm{mod}\ 16)$, a can have only the values 1 and 9 modulo 16. The solutions of $x^2 \equiv 1(\mathrm{mod}\ 16)$ are 1, 7, 9, and 15 modulo 16, and those of $x^2 \equiv 9(\mathrm{mod}\ 16)$ are 3, 5, 11, and 13 modulo 16.

EXERCISE

First find the values that a can have in order that there be a solution of $x^2 \equiv a(\mathrm{mod}\ 64)$, and then find all the solutions of these congruences.

CHAPTER 10

SOME FAMOUS PROBLEMS

10-1. The Waring Problem.   In 1770 Waring published the statement that every positive integer is a sum of not more than 4 squares, not more than 9 cubes, not more than 19 fourth powers.   He gave no proof of his assertion and may have had only calculations to support it, but the problem implied by his statement has ever since challenged the best mathematicians and has been only recently solved.   It is generally agreed that Waring meant to imply that for every positive integer k there exists a smallest positive integer $g(k)$ such that any positive integer n can be expressed as a sum of at most $g(k)$ positive kth powers.*

Certain results connected with this problem of representing a positive integer as a sum of like powers of integers had long been conjectured even though not much progress in proving them was made until the eighteenth century.   Fermat, for instance, was much interested in the theorem that every prime of the form $4n + 1$ can be expressed as a sum of two squares and, barring the use of negative integers, in but one way.   Thus $5 = 1^2 + 2^2$, and $13 = 2^2 + 3^2$.   It remained for Euler, however, to demonstrate the theorem satisfactorily.   Moreover, that any integer n is a sum of two squares if and only if it has the form $n = 2^t a^2 P$, with $t \geq 0$ and P a product of different primes of the form $4s + 1$, had been determined in the seventeenth century.   Again, mathematicians had asserted that any integer not of the form $4^r(8s + 7)$ is expressible as a sum of three squares and that integers of this form fail to be expressible as such a sum.   Furthermore, by 1770 Lagrange had proved that every integer is a sum of at most four squares.

From the time Waring enunciated his theorem, it took 139 years to prove that every integer is a sum of at most nine cubes.   Although Liouville proved in 1859 that there exists a smallest integer $g(4)$ such that every n is a sum of at most $g(4)$ fourth powers, still it has not yet been proved that in this case $g(4)$ actually is 19.   In 1909 Hilbert proved the general theorem that for each k there exists a positive integer $g(k)$, independent of n, such that every integer n is a sum of at most $g(k)$ kth powers, but his proof merely shows the existence of algebraic identities for deter-

* G. H. Hardy, "Some Famous Problems of the Theory of Numbers."

mining $g(k)$ and sheds no light on the actual value of $g(k)$. Since then Hardy and Littlewood have developed by analytical means a formula that determines an upper bound for $g(k)$ for every k.

From these few remarks we can obtain some idea of the magnitude of this problem, and certainly a perusal of a few of the original proofs will give an appreciation of the ingenious adaptation of the tools of the theory of functions of a complex variable to the problems of the integers. We are not concerned here with the presentation of any of these powerful methods, but we shall give two of Euler's* proofs that every prime of the form $4n + 1$ can be represented uniquely as a sum of two squares and then reproduce a proof, due to Euler and Lagrange,† that uses only the ideas of the classical theory of numbers to show that every integer can be expressed as a sum of at most four squares.

Let us recognize first that the identity

$$(a^2 + b^2)(c^2 + d^2) = (ac \pm bd)^2 + (ad \mp bc)^2$$

expresses the product of two sums of squares as a sum of two squares. For instance, $(2^2 + 1^2)(3^2 + 2^2) = 8^2 + 1^2 = 4^2 + 7^2$. We notice, however, that $(2^2 + 1)(2^2 + 1) = 5^2 + 0^2 = 3^2 + 4^2$, and so in this case the formula gives but one representation of the product as a sum of two positive squares. Does the formula ever fail to give at least one solution when $(a, b) = 1$ and $(c, d) = 1$? In this case $ac = bd$, and $ad = bc$. But if $ac = bd$, then $a = d$ and $b = c$, and so the two given sums are identical. If $ad = bc$ as well, then $a^2 = b^2 = 1$. Hence, in the single case $(1 + 1)(1 + 1) = 2^2 + 0$, the formula fails to give a sum of two positive squares.

It is also apparent that when $(a, b) = 1$ and $(c, d) = 1$, the squares in the expression for the result of the product need not be relatively prime, for example, $(8^2 + 1^2)(9^2 + 2^2) = 70^2 + 25^2$. On the other hand, if $(ac \pm bd, ad \mp bc) = 1$, then $(a, b) = 1$ and $(c, d) = 1$, for if $(a, b) = k$, or if $(c, d) = k$, it is clear that k divides both $ac \pm bd$ and $ad \mp bc$.

Euler's first proof of the fact that a prime of the form $4n + 1$ can be represented as a sum of two squares is a little cumbersome, but it is instructive to study it and to compare it with the second, more elegant proof which Euler published about 25 years later. The second proof exemplifies the enormous improvement in the directness of the presentation that a mathematician often attains when the initial proof is reviewed.

Lemma 10-1a. If a prime $p = c^2 + d^2$, and if there is a $q > 1$ such that $pq = a^2 + b^2$ with $(a, b) = 1$, then q is a sum of two relatively prime squares.

* L. E. Dickson, "History of the Theory of Numbers," Vol. 2, pp. 230–231.
† *Ibid.*, Vol. 2, p. 281.

If the prime $p = c^2 + d^2$, then $(c, d) = 1$, and if $pq = a^2 + b^2$, we have

$$c^2(a^2 + b^2) - a^2(c^2 + d^2) = c^2pq - a^2p = mp$$

But

$$c^2(a^2 + b^2) - a^2(c^2 + d^2) = b^2c^2 - a^2d^2 = (bc - ad)(bc + ad)$$

Consequently, the prime p divides at least one of $bc - ad$ and $bc + ad$. Moreover, $bc - ad \neq 0$, for if $bc = ad$, then $a = c$ and $b = d$. Under these conditions p and pq would not be distinct. If $bc - ad = tp$, let

$$b = tc + r$$

and

$$a = -td + s$$

Then

$$cr = bc - tc^2$$

and

$$ds = ad + td^2$$

so that

$$cr - ds = bc - ad - t(c^2 + d^2) = 0$$

Hence,

$$cr = ds$$
$$r = dn \qquad \text{and} \qquad s = cn$$

But if $bc + ad = kp$, the equations

$$b = kc + r$$

and

$$a = kd + s$$

give

$$cr = bc - kc^2$$

and

$$ds = ad - kd^2$$

Hence,

$$cr + ds = bc + ad - k(c^2 + d^2) = 0$$

and

$$cr = -ds$$

In this case

$$r = dn \qquad \text{and} \qquad s = -cn$$

In the first case

$$pq = a^2 + b^2 = (-td + cn)^2 + (tc + dn)^2$$
$$= (t^2 + n^2)(c^2 + d^2)$$
$$= p(t^2 + n^2)$$

and in the second

$$pq = (kd - cn)^2 + (kc + dn)^2$$
$$= (k^2 + n^2)(c^2 + d^2)$$
$$= p(k^2 + n^2)$$

Therefore, q is a sum of two positive squares. These squares are relatively prime if $(a, b) = 1$, for if in the first case $(t, n) = u$, the equations $b = tc + dn$, $a = -td + cn$ show that u divides both a and b. Likewise, $(k, n) = 1$ in the second case.

Lemma 10-2a. If PQ is a sum of two relatively prime squares and Q is not a sum of two relatively prime squares, then P has a prime factor that is not a sum of two squares.

Consider Lemma 10-1a, and let $P = p_1 p_2 \cdots p_k$, where each prime p_i, with $i = 1, 2, \ldots, k$, is a sum of two squares. Then $p_1(p_2 \cdots p_k Q) = PQ$ is a sum of two relatively prime squares, and it follows immediately that $p_2 \cdots p_k Q$ is a sum of two relatively prime squares. By repeating this process, we find that Q is a sum of two relatively prime squares. We must conclude, then, that if PQ is a sum of two relatively prime squares and Q is not, P must have a prime factor that is not a sum of two squares.

Lemma 10-3a. If a prime p divides $a^2 + b^2$, where $(a, b) = 1$, then p is a sum of two squares.

Let the prime p divide $a^2 + b^2$ with $(a, b) = 1$, and suppose that p is not a sum of two squares. Set

$$a = mp \pm r_1 \qquad 0 < r_1 \leq \frac{p}{2}$$

and

$$b = np \pm r_2 \qquad 0 < r_2 \leq \frac{p}{2}$$

Then

$$r_1{}^2 + r_2{}^2 = a^2 + b^2 + kp$$
$$= Qp \leq \frac{p^2}{2}$$

Any common divisor of r_1 and r_2 must divide Q, and thus the last equation can be reduced to $a_1{}^2 + b_1{}^2 = Pp$, with $(a_1, b_1) = 1$. According to Lemma 10-2a, it is now evident that P has a prime factor p_1 that is not a sum of two squares, and furthermore, $p_1 \leq p/2$. Using the fact that p_1 divides $a_1{}^2 + b_1{}^2$, we can repeat this process. The method, therefore, always produces a sum of two relatively prime squares, $a_i{}^2 + b_i{}^2 \leq (p_{i-1}{}^2)/2$, which has a prime factor $p_i < p_{i-1}$ that is not a sum of two squares. But this statement is contrary to fact, for the prime factors of all sums of two sufficiently small relatively prime squares are themselves a sum of two squares. ($3^2 + 2^2 = 13$, $3^2 + 1^2 = 10$, $2^2 + 1^2 = 5$, $1^2 + 1^2 = 2$.) Consequently, the prime factor p of $a^2 + b^2$ must be a sum of two squares.

Theorem 10-1. Every prime of the form $4n + 1$ is a sum of two squares in just one way.

The integer -1 is a quadratic residue of all primes of the form $4n + 1$. Hence, there is an integer a such that $a^2 \equiv -1 (\text{mod } p)$, where $p = 4n + 1$. It is immediately evident that p divides $a^2 + 1$, and accordingly p is expressible as a sum of two squares.

Now suppose that $p = a^2 + b^2 = c^2 + d^2$, where it is evident that, of each of the pairs a and b, c and d, one integer is even while the other is odd. Then

$$a^2 - c^2 = d^2 - b^2$$

and

$$(a - c)(a + c) = (d - b)(d + b)$$

Let $(a - c, \ d - b) = r$, so that $a - c = rm$ and $d - b = rn$, with $(m, n) = 1$. Therefore,

$$m(a + c) = n(d + b)$$

Hence, if we let $(a + c, d + b) = s$, we have

$$a + c = ns$$

and

$$d + b = ms$$

If a and c are both even or both odd, it is clear that r is even, and so is s. But if only one of a and c is even, then r is odd, and so is s. In the latter case both m and n are also odd. Moreover,

$$(r^2 + s^2)(m^2 + n^2) = m^2r^2 + m^2s^2 + n^2r^2 + n^2s^2$$
$$= (a - c)^2 + (d + b)^2 + (d - b)^2 + (a + c)^2$$

Hence, the integer

$$\frac{(r^2 + s^2)(m^2 + n^2)}{4} = \frac{a^2 + b^2}{2} + \frac{c^2 + d^2}{2}$$
$$= p$$

Thus, if r and s are even, p has been factored into the integers $(r^2 + s^2)/4$ and $m^2 + n^2$, both of which are greater than 1. But if r and s are odd, r and s cannot both be 1, nor can both m and n be 1, for in either case $a = d$ and $b = c$. Consequently, when r and s are odd, p is equal to the product of the integers $(r^2 + s^2)/2$ and $(m^2 + n^2)/2$, neither of which is 1. Since such a factorization is impossible, we must conclude that the prime $p = 4n + 1$ has a unique representation as a sum of two squares.

Let us start the second proof of Theorem 10-1 with the statement that since -1 is a quadratic residue of every prime of the form $4n + 1$, there are integers a and m that satisfy the equation $a^2 + 1 = mp$. The fact that a is a quadratic residue of p means that a can be chosen positive and not greater than $(p - 1)/2$. Consequently, $a^2 + 1 < (p^2/4) + 1$. But

$(p^2/4) + 1 < p^2$. Thus $mp < p^2$, and $m < p$. Hence, it is true that there are integers a and b, with $(a, b) = 1$ and $0 < a, b \leq (p - 1)/2$, which satisfy the equation $a^2 + b^2 = mp$, m being an integer in the interval $1 \leq m < p$. If $m > 1$, we shall show that we can produce a positive integer $m_1 < m$ such that $m_1 p$ is a sum of two squares.

Set $a = q_1 m + r_1$ and $b = q_2 m + r_2$, with $|r_1|$ and $|r_2|$ not greater than $m/2$. As a result

$$a^2 + b^2 = r_1{}^2 + r_2{}^2 + m^2(q_1{}^2 + q_2{}^2) + 2m(r_1 q_1 + r_2 q_2) \tag{1}$$

and

$$mp = r_1{}^2 + r_2{}^2 + mK$$

so that

$$r_1{}^2 + r_2{}^2 = m_1 m$$

But

$$r_1{}^2 + r_2{}^2 < 2\left(\frac{m}{2}\right)^2$$

for not both $|r_1|$ and $|r_2|$ can be $m/2$ because $(a, b) = 1$. Hence,

$$m_1 m < \frac{m^2}{2}$$

and

$$m_1 < m$$

Applying the identity exhibited just before Lemma 10-1a, we have

$$(r_1{}^2 + r_2{}^2)(q_1{}^2 + q_2{}^2) = (r_1 q_1 + r_2 q_2)^2 + (r_1 q_2 - r_2 q_1)^2$$

or

$$m_1 m(q_1{}^2 + q_2{}^2) = s^2 + t^2 \tag{2}$$

where

$$s = r_1 q_1 + r_2 q_2$$

and

$$t = r_1 q_2 - r_2 q_1$$

Recalling Eq. (1), we observe that

$$mp = m_1 m + m^2(q_1{}^2 + q_2{}^2) + 2ms$$

and

$$p = m_1 + m(q_1{}^2 + q_2{}^2) + 2s$$

Therefore,

$$m_1 p = m_1{}^2 + m_1 m(q_1{}^2 + q_2{}^2) + 2m_1 s$$

and, according to (2),

$$m_1 p = m_1{}^2 + s^2 + t^2 + 2m_1 s$$

or

$$m_1 p = (m_1 + s)^2 + t^2$$

Hence, it is clear that upon the assumption that $m > 1$ we have constructed another integer $m_1 < m$ such that $m_1 p$ is a sum of two squares. We must conclude, therefore, that $m = 1$.

The unicity of this representation of the prime $p = 4n + 1$ was proved at the end of the first proof of Theorem 10-1.

Recalling that the even prime $2 = 1^2 + 1^2$, we shall now proceed to the second problem stated above by showing in the following steps that any odd prime can be expressed as a sum of four squares or fewer:

Lemma 10-1b (Euler's Identity). $(x_1{}^2 + x_2{}^2 + x_3{}^2 + x_4{}^2)(y_1{}^2 + y_2{}^2 + y_3{}^2 + y_4{}^2) = (x_1 y_1 + x_2 y_2 + x_3 y_3 + x_4 y_4)^2 + (x_1 y_2 - x_2 y_1 + x_3 y_4 - x_4 y_3)^2 + (x_1 y_3 - x_3 y_1 + x_4 y_2 - x_2 y_4)^2 + (x_1 y_4 - x_4 y_1 + x_2 y_3 - x_3 y_2)^2$.

If i has the usual meaning, $\sqrt{-1}$, this identity can be proved by finding the following product of two determinants whose values are $x_1{}^2 + x_2{}^2 + x_3{}^2 + x_4{}^2$ and $y_1{}^2 + y_2{}^2 + y_3{}^2 + y_4{}^2$:

$$\begin{vmatrix} x_1 + ix_2 & x_3 + ix_4 \\ -x_3 + ix_4 & x_1 - ix_2 \end{vmatrix} \cdot \begin{vmatrix} y_1 - iy_2 & -y_3 - iy_4 \\ y_3 - iy_4 & y_1 + iy_2 \end{vmatrix} = \begin{vmatrix} A - iB & C - iD \\ -C - iD & A + iB \end{vmatrix}$$
$$= A^2 + B^2 + C^2 + D^2$$

where

$$A = x_1 y_1 + x_2 y_2 + x_3 y_3 + x_4 y_4$$
$$B = x_1 y_2 - x_2 y_1 + x_3 y_4 - x_4 y_3$$
$$-C = x_1 y_3 - x_3 y_1 + x_4 y_2 - x_2 y_4$$
$$D = x_1 y_4 - x_4 y_1 + x_2 y_3 - x_3 y_2$$

Lemma 10-2b. If p is an odd prime, there exists an integer t, where $1 \leq t < p$, such that $tp = x_1{}^2 + x_2{}^2 + x_3{}^2 + x_4{}^2$.

Let x_i, where $i = 0, 1, 2, \ldots, (p - 1)/2$, represent the integers that lie in the interval $0 \leq x_i \leq (p - 1)/2$. There are then $(p + 1)/2$ values of $x_i{}^2$, and no two of these values are congruent modulo p, for if $x_i{}^2 \equiv x_j{}^2 \pmod{p}$, where $i \neq j$ and $j = 0, 1, 2, \ldots, (p - 1)/2$, it follows that $(x_i - x_j)(x_i + x_j) \equiv 0 \pmod{p}$. Hence, at least one of $x_i - x_j$ and $x_i + x_j$ would be divisible by p, which is impossible because each is less than p.

Again, let y_i represent the integers in the same interval and form the numbers $-1 - y_i{}^2$. These integers are also incongruent modulo p, for if $-1 - y_i{}^2 \equiv -1 - y_j{}^2 \pmod{p}$, where $i \neq j$, then $y_j{}^2 - y_i{}^2 \equiv 0 \pmod{p}$, and we have seen that this congruence is impossible.

Because the $x_i{}^2$ and $-1 - y_i{}^2$ taken together form a set of $p + 1$ integers, two of them must be congruent modulo p. Therefore, some $x_i{}^2$ must be congruent to a particular $-1 - y_j{}^2$. Calling these integers x^2 and $-1 - y^2$, respectively, we have

$$x^2 \equiv -1 - y^2 \pmod{p}$$

and
$$x^2 + y^2 + 1^2 + 0^2 \equiv 0(\mathrm{mod}\ p)$$

so that $x^2 + y^2 + 1^2 + 0^2 = tp$, where t is a positive integer.

Moreover, $x^2 < p^2/4$, and $y^2 < p^2/4$. Therefore, $(p^2/4) + (p^2/4) + 1 \geq tp$, and $(p^2/2) + 1 \geq tp$. However, since $p^2 > 2$, it is evident that $2p^2 > p^2 + 2$, and $p^2 > (p^2/2) + 1$. Hence, $p^2 > (p^2/2) + 1 \geq tp$, which shows that $p > t$. As a result, $1 \leq t < p$.

Lemma 10-3b. If p is an odd prime and t is the least positive integer such that $tp = x_1^2 + x_2^2 + x_3^2 + x_4^2$, then t is odd.

Suppose that t is even and that $x_1^2 + x_2^2 + x_3^2 + x_4^2 = tp$. Then the x_i, where $i = 1, 2, 3, 4$, are (1) all even, (2) all odd, or (3) two are even and two are odd. In any of these cases the x_i can be grouped in pairs so that $x_1 + x_2 \equiv 0(\mathrm{mod}\ 2)$ and $x_3 + x_4 \equiv 0(\mathrm{mod}\ 2)$. Hence, $(x_1 + x_2)/2$ and $(x_3 + x_4)/2$ are integers, and so are $(x_1 - x_2)/2$ and $(x_3 - x_4)/2$. Therefore,

$$\left(\frac{x_1 + x_2}{2}\right)^2 + \left(\frac{x_1 - x_2}{2}\right)^2 + \left(\frac{x_3 + x_4}{2}\right)^2 + \left(\frac{x_3 - x_4}{2}\right)^2 = \frac{x_1^2}{2} + \frac{x_2^2}{2}$$
$$+ \frac{x_3^2}{2} + \frac{x_4^2}{2} = \frac{t}{2}p$$

Thus there is an integer $t/2$ smaller than t and such that $tp/2$ is a sum of four squares. Consequently, t must be odd.

Lemma 10-4b. If p is an odd prime and if the least positive integer t, less than p, satisfying the condition $tp = x_1^2 + x_2^2 + x_3^2 + x_4^2$ is not 1, then there exists a positive integer s less than t and such that $st = y_1^2 + y_2^2 + y_3^2 + y_4^2$.

Choose y_i, where $i = 1, 2, 3, 4$, so that $y_i \equiv x_i(\mathrm{mod}\ t)$, and let $|y_i| < t/2$. Then $y_i^2 \equiv x_i^2(\mathrm{mod}\ t)$, and

$$\sum_{i=1}^{4} y_i^2 \equiv \sum_{i=1}^{4} x_i^2(\mathrm{mod}\ t)$$

Hence,

$$\sum_{i=1}^{4} y_i^2 \equiv tp \equiv 0(\mathrm{mod}\ t)$$

Therefore, $y_1^2 + y_2^2 + y_3^2 + y_4^2 = st$. The integer s is not 0 or each y_i would be 0, and then each x_i would be divisible by t. In this case t^2 would divide tp, and t would divide p. Hence, t would be 1. Moreover, since $|y_i| < t/2$, it follows that $y_i^2 < t^2/4$ and $\sum_{i=1}^{4} y_i^2 < t^2$. Hence, $st < t^2$, and $s < t$. Consequently, $1 \leq s < t$.

Theorem 10-2. Every odd prime is a sum of at most four positive squares.

If $p = 3$, observe that $3 = 1^2 + 1^2 + 1^2$.

If $p > 3$, multiply corresponding members of the equations

$$x_1^2 + x_2^2 + x_3^2 + x_4^2 = tp \qquad 3 \le t < p$$
$$y_1^2 + y_2^2 + y_3^2 + y_4^2 = st \qquad 1 \le s < t$$

developed in the preceding lemmas. Remember that t is the least positive integer satisfying the first equation. We find upon applying Euler's identity that

$$t^2 sp = (x_1 y_1 + x_2 y_2 + x_3 y_3 + x_4 y_4)^2 + (x_1 y_2 - x_2 y_1 + x_3 y_4 - x_4 y_3)^2$$
$$+ (x_1 y_3 - x_3 y_1 + x_4 y_2 - x_2 y_4)^2 + (x_1 y_4 - x_4 y_1 + x_2 y_3 - x_3 y_2)^2 \quad (3)$$

But since $y_i \equiv x_i \pmod{t}$,

$$x_1 y_1 + x_2 y_2 + x_3 y_3 + x_4 y_4 \equiv x_1^2 + x_2^2 + x_3^2 + x_4^2 \equiv tp \equiv 0 \pmod{t}$$

Also,

$$x_1 y_2 - x_2 y_1 + x_3 y_4 - x_4 y_3 \equiv x_1 x_2 - x_1 x_2 + x_3 x_4 - x_3 x_4 \equiv 0 \pmod{t}, \ldots$$

It is apparent, therefore, that t^2 divides each of the four squares in the right-hand member of (3) and that sp, with $s < t$, is a sum of four squares. But this conclusion contradicts the fact that t was chosen the least positive integer such that tp is a sum of four squares. Hence, $t = 1$, and the theorem is proved.

Theorem 10-3. Every integer is a sum of at most four positive squares.

Upon factoring the given integer into primes, the theorem follows immediately from Euler's identity.

It may also be added that we must use at least four positive squares to express some integers as a sum of squares, for we shall show that no integer that is congruent to 7 for the modulus 8 can be a sum of three squares.

Suppose that $x_1^2 + x_2^2 + x_3^2 = n$. Not all the x_i, where $i = 1, 2, 3$, can be even, nor can just one be, for $n = 8k + 7$ is odd. But if all the x_i are odd so that $x_i^2 \equiv 1 \pmod{8}$, then $x_1^2 + x_2^2 + x_3^2 \equiv 3 \pmod{8}$. Finally, if two of the x_i are even and one is odd, $x_1^2 + x_2^2 + x_3^2 \equiv 1 \pmod{8}$ or $x_1^2 + x_2^2 + x_3^2 \equiv 5 \pmod{8}$. Consequently, a sum of three squares cannot be equal to any integer that is congruent to 7 modulo 8.

EXERCISES

1. Prove that integers of the form $4^r(8n + 7)$ with r and $n \ge 0$ cannot be expressed as a sum of three squares.

2. Write $(x_1^2 + x_2^2 + x_3^2 + x_4^2)^2$ as a sum of three squares. What does the result prove?

10-2. The Equation $x^2 + y^2 = z^2$. From the point of view of the theory of numbers the solution of the Pythagorean triangle means the determining of formulas for expressing all triplets of positive integral values that satisfy the equation $x^2 + y^2 = z^2$. When x, y, z is a solution of this equation, it is evident that kx, ky, kz is also a solution. We shall, therefore, confine ourselves to the solutions, called *primitive solutions*, in which the values x, y, z are relatively prime. This restriction together with the equation implies that x, y, z are relatively prime in pairs, for a common divisor of any two of them divides the third. We infer, then, that two of these integers cannot be even. But neither can both the integers x and y be odd, for the square of an odd integer has the form $8n + 1$, and thus the sum of two odd squares is divisible by 2 but not by 4. Consequently, one of x and y is even, and the other is odd. Let $x = 2u$. Then y and z are odd, and $x^2 = 4u^2 = z^2 - y^2 = (z + y)(z - y)$. However, $(z + y) + (z - y) = 2z$, and therefore any common divisor of $z + y$ and $z - y$ divides $2z$. But a divisor greater than 1 of z cannot divide $z + y$. Hence, 2 is the greatest common divisor of $z + y$ and $z - y$. Therefore, let $z + y = 2v^2$ and $z - y = 2w^2$, where $(v, w) = 1$. Then $4u^2 = (2v^2)(2w^2)$, and $x = 2u = 2vw$. By adding the members of $z + y = 2v^2$ and $z - y = 2w^2$, we find, furthermore, that $z = v^2 + w^2$ and $y = v^2 - w^2$. Moreover, because $(y, z) = 1$, one of the integers v, w is even, while the other is odd.

If $(v, w) = 1$ and one is even, while the other is odd, and k is an arbitrary integer, the substitution of

$$x = 2kvw \qquad y = k(v^2 - w^2) \qquad z = k(v^2 + w^2)$$

in the given equation makes it clear that the equation is actually satisfied by these values. They, therefore, form the general solution of $x^2 + y^2 = z^2$ except for the fact that the values of x and y may be interchanged. Hence, we have proved that:

Theorem 10-4. If k is an arbitrary integer, the solutions of $x^2 + y^2 = z^2$ are $x = 2kvw$, $y = k(v^2 - w^2)$, and $z = k(v^2 + w^2)$ for all integers v and w so chosen that $(v, w) = 1$ and one is even, while the other is odd.

EXERCISES

1. Express 21, 31, and 39 as a sum of squares.

2. Solve each of the equations $x^2 + y^2 = 169$, $x^2 + y^2 = 625$, and $x^2 + y^2 = 2704$.

3. Is there an isosceles right triangle whose three sides are integers?

4. Find expressions for the sides of all integral right triangles whose hypotenuse is one greater than a side.

5. Show that if $x^2 + y^2 = 2z^2$, then $x = k(v^2 + 2vw - w^2)$, $y = \pm k(v^2 - 2vw - w^2)$, $z = k(v^2 + w^2)$, where k is an arbitrary integer, $(v, w) = 1$ and one of v and w is even, while the other is odd.

10-3. Fermat's Last Theorem. About 1637 Fermat stated that there is no solution in positive integers of the equation $x^n + y^n = z^n$ if $n > 2$. This theorem is known as Fermat's last theorem, and about it he wrote, "I have discovered a truly remarkable proof but this margin is too small to contain it." To this day mathematicians have been baffled by the statement, for they have been able neither to prove nor to disprove the general theorem. The equations $(x^m)^4 + (y^m)^4 = (z^m)^4$ and $(x^m)^p + (y^m)^p = (z^m)^p$ show that the proof can be broken up into the cases in which $n = 4$ and n is an odd prime. In 1747 Euler published a proof, which we shall reproduce below, that there is no solution in the first case. No proof for every odd prime has been discovered although by 1857 Kummer had shown the impossibility of solving the equation if $n < 100$. It was Kummer's reflection on his own error made in attempting to prove this theorem, as well as the misconceptions of Cauchy and Lamé, that led to his invention of the theory of ideals. With this new tool he and other mathematicians were able to set up various conditions for the insolvability of the equation. H. S. Vandiver* has given a complete account of the present status of the problem, including his own recent contributions toward its solution and his conjectures as to its truth.

Theorem 10-5. There is no solution in positive integers of the equation $x^4 + y^4 = z^2$.

The method we shall use in proving this theorem is a neat example of Fermat's method of infinite descent. We shall assume that there are integers that satisfy the equation and shall show that under this condition there must always be another set having a smaller z. It is evident that if there is a solution of the equation in which the integers x, y, z are not relatively prime in pairs, then there is another in which the restriction holds. We shall assume, therefore, that x, y, and z are prime each to each. Then $(x^2)^2 + (y^2)^2 = z^2$, so that according to Theorem 10-4 we have $x^2 = a^2 - b^2$, $y^2 = 2ab$, and $z = a^2 + b^2$, with $(a, b) = 1$, and where we may choose a odd and b even. Because $y^2 = a(2b)$, it follows that $a = u^2$ and $2b = v^2$. But $a^2 = x^2 + b^2$. Therefore, $a = r^2 + s^2$, and $b = 2rs$ with $(r, s) = 1$. Hence, $2b = 4rs = v^2$, and $r = x_1^2$, $s = y_1^2$. Thus $x_1^4 + y_1^4 = u^2$, and, furthermore, $1 < u < a < z$. Thus there is a set of integers with a smaller z that satisfies the given equation. It is impossible that this always be so, and consequently there is no solution of $x^4 + y^4 = z^2$.

Corollary. There is no solution in positive integers of the equation $x^4 + y^4 = z^4$.

10-4. The Area of an Integral Right Triangle

Theorem 10-6. If the sides of a right triangle are integers, the area cannot be a perfect square.

* *Am. Math. Monthly*, Vol. 53, No. 10, pp. 555–578, 1946; *ibid.*, Vol. 60, No. 3, pp. 164–167, 1953.

We shall develop the proof of this theorem as another example of Fermat's method of infinite descent, using basically the very method he outlined in the marginal notes of his copy of Bachet's edition of Diophantus's "Arithmetica."[*]

If x, y, and z are the sides of a right triangle, again restricting ourselves to the case where these integers are relatively prime in pairs, let $x = 2ab$, $y = a^2 - b^2$, $z = a^2 + b^2$, where a and b are relatively prime and one is even, the other odd. Then the area of this triangle, which we assume is a perfect square, is $A = ab(a^2 - b^2) = r^2$. Since $(a, b) = 1$, the integers a, b, and $a^2 - b^2$ are relatively prime in pairs, and each is, therefore, a perfect square. Let $a = m^2$, $b = n^2$, $a^2 - b^2 = k^2$. But $a + b$ and $a - b$ are also relatively prime; so let

$$a + b = m^2 + n^2 = u^2$$

and

$$a - b = m^2 - n^2 = v^2$$

As a result

$$2m^2 = u^2 + v^2$$

and

$$2n^2 = u^2 - v^2 = (u - v)(u + v)$$

Thus $(u, v) = 1$, and the last equation shows that $u - v$ and $u + v$ are even integers. Hence, n is even, and $2n^2 = 8q^2 = (u - v)(u + v)$. Therefore, one of the integers $\dfrac{u - v}{2}, \dfrac{u + v}{2}$ is even. Accordingly, let either

$$\frac{u - v}{2} = 2s^2 \qquad \text{and} \qquad \frac{u + v}{2} = t^2$$

or

$$\frac{u - v}{2} = t^2 \qquad \text{and} \qquad \frac{u + v}{2} = 2s^2$$

Then

$$2n^2 = 8s^2t^2$$

and

$$n^2 = 4s^2t^2$$

Furthermore, in the first case

$$u = 2s^2 + t^2 \qquad \text{and} \qquad v = t^2 - 2s^2$$

and in the second

$$u = 2s^2 + t^2 \qquad \text{and} \qquad v = 2s^2 - t^2$$

But $m^2 = v^2 + n^2 = t^4 - 4s^2t^2 + 4s^4 + 4s^2t^2 = (t^2)^2 + (2s^2)^2$. Thus m is the hypotenuse of a right triangle in which t^2 and $2s^2$ are the arms. But

[*] Dickson, *op. cit.*, Vol. 2, p. 615.

notice that since $z = a^2 + b^2$ and $a = m^2$, it follows that $z > a > m$, so that the hypotenuse of the new triangle is smaller than that of the original. Moreover, the area A_1 of the new triangle is the integer $s^2t^2 = (u^2 - v^2)/8$, and the area of the original triangle is

$$A = ab(a^2 - b^2) = \left(\frac{u^2 + v^2}{2}\right)\left(\frac{u^2 - v^2}{2}\right)(u^2v^2)$$

But

$$\frac{(u^2 + v^2)(u^2 - v^2)}{4}(u^2v^2) > \frac{u^2 - v^2}{8}, \text{ for } \quad (u^2 + v^2)u^2v^2 > 1$$

The assumption of the existence of a triangle whose sides are integers and whose area is a perfect square has led to the conclusion that a triangle having these properties but of smaller area and shorter hypotenuse must also exist. Thus there would always be a smaller triangle of this kind, and that is impossible. We must conclude that such a triangle cannot exist.

On the basis of the last theorem it is easy to show that the following statement is true:

Theorem 10-7. There are no integers that satisfy the set of equations $x^2 + y^2 = z^2$, $x^2 - y^2 = w^2$.

If both $p^2 + q^2 = m^2$ and $p^2 - q^2 = n^2$, consider the right triangle whose sides are $2p^2q^2$, $p^4 - q^4$, and $p^4 + q^4$. Hence, the area is

$$p^2q^2(p^4 - q^4) = p^2q^2m^2n^2$$

But we have shown that if the sides are integers, the area cannot be a perfect square. Consequently, there is no solution in integers of the given set of equations.

10-5. The Generalized Wilson Theorem

Theorem 10-8. The product of the positive integers less than m and prime to m is congruent to -1 modulo m if $m = 4$, p^n, or $2p^n$ with p an odd prime, but the product is congruent to $+1$ modulo m for all other moduli.

If $m = 4$, the product $1 \cdot 3 \equiv -1 \pmod 4$.

If $m = p^n$, let t be a quadratic nonresidue of the odd prime p, and let a_i, where $i = 1, 2, \ldots, \phi(p^n)$, be the least positive integers forming a reduced residue system modulo p^n. Then, for each a_i, the congruence $a_ix \equiv t \pmod{p^n}$ has a solution $x \equiv a_j \pmod{p^n}$ from the set of the a_i, and each integer a_i is thus paired with an a_j distinct from the a_i modulo p^n, for $a_i^2 \not\equiv t \pmod p$. The integers a_i are, therefore, separated into $\phi(p^n)/2$ pairs, and if P is the product of these pairs,

$$P \equiv t^{\phi(p^n)/2} \pmod{p^n}$$

But $t^{(p-1)/2} \equiv -1 (\mathrm{mod}\ p)$, and hence

and

$$(t^{(p-1)/2})^{p^{n-1}} = (-1 + kp)^{p^{n-1}}$$

$$t^{p^{n-1}(p-1)/2} = -1 + Mp^n$$

Therefore,

$$t^{\phi(p^n)/2} \equiv -1 (\mathrm{mod}\ p^n)$$

and

$$P \equiv -1 (\mathrm{mod}\ p^n)$$

If $m = 2p^n$, let s be a quadratic nonresidue modulo p, and let t satisfy both of the congruences

$$x \equiv s (\mathrm{mod}\ p)$$
$$x \equiv 1 (\mathrm{mod}\ 2)$$

Therefore, t is an odd quadratic nonresidue of $2p^n$, for if $x^2 \equiv t (\mathrm{mod}\ 2p^n)$ had a solution, then $t \equiv s (\mathrm{mod}\ p)$ would be a quadratic residue of p. The congruences $a_i x \equiv t (\mathrm{mod}\ 2p^n)$ now pair the positive integers a_i, where $i = 1, 2, \ldots, \phi(2p^n)$, that are less than $2p^n$ and prime to $2p^n$. If P represents the product of these pairs, we find that

$$P \equiv t^{\phi(2p^n)/2} (\mathrm{mod}\ 2p^n)$$

But $t^{(p-1)/2} \equiv -1 (\mathrm{mod}\ p)$, and thus $t^{\phi(p^n)/2} \equiv -1 (\mathrm{mod}\ p^n)$. However, t is odd, and $\phi(2p^n) = \phi(p^n)$. Therefore, $P \equiv -1 (\mathrm{mod}\ 2p^n)$.

If $m = 2^u$, where $u > 2$, then -1 is a quadratic nonresidue of 2^u. Hence, the congruences $a_i x \equiv -1 (\mathrm{mod}\ 2^u)$, where the a_i range through the positive integers less than 2^u and prime to 2, separate these integers into 2^{u-2} pairs. In this case, therefore, if P again represents the product of these pairs, $P \equiv (-1)^{2^{u-2}} \equiv +1 (\mathrm{mod}\ 2^u)$.

When $m = 2$, moreover, the above congruence is obviously true.

Finally, suppose that m contains at least two distinct odd primes as factors or at least one odd prime and the factor 2^u with $u > 1$. Let $m = 2^u p_1{}^{n_1} p_2{}^{n_2} \cdots p_r{}^{n_r}$. Let s be a quadratic nonresidue modulo p_1, and let t satisfy both the congruences

$$x \equiv s (\mathrm{mod}\ p_1)$$
$$x \equiv 1 (\mathrm{mod}\ 2p_2 p_3 \cdots p_r)$$

Then t is a quadratic nonresidue of m. Again, if the a_i, where $i = 1, 2, \ldots, \phi(m)$, are the positive integers less than m and prime to m, then the congruences $a_i x \equiv t (\mathrm{mod}\ m)$ pair the a_i and, as before, the product P of the a_i is such that

$$P \equiv t^{\phi(m)/2} (\mathrm{mod}\ m)$$

But $t^{(p_1-1)/2} \equiv -1 (\mathrm{mod}\ p_1)$, and $t^{\phi(p_1{}^{n_1})/2} \equiv -1 (\mathrm{mod}\ p_1{}^{n_1})$. However, since $\phi(p_i{}^{n_i})$ is even and $\phi(m) = \phi(p_1{}^{n_1}) \phi(p_2{}^{n_2}) \cdots \phi(p_r{}^{n_r})$,

$$t^{\phi(m)/2} \equiv +1 (\mathrm{mod}\ p_1{}^{n_1})$$

Moreover, $t = 1 + 2p_2p_3 \cdots p_rk$, so that $t^{\phi(m)/2} = (1 + 2p_2p_3 \cdots p_rk)^{\phi(m)/2}$, and $t^{\phi(m)/2} \equiv +1 \pmod{p_2^{n_2}p_3^{n_3} \cdots p_r^{n_r}}$. Furthermore, $t^{2^{u-1}} \equiv +1 \pmod{2^u}$, and thus $t^{\phi(m)/2} \equiv +1 \pmod{2^u}$. Therefore, $t^{\phi(m)/2} \equiv +1 \pmod{m}$, and $P \equiv +1 \pmod{m}$.

10-6. The Pellian Equation. The equation $x^2 - by^2 = 1$, in which b is a positive integer that is not a square, is known as the Pellian equation, but it should really be called Fermat's equation, for it was he who proposed the problem of finding its integral solutions. As a matter of fact the problem is a very old one, having been solved in the Middle Ages by the Hindus. We have but an outline of Fermat's proof showing that the equation is satisfied by an infinite number of pairs of integers all of which can be obtained from a particular pair, but a proof was also found conjointly by Wallis and Lord Brouncker and was published in 1658. Both Euler and Lagrange contributed to the further development of the problem. The following argument is based upon that devised by Dirichlet:

Lemma 10-1c. If α is any real, irrational number and $m > 0$ is an integer, then there exist integers r and s such that $0 < |r - s\alpha| < 1/m$ and $0 < s \leq m$.

Let x have the values $0, 1, 2, \ldots, m$, and determine corresponding integral values of y so that $0 < y - x\alpha \leq 1$ by taking $y = [x\alpha] + 1$. There are, then, $m + 1$ values of $y - x\alpha$ that lie in the interval from 0 to 1, excluding 0 but including 1. Separate this interval into m equal parts, the first one extending from, but not including, 0 up to and including $1/m$; the second, extending from, but not including, $1/m$ up to and including $2/m$; .... At least two of the $m + 1$ values determined for $y - x\alpha$ lie in one of these m intervals. Suppose that these values are $y_1 - x_1\alpha$ and $y_2 - x_2\alpha$ with $x_2 > x_1$. Then

$$|(y_2 - x_2\alpha) - (y_1 - x_1\alpha)| < \frac{1}{m}$$

or

$$|(y_2 - y_1) - (x_2 - x_1)\alpha| < \frac{1}{m}$$

But the difference cannot be 0, for $x_1 \neq x_2$. Hence, if $r = y_2 - y_1$ and $s = x_2 - x_1$, we conclude that

$$0 < |r - s\alpha| < \frac{1}{m} \quad \text{and} \quad 0 < s \leq m$$

Lemma 10-2c. If b is a positive integer that is not a square, there is an infinite number of pairs of integers r and s with $s > 0$ that satisfy the inequality $0 < |r^2 - s^2b| < 1 + 2\sqrt{b}$.

Lemma 10-1c shows that when m is a positive integer, integers r_1 and s_1 exist such that

$$0 < |r_1 - s_1 \sqrt{b}| < \frac{1}{m} \qquad 0 < s_1 \leq m$$

Now choose a positive integer m_1 sufficiently large so that

$$\frac{1}{m_1} < |r_1 - s_1 \sqrt{b}|$$

Then r_2 and s_2 can be determined so that

$$0 < |r_2 - s_2 \sqrt{b}| < \frac{1}{m_1} \qquad 0 < s_2 \leq m_1$$

Hence,

$$|r_2 - s_2 \sqrt{b}| < |r_1 - s_1 \sqrt{b}| < \frac{1}{m}$$

By continuing to choose m_i sufficiently large, we obtain

$$\frac{1}{m_i} < |r_i - s_i \sqrt{b}|$$

for $i = 1, 2, 3, \ldots$. This means we can find integers r_{i+1}, s_{i+1} that give

$$0 < |r_{i+1} - s_{i+1} \sqrt{b}| < \frac{1}{m_i} \qquad 0 < s_{i+1} \leq m_i$$

Thus

$$|r_{i+1} - s_{i+1} \sqrt{b}| < |r_i - s_i \sqrt{b}|$$

and in this way we can set up an infinite number of pairs of integers r_i, s_i satisfying the above condition.

But for any pair r_i, s_i,

$$0 < |r_i - s_i \sqrt{b}| < \frac{1}{m_{i-1}} \leq \frac{1}{s_i}$$

Hence,

$$0 < |r_i + s_i \sqrt{b}| < \frac{1}{s_i} + 2s_i \sqrt{b}$$

and

$$0 < |r_i{}^2 - s_i{}^2 b| < \frac{1}{s_i{}^2} + 2 \sqrt{b} \leq 1 + 2 \sqrt{b}$$

Therefore, there are infinitely many pairs of integral values of r and s with $s > 0$, such that $|r^2 - s^2 b|$ lies between 0 and $1 + 2 \sqrt{b}$.

Lemma 10-3c. If b is a positive integer that is not a square, there exists an integer $k \neq 0$ such that the equation $x^2 - by^2 = k$ is satisfied by an infinite number of pairs of integers x and y.

We have seen in lemma 10-2c that an infinite number of pairs of integers r, s give integral values for $|r^2 - s^2 b|$ that lie between 0 and $1 + 2\sqrt{b}$. Since b is not a square, $r^2 - s^2 b \neq 0$, and thus the expression can have at most $2[1 + 2\sqrt{b}]$ values so determined. Consequently, at least one of these integral values, $k \neq 0$, is determined by an infinite number of the pairs of integers r, s, and these are the values of x, y that satisfy $x^2 - by^2 = k$.

Theorem 10-9. If b is a positive integer that is not a perfect square, the equation $x^2 - by^2 = 1$ has a solution distinct from $x = \pm 1$, $y = 0$.

Select $k \neq 0$ so that the equation $x^2 - by^2 = k$ is satisfied by an infinite number of pairs of values of x, y. Now separate the values of x, and in like manner of y, into the $|k|$ residue classes modulo k. There are, therefore, k^2 pairs of classes modulo k into which the solutions x, y can fit. Having excluded the finite number of solutions with either x or y zero, we recognize that the equation shows that for any solution in which either or both x and y are negative there is one in which both are positive. Hence, there is an infinite number of solutions having both x and y positive. Accordingly, if these positive solutions are distributed among the k^2 pairs of residue classes modulo k, at least one of these pairs of classes must contain at least two of these solutions. Consequently, two pairs x_1, y_1 and x_2, y_2 can be so selected that

$$x_1 \equiv x_2 (\text{mod } k) \qquad x_1 \neq x_2 \qquad x_1, x_2 > 0$$
$$y_1 \equiv y_2 (\text{mod } k) \qquad y_1 \neq y_2 \qquad y_1, y_2 > 0$$
$$x_1{}^2 - by_1{}^2 = k$$
$$x_2{}^2 - by_2{}^2 = k$$

Now consider the quotient

$$\frac{x_1 - y_1\sqrt{b}}{x_2 - y_2\sqrt{b}} = \frac{x_1x_2 - y_1y_2 b + (x_1y_2 - x_2y_1)\sqrt{b}}{x_2{}^2 - y_2{}^2 b}$$

From the above congruences

$$x_1x_2 - y_1y_2 b \equiv x_1{}^2 - by_1{}^2 \equiv 0 (\text{mod } k)$$

and

$$x_1y_2 - x_2y_1 \equiv x_1y_1 - x_1y_1 \equiv 0 (\text{mod } k)$$

Therefore, let

$$\frac{x_1x_2 - y_1y_2 b}{k} = u \qquad \text{and} \qquad \frac{x_1y_2 - x_2y_1}{k} = v$$

and thus

$$x_1 - y_1\sqrt{b} = (u + v\sqrt{b})(x_2 - y_2\sqrt{b})$$

Likewise,

$$x_1 + y_1\sqrt{b} = (u - v\sqrt{b})(x_2 + y_2\sqrt{b})$$

Hence,
$$x_1^2 - by_1^2 = (u^2 - bv^2)(x_2^2 - by_2^2)$$
or
$$k = k(u^2 - v^2 b)$$
so that
$$u^2 - bv^2 = 1$$

and the integers u and v satisfy the equation $x^2 - by^2 = 1$.

If $v = 0$, then $u = \pm 1$ and then $x_1 - y_1 \sqrt{b} = \pm(x_2 - y_2 \sqrt{b})$. Thus $x_1 = \pm x_2$, $y_1 = \pm y_2$. But since x_1, x_2, y_1, y_2 are positive, $x_1 = x_2$ and $y_1 = y_2$, whereas we chose x_1, y_1 and x_2, y_2 as distinct solutions of $x^2 - by^2 = k$. We have, therefore, found a solution $x = u$, $y = v$ of the equation $x^2 - by^2 = 1$ that is distinct from the solutions $x = \pm 1$, $y = 0$.

Theorem 10-10. If b is a positive integer that is not a square and if x_1, y_1 is the solution of $x^2 - by^2 = 1$ for which x_1 and y_1 are positive and $x_1 + y_1 \sqrt{b}$ has the least positive value, then any solution x, y of the equation is determined by the formula $x + y \sqrt{b} = \pm(x_1 + y_1 \sqrt{b})^n$ for $n = 0$, ± 1, ± 2, ...

Since $x^2 - by^2 = 1$ has a solution in which $y \neq 0$, there must be one, x_1, y_1, with x_1 and y_1 positive integers, for which $x_1 + y_1 \sqrt{b}$ is a minimum. Then $x_1^2 - by_1^2 = 1$, and if $x_2^2 - by_2^2 = 1$, let
$$(x_1 - y_1 \sqrt{b})(x_2 - y_2 \sqrt{b}) = x_3 - y_3 \sqrt{b}$$
and also
$$(x_1 + y_1 \sqrt{b})(x_2 + y_2 \sqrt{b}) = x_3 + y_3 \sqrt{b}$$

Consequently, $x_3^2 - by_3^2 = 1$, and the pair of integers x_3, y_3 so determined is a solution of the given equation. It follows, by induction, that $(x_1 + y_1 \sqrt{b})^n$ determines a solution of $x^2 - by^2 = 1$ for each positive integral n.

Moreover,
$$\frac{1}{(x_1 + y_1 \sqrt{b})^n} = (x_1 - y_1 \sqrt{b})^n$$

and if x_1, y_1, is a solution of the given equation, then x_4, y_4 determined by $x_4 - y_4 \sqrt{b} = (x_1 - y_1 \sqrt{b})^n$, for $n = 1, 2, . . .$, is also a solution of $x^2 - by^2 = 1$.

Again, if $n = 0$, we find $(x_1 + y_1 \sqrt{b})^n = (x_1 - y_1 \sqrt{b})^n = 1$ and $x = \pm 1$, $y = 0$.

Furthermore, when x, y is a solution, x, $-y$ and $-x$, y, as well as $-x$, $-y$, are solutions. Consequently, for $n = 0$, ± 1, ± 2, . . . , all pairs of integers x, y determined by $x + y \sqrt{b} = \pm(x_1 + y_1 \sqrt{b})^n$ are solutions of $x^2 - by^2 = 1$.

But the pairs of integers x, y determined by the formula constitute all the solutions of $x^2 - by^2 = 1$, for if X, Y with both X and Y positive is any solution that cannot be developed by the formula, then $X + Y \sqrt{b}$ lies between two consecutive powers of the positive number $x_1 + y_1 \sqrt{b}$; that is,

$$(x_1 + y_1 \sqrt{b})^n < X + Y \sqrt{b} < (x_1 + y_1 \sqrt{b})^{n+1}$$

By multiplying each member of this statement by $(x_1 - y_1 \sqrt{b})^n$ and using the fact that $x_1{}^2 - y_1{}^2 b = 1$, we see that

$$1 < (X + Y \sqrt{b})(x_1 - y_1 \sqrt{b})^n < x_1 + y_1 \sqrt{b}$$

But if we let

$$(X + Y \sqrt{b})(x_1 - y_1 \sqrt{b})^n = x' + y' \sqrt{b}$$

necessarily giving

$$(X - Y \sqrt{b})(x_1 + y_1 \sqrt{b})^n = x' - y' \sqrt{b}$$

then $x'^2 - by'^2 = 1$ and

$$1 < x' + y' \sqrt{b} < x_1 + y_1 \sqrt{b} \tag{4}$$

But $x' - y' \sqrt{b} = (x' + y' \sqrt{b})^{-1}$, and therefore

$$0 < x' - y' \sqrt{b} < 1 \tag{5}$$

Adding (4) and (5) shows that $x' > 0$, and subtracting (5) from (4) gives $0 < 2y' \sqrt{b}$, which implies that $y' > 0$. Under these circumstances, however, it is impossible that $x' + y' \sqrt{b}$ be less than $x_1 + y_1 \sqrt{b}$, for $x_1 + y_1 \sqrt{b}$ was chosen as the smallest of these numbers. Therefore, $X + Y \sqrt{b} = (x_1 + y_1 \sqrt{b})^n$. Since to each solution, not $x = \pm 1$, $y = 0$, of $x^2 - by^2 = 1$ in which one or both the integers x and y are negative must correspond a solution in which both are positive, we conclude that all values of x and y that satisfy the equation can be obtained from the formula $x + y \sqrt{b} = \pm(x_1 + y_1 \sqrt{b})^n$.

EXERCISES

1. Show that all solutions of $x^2 - 2y^2 = 1$ can be developed from $x = 3$, $y = 2$.

2. Can you discover a method for developing solutions of both $x^2 - 2y^2 = 1$ and $x^2 - 2y^2 = -1$ from $x = 1$, $y = 1$?

3. Show that the formula for developing all solutions of $x^2 - 3y^2 = 1$ is $x + y\sqrt{3} = \pm(2 + \sqrt{3})^n$.

CHAPTER 11

POLYNOMIALS

11-1. Integral Domains and Fields. Let us recall that the set of rational integers has certain salient properties with respect to the operation of addition which can be summarized in the following manner:

1. The sum of two elements in a certain order is a unique element of the set.
2. Addition is commutative.
3. Addition is associative.
4. Each element has an inverse with respect to addition.

It follows then that there is an element 0 such that $a + 0 = a$ for any a.

There is a second law of combination for the set of rational integers which we called multiplication, and it has the following properties.

1. Multiplication is unique, and the product is in the set.
2. Multiplication is commutative.
3. Multiplication is associative.
4. Multiplication is distributive with respect to addition.
5. There is an element 1, called the *unity element*, or *unity*, such that $a \cdot 1 = a$ for any a.
6. The elements obey the cancellation law, so that if $ab = ac$ and $a \neq 0$, then $b = c$.

Any set of elements that fulfills these 10 conditions is said to be an *integral domain*.

When the set has at least two elements and in addition to the above properties each element of the set except zero has an inverse with respect to multiplication, the set is called a *field*. Thus, in a field, $ax = 1$ with $a \neq 0$ can be solved for x, and the value is unique. Hence, division by $a \neq 0$ is possible, for if $ax_0 = 1$, then $a(bx_0) = b$ and a divides b. The rational integers fail to form a field, for division of an integer b by $a \neq 0$ is not always possible, but the set of the rational numbers (ratios a/b of two rational integers with $b \neq 0$) is a field. The real numbers as well as the complex numbers also form fields.

Now consider the set of all polynomials $f(x) = a_0x^n + a_1x^{n-1} + \cdots + a_n$, where the coefficients a_i, with $i = 0, 1, \ldots, n$, are selected from a field. This set includes the field of the coefficients itself, and consequently it contains the numbers 0 and 1, which are called the *identity elements* with respect to addition and multiplication, respectively. Constants not 0 are polynomials of degree zero, whereas 0 is said to have no degree. The laws of elementary algebra show very easily that this set of polynomials $f(x)$ has the first nine characteristics enumerated above, but we must clear up another idea before showing that the cancellation law also holds.

Two polynomials in x are said to be *identically equal* if and only if they have equal values for all values of the variable x. But a polynomial in x of the nth degree with $n > 0$ is not reduced to zero by more than n values of x, and therefore $f(x)$ *vanishes identically* if and only if all of its coefficients are zero. If, then, the product of two polynomials with coefficients in a field F is identically zero, at least one factor must vanish identically, for otherwise the product would be a polynomial of at least degree zero and could not vanish identically. In short, there are no divisors of zero in the domain of these polynomials, and that is equivalent to saying that the cancellation law is observed. The polynomials with coefficients in a field F, therefore, form an integral domain.

After recalling the early definitions and theorems that pertain to the elements of the integral domain of the rational integers, it is easy to set up the following analogous definitions and theorems concerning the elements of the domain of the polynomials $f(x)$ with coefficients in a field F:

If two polynomials $f(x)$ and $g(x)$ have coefficients in a field F, $f(x)$ is said to *divide* $g(x)$ if there is a polynomial $q(x)$ with coefficients in F such that $g(x) = f(x)q(x)$ identically. Then $f(x)$ is a *factor* of $g(x)$ and $q(x)$ is the *quotient* of $g(x)$ by $f(x)$. Furthermore, if $g(x) \not\equiv 0$, the degree of $f(x)$ is at most that of $g(x)$.

A polynomial that divides only itself is a *null polynomial*.

A polynomial that divides every polynomial with coefficients in F is a *unit polynomial*, or a *unit*.

Theorem 11-1. If $g(x) = f(x)q(x)$, where $f(x) \not\equiv 0$ and the polynomials have coefficients in a field F, the quotient $q(x)$ is unique.

If

$$g(x) = f(x)q_1(x) = f(x)q_2(x)$$

then

$$f(x)[q_1(x) - q_2(x)] \equiv 0$$

Hence,

$$q_1(x) - q_2(x) \equiv 0 \quad \text{and} \quad q_1(x) \equiv q_2(x)$$

Theorem 11-2. Zero is the null polynomial of the set of polynomials $f(x)$ with coefficients in F.

The equation $0 \cdot f(x) = 0$ shows that the quotient of zero by zero exists but is indeterminate. It also shows that zero divides only itself. Furthermore, every polynomial $f(x)$ divides zero, so that there can be but one null polynomial.

Theorem 11-3. All the elements except zero of a field F are unit polynomials of the set of polynomials with coefficients in F.

It is evident that a constant not zero of F divides every polynomial whose coefficients are in this field. But a polynomial of degree $n > 0$ cannot divide any constant except zero.

A polynomial with coefficients in a field F whose leading coefficient is unity is a *monic polynomial*.

The *associates* of a polynomial with coefficients in a field F are the products of that polynomial by the unit polynomials of the set of polynomials.

A polynomial with coefficients in F that is not a unit and that is divisible only by its associates and the units is a *prime polynomial*.

A polynomial with coefficients in F that is not zero, a unit, or a prime polynomial is a *composite polynomial*.

A *common divisor* of two or more polynomials with coefficients in F is a polynomial of the set that divides each of the given polynomials.

A *greatest common divisor* of two or more polynomials, not all zero, with coefficients in F is a common divisor that is divisible by every common divisor of the given polynomials. When the coefficients of the given polynomials are in a field F, the monic polynomial that is an associate of a greatest common divisor is called *the greatest common divisor* of the set.

If the greatest common divisor of two or more polynomials with coefficients in a field F is 1, the polynomials are *relatively prime*.

Theorem 11-4. If $f(x) \not\equiv 0$ and $g(x)$ are polynomials with coefficients in a field F, there exists a unique pair of polynomials $q(x)$ and $r(x)$ with coefficients in F that satisfy the identity $g(x) = f(x)q(x) + r(x)$ with either $r(x) \equiv 0$ or of lower degree than $f(x)$.

If $g(x) = a_0 x^n + a_1 x^{n-1} + \cdots + a_n$ is of lower degree than $f(x) = b_0 x^m + b_1 x^{m-1} + \cdots + b_m$, take $q(x) \equiv 0$ and $r(x) \equiv g(x)$ and the theorem is satisfied. Do likewise if $g(x) \equiv 0$.

If $g(x)$ is not of lower degree than $f(x)$, take $q_1(x) = kx^{n-m}$, where $a_0 = kb_0$. Then $r_1(x) = g(x) - kx^{n-m}f(x)$ is lower in degree than $g(x)$ and

$$g(x) = f(x)q_1(x) + r_1(x)$$

If $r_1(x) \equiv 0$ or if its degree is lower than that of $f(x)$, the existence of the pair of polynomials has been demonstrated, but if neither is the case, repeat the operation, using $f(x)$ and $r_1(x)$. Thus we obtain

$$r_1(x) = f(x)q_2(x) + r_2(x)$$

and

$$g(x) = f(x)[q_1(x) + q_2(x)] + r_2(x)$$

Again, if $r_2(x) \equiv 0$ or if its degree is lower than that of $f(x)$, the required polynomials are $q_1(x) + q_2(x)$ and $r_2(x)$, but if not, the process is repeated until after a finite number of steps we obtain

$$r_{s-1}(x) = f(x)q_s(x) + r_s(x)$$

Hence,

$$g(x) = f(x)[q_1(x) + q_2(x) + \cdots + q_s(x)] + r_s(x)$$

and either $r_s(x) \equiv 0$, or it is lower in degree than $f(x)$.

Now suppose that there are two pairs of polynomials that satisfy the stated conditions. Then

$$g(x) = f(x)q(x) + r(x) = f(x)Q(x) + R(x)$$

and

$$f(x)[q(x) - Q(x)] + r(x) - R(x) \equiv 0$$

Consequently, $q(x) \equiv Q(x)$, or the degree of the above expression would be at least that of $f(x)$. Accordingly, $r(x) \equiv R(x)$.

Theorem 11-5. The greatest common divisor $D(x)$ of two polynomials $f(x)$ and $g(x)$, not both zero, with coefficients in a field F exists and can be expressed in the form $D(x) = F(x)f(x) + G(x)g(x)$, where the polynomials $F(x)$ and $G(x)$ have coefficients in F.

Using Theorem 11-4 we apply the analogue of the Euclidean algorithm to the polynomials $f(x)$ and $g(x)$ of degrees m and n, respectively, with $0 < m \leq n$. Then

$$
\begin{aligned}
g(x) &= f(x)Q_1(x) + R_1(x) && R_1(x) \text{ is of degree } m_1 < m \\
f(x) &= R_1(x)Q_2(x) + R_2(x) && R_2(x) \text{ is of degree } m_2 < m_1 \\
R_1(x) &= R_2(x)Q_3(x) + R_3(x) && R_3(x) \text{ is of degree } m_3 < m_2
\end{aligned}
$$

$$\cdots \cdots \cdots \cdots \cdots \cdots \cdots \cdots \cdots \cdots \cdots \cdots \cdots$$

$$R_{t-1}(x) = R_t(x)Q_{t+1}(x) + R_{t+1}$$

We must finally arrive at a step in which R_{t+1} is a constant, for the polynomials $R_i(x)$, where $i = 1, 2, \ldots, t + 1$, decrease in degree. Then by making use of an argument that parallels that in the proof of the Euclidean algorithm, we see that $f(x)$ and $g(x)$ have a greatest common divisor $R_t(x)$ different from a constant if and only if $R_{t+1} \equiv 0$. It is also evident that a necessary and sufficient condition that $f(x)$ and $g(x)$ be relatively prime is that R_{t+1} be a constant different from zero.

If $R_1(x) \not\equiv 0$, solve for each $R_i(x)$ that is not zero, and substitute the expression in the succeeding equation of the algorithm. Thus when $R_{t+1} \equiv 0$, we find that

$$R_1(x) = g(x) - f(x)Q_1(x)$$
$$R_2(x) = [1 + Q_1(x)Q_2(x)]f(x) - Q_2(x)g(x)$$
$$R_3(x) = [1 + Q_2(x)Q_3(x)]g(x) - [Q_1(x)Q_2(x)Q_3(x) + Q_1(x) + Q_3(x)]f(x)$$

$$\cdots \cdots \cdots \cdots \cdots \cdots \cdots \cdots \cdots \cdots \cdots \cdots \cdots$$

$$R_t(x) = F_1(x)f(x) + G_1(x)g(x)$$

Hence if $f(x)$ and $g(x)$ are not relatively prime and if $R_t(x)$ is not a monic polynomial, by dividing through by its leading coefficient, we have

$$D(x) = F_3(x)f(x) + G_3(x)g(x)$$

However, if $f(x)$ and $g(x)$ are relatively prime, we find

$$R_{t+1} = F_2(x)f(x) + G_2(x)g(x)$$

and dividing by R_{t+1}, we obtain

$$1 = F(x)f(x) + G(x)g(x)$$

In the last case the term of highest degree of $F(x)$ comes from the product $Q_1(x)Q_2(x) \cdots Q_{t+1}(x)$. The degree of $Q_1(x)$ is $n - m$, of $Q_2(x)$ is $m - m_1$, and the degree of each $Q_j(x)$, where $j = 3, 4, \ldots,$ $t + 1$, is $m_{j-2} - m_{j-1}$. Therefore, when $m \geq 1$, the degree of their product is less than n, the degree of $g(x)$, for $n - m + (m - m_1) + (m_1 - m_2) + \cdots + (m_{t-1} - m_t) = n - m_t$. In like manner, when $m \geq 1$, the degree of $G(x)$ is determined by the degree of $Q_2(x)Q_3(x) \cdots$ $Q_{t+1}(x)$ and is less than m, the degree of $f(x)$.

In the special case where $R_1(x) \equiv 0$, $f(x)$ is a greatest common divisor, and then $f(x) = f(x) + 0 \cdot g(x)$, and the theorem holds.

Notice that although the method is applicable when the polynomial $f(x)$ is a constant not zero, the statement about the degrees of $F(x)$ and $G(x)$ does not hold. For example, if $g(x) = 4x + 3$ and $f(x) = 2$, we write $1 = 2 \cdot \frac{1}{2} + 0 \cdot (4x + 3)$. If $f(x) \equiv 0$, the result is obvious.

The following theorem is now evident:

Theorem 11-6.   The polynomials $f(x)$ and $g(x)$ with coefficients in a field F are relatively prime if and only if there exist polynomials $F(x)$ and $G(x)$ with coefficients in F such that $F(x)f(x) + G(x)g(x) = 1$.

Theorem 11-7.   The greatest common divisor of the polynomials $f(x)$ and $g(x)$ with coefficients in a field F is unique.

If $D_1(x)$ and $D_2(x)$ are two greatest common divisors of $f(x)$ and $g(x)$, then $D_1(x) \mid D_2(x)$ and the degree d_1 of $D_1(x)$ is less than or equal to the degree d_2 of $D_2(x)$. Also $D_2(x) \mid D_1(x)$, so that $d_2 \leq d_1$. Hence, $d_1 = d_2$. As a result $D_1(x)$ and $D_2(x)$ can differ only by a constant factor; that is, $D_1(x) = cD_2(x)$. But each one is a monic polynomial. Therefore, $c = 1$, and $D_1(x) = D_2(x)$.

Theorem 11-8.   If $f_1(x)$ and $f_2(x)$ are relatively prime polynomials with coefficients in a field F and if $f_1(x)$ divides the product $f_2(x)f_3(x)$, then $f_1(x)$ divides $f_3(x)$.

Since $(f_1(x), f_2(x)) = 1$,

$$f_1(x)F_1(x) + f_2(x)F_2(x) = 1$$

Then
$$f_1(x)f_3(x)F_1(x) + f_2(x)f_3(x)F_2(x) = f_3(x)$$

Applying the distributive law, it is evident that $f_1(x)$ divides $f_3(x)$.

   Theorem 11-9.   If $f(x)$ and $g(x)$ are relatively prime polynomials of at least the first degree with coefficients in a field F, there exists one and only one pair of polynomials $F(x)$ and $G(x)$ with coefficients in F satisfying the condition $F(x)f(x) + G(x)g(x) = 1$ and such that the degree of $F(x)$ is less than that of $g(x)$ and the degree of $G(x)$ is less than that of $f(x)$.

   That the required polynomials $F(x)$ and $G(x)$ exist has been proved in Theorem 11-5, but if there is a second pair $F_1(x)$ and $G_1(x)$ of such polynomials, then

$$F(x)f(x) + G(x)g(x) = F_1(x)f(x) + G_1(x)g(x)$$

Hence,

$$f(x)[F(x) - F_1(x)] = g(x)[G_1(x) - G(x)]$$

But since $f(x)$ and $g(x)$ are relatively prime, $g(x)$ divides $F(x) - F_1(x)$. Unless $F(x) \equiv F_1(x)$, this division would be impossible, for the degree of $F(x) - F_1(x)$ is less than that of $g(x)$.   It is then obvious that $G(x) \equiv G_1(x)$.

   It is important to observe the conditions set by the last theorem.   We admit that when the given polynomials are the constants a and b, there are infinitely many solutions of $ax + by = 1$.   But it is to be noticed that Theorem 11-9 requires $f(x)$ and $g(x)$ to be of at least the first degree and places a restriction on the degree of both $F(x)$ and $G(x)$.   If the second condition is removed, we can find many pairs of polynomials $F(x)$ and $G(x)$ that will satisfy the equation $F(x)f(x) + G(x)g(x) = 1$, for if $F(x)$ and $G(x)$ do, then all pairs of the form $F(x) + k(x)g(x)$ and $G(x) - k(x)f(x)$ will also.   Are there any others?   When one of the given polynomials is a constant, the results should now be obvious.

   On the other hand when the greatest common divisor of the given polynomials is not 1, even so simple a case as expressing the greatest common divisor of $x^2 - 4x + 3$ and $2x - 6$ shows the lack of unicity in the pair of polynomials $F(x)$ and $G(x)$ having the restriction on degree stated in Theorem 11-9, for

$$(x^2 - 4x + 3)(+1) + (2x - 6)\left(-\frac{x}{2} + 1\right) = x - 3$$

and

$$(x^2 - 4x + 3)(-1) + (2x - 6)\left(\frac{x}{2}\right) = x - 3$$

   When the field F containing the coefficients of $f(x)$ is the set of complex numbers, on the basis of the fundamental theorem of algebra, we know that, except for the order of the factors, $f(x)$ can be factored into linear factors, each with leading coefficient unity and absolute term in F, and a constant factor, in exactly one way. Hence, the identity

$$f(x) = a_0 x^n + a_1 x^{n-1} + \cdots + a_n = a_0(x - r_1)(x - r_2) \cdots (x - r_n)$$

where the r_i, with $i = 1, 2, \ldots, n$, are in F, expresses this unique factorization of $f(x)$. The reader realizes, however, that such a factorization of $f(x)$ does not exist in all fields. In the field of the real numbers $x^2 + 1$ cannot be so factored, but in the field of the complex numbers $x^2 + 1 = (x - i)(x + i)$. Although $x^2 - 2 = (x - \sqrt{2})(x + \sqrt{2})$ in the field of the real numbers, it cannot be factored into linear factors in the field of the rational numbers.

If a polynomial $f(x)$ of degree n with coefficients in a domain F cannot be factored into two polynomials of at least the first degree with coefficients in F, then $f(x)$ is said to be *irreducible in* F. Otherwise $f(x)$ is *reducible in* F. Thus $x^3 - 5$ is irreducible in the integral domain of the rational integers and also in the field of the rational numbers, but it is reducible in the field of the real numbers.

The field of the rational numbers is the smallest infinite field that contains the rational integers, and so we shall consider a few important characteristics of polynomials with coefficients in this field. We are especially concerned with being able to classify the coefficients of the factors of an integral polynomial.

A *primitive* polynomial is an integral polynomial whose coefficients are relatively prime.

The *primary associate* of an integral polynomial is that associate of the polynomial whose coefficients are relatively prime integers and whose leading coefficient is positive.

Theorem 11-10. If $f_1(x)$ and $f_2(x)$ are integral polynomials, a necessary and sufficient condition that their product be a primitive polynomial is that both $f_1(x)$ and $f_2(x)$ be primitive polynomials.

Suppose that

$$f_1(x) = a_0 x^n + a_1 x^{n-1} + \cdots + a_n$$

and

$$f_2(x) = b_0 x^m + b_1 x^{m-1} + \cdots + b_m$$

with $n \geq m$, have integral coefficients that are relatively prime. Their product necessarily has integral coefficients, but suppose that a prime p divides each of these coefficients. Then there is a first a_i, say a_r, and a first b_j, say b_s, that is not divisible by p. Now consider the coefficient of $x^{n+m-r-s}$, which is

$$a_{r+s}b_0 + \cdots + a_{r+1}b_{s-1} + a_r b_s + a_{r-1}b_{s+1} + \cdots + a_{r+s-m}b_m$$

Each term except $a_r b_s$ of this expression is divisible by p, and thus it is impossible that all the coefficients of the product be divisible by p. Hence, the product is a primitive polynomial.

On the other hand, if $f_1(x) = pg(x)$, where $g(x)$ is an integral polynomial and p is a prime, then $f_1(x)f_2(x) = p[g(x)f_2(x)]$ and the product is not primitive.

Theorem 11-11. If $f(x)$ is a polynomial with integral coefficients and leading coefficient unity, $f(x)$ is factorable into the product of two monic polynomials in the field of the rational numbers if and only if it is factorable in the domain of the rational integers.

Let $f(x) = f_1(x)f_2(x)$, where $f_1(x)$ and $f_2(x)$ are monic polynomials with rational coefficients, and suppose that not all the coefficients of the factors are integers. Reduce all fractional coefficients to their lowest terms, and let d_1 and d_2 be the least common multiples of the denominators of the coefficients of $f_1(x)$ and $f_2(x)$, respectively. Then the coefficients of both $g(x) = d_1 f_1(x)$ and $h(x) = d_2 f_2(x)$ are relatively prime integers. Consequently, the product $g(x)h(x) = d_1 d_2 f_1(x)f_2(x)$ is a primitive polynomial. But then $f(x) = f_1(x)f_2(x) = g(x)h(x)/d_1 d_2$ cannot have integral coefficients unless $d_1 d_2 = 1$. In short, the coefficients of both $f_1(x)$ and $f_2(x)$ are integers.

If $f(x)$ is factorable in the domain of the integers, it is, of course, factorable rationally and so the converse is obvious.

Theorem 11-12. If a polynomial $f(x)$ with coefficients in the field R of the rational numbers is irreducible in R, and if $f(x)$ divides the product of the polynomials $g(x)$ and $h(x)$ with coefficients in R, then $f(x)$ divides at least one of $g(x)$ and $h(x)$.

Because $f(x)$ is irreducible in R, the greatest common divisor of $f(x)$ and $g(x)$ either is the monic polynomial that is an associate of $f(x)$, or is 1. In the first case $f(x) \mid g(x)$. In the second, we have shown that $f(x) \mid h(x)$.

Theorem 11-13. Any polynomial of at least the first degree with rational coefficients can be resolved into a product of a rational constant and one or more monic irreducible polynomials of at least the first degree with coefficients that are rational. Except for the order of the factors this factorization is unique.

If $f(x)$ is either of the first degree or of higher degree and irreducible in the field R of the rational numbers, then $f(x) = cg(x)$, where $g(x)$ is a monic polynomial, and c is a rational number.

If $f(x)$ is reducible in R, let $f(x) = f_1(x)f_2(x)$. Each of the new polynomials is of lower degree than $f(x)$. Either $f_1(x)$ is irreducible in R, or it has a factor $f_3(x)$ which is lower in degree than $f_1(x)$ and is in turn a factor of $f(x)$. Continuing in this manner, we observe that the degree of each factor is lower than that of its predecessor and so the process must end; that is, there must be an irreducible factor, say $p(x)$, of $f(x)$. Then

$f(x) = p(x)q(x)$. We now operate on $q(x)$ in the same way and after a finite number of steps determine that

$$f(x) = cp_1(x)p_2(x) \cdots p_r(x)$$

where c is a constant and the $p_j(x)$ are monic irreducible polynomials.

Suppose that there are two such factorizations of $f(x)$. Then

$$cp_1(x)p_2(x) \cdots p_r(x) = kq_1(x)q_2(x) \cdots q_s(x)$$

Clearly, $c = k$, for the other factors are monic polynomials. Moreover, $p_1(x)$ divides the product of the $q_i(x)$, where $i = 1, 2, \ldots, s$. Hence, $p_1(x)$ divides one of the $q_i(x)$, say $q_1(x)$. But $q_1(x)$ is irreducible in R. Thus $q_1(x) = tp_1(x)$, and since each is monic, $q_1(x) = p_1(x)$. Canceling the identical factors and repeating the argument, supposing that $s > r$, we have

$$1 = q_{r+1}(x) \cdots q_s(x)$$

Consequently, each of these factors is 1, and the original factorization is unique.

Theorem 11-14. If $f_1(x)$ and $f_2(x)$ are integral polynomials, not both zero, we can choose a greatest common divisor of them so that it is an integral polynomial.

Since the coefficients of $f_1(x)$ and $f_2(x)$ are rational, their greatest common divisor $D(x)$ exists and can be written

$$D(x) = f_1(x)F_1(x) + f_2(x)F_2(x)$$

Let d, g, and h be the least common multiples of the denominators of the coefficients of $D(x)$, $F_1(x)$, and $F_2(x)$, respectively. Let $D(x) = d(x)/d$, $F_1(x) = g(x)/g$, and $F_2(x) = h(x)/h$. Then

$$\frac{d(x)}{d} = f_1(x)\frac{g(x)}{g} + f_2(x)\frac{h(x)}{h}$$

Multiply both members of this equation by the least common multiple of d, g, and h. Thus

$$k_1d(x) = f_1(x)[k_2g(x)] + f_2(x)[k_3h(x)]$$

where $k_1d(x)$ is an associate of the monic polynomial $D(x)$ and has integral coefficients.

Very often we use the primary associate of $k_1d(x)$ in place of the greatest common divisor of $f_1(x)$ and $f_2(x)$ even though we may not be able to write it in the above form with $k_2g(x)$ and $k_3h(x)$ integral polynomials.

Example. The greatest common divisor $x - \frac{2}{3}$ of $3x^3 - 2x^2 - 3x + 2$ and $3x^2 - 8x + 4$ can be expressed in the form

$$x - \tfrac{2}{3} = \tfrac{1}{9}(3x^3 - 2x^2 - 3x + 2) - \tfrac{1}{9}(x + 2)(3x^2 - 8x + 4)$$

Its associate $9x - 6$ can be written

$$9x - 6 = (3x^3 - 2x^2 - 3x + 2) - (3x^2 - 8x + 4)(x + 2)$$

Instead of $9x - 6$, however, we may prefer to use its primary associate $3x - 2$.

EXERCISES

1. Can the primary associate of the greatest common divisor of $2x^2 - x - 3$ and $2x^2 - 5x + 3$ be expressed in the form developed in Theorem 11-14 that uses integral polynomials?

2. Find the greatest common divisor of $6x^3 + 13x^2 + 4x - 3$ and $2x^3 + 9x^2 + 13x + 6$, and express it in terms of the given polynomials. Write its primary associate.

3. Do the rational integers modulo p, a prime, form a field?

4. A number r is said to be an algebraic integer if it satisfies a rational integral equation $x^n + a_1 x^{n-1} + \cdots + a_n = 0$, where the coefficients a_i, for $i = 1, 2, \ldots, n$, are rational integers. If a is a rational integer, apply this definition to the roots of the equation $x^m = a$ and consider the problem of factoring a.

11-2. Polynomials with Respect to a Prime Modulus. When the modulus is a prime p, we pointed out in Chap. 5 that the division of $f_1(x)$ by $f_2(x) \not\equiv 0 \pmod{p}$, where these are integral polynomials, exists. To carry out the division, we may use the method of choosing k so that the leading coefficient of $kf_2(x)$ is congruent to 1 modulo p, and then dividing $f_1(x)$ by $kf_2(x)$ according to the process of ordinary long division, so that

$$f_1(x) = kf_2(x)g(x) + r(x)$$

where $r(x)$ is 0 or an integral polynomial lower in degree than $f_2(x)$. Hence,

$$f_1(x) \equiv f_2(x)[kg(x)] + r(x) \pmod{p}$$

and $kg(x)$ is the *quotient* while $r(x)$ is the *remainder* in the *division modulo p* of $f_1(x)$ by $f_2(x)$. This division has already been shown to be unique.

Definitions analogous to those in the first paragraph of this chapter show that the set of integral polynomials modulo p, a prime, forms an integral domain. The unit polynomials, or units, modulo p are the rational integers that are prime to p, for when $(a, p) = 1$, the congruence $ax \equiv b \pmod{p}$ has a solution and we can infer that a divides any integral polynomial modulo p. There can be no other units modulo p, for 1 is not divisible modulo p by a multiple of p or by any polynomial of the first degree or higher. Since r is identically congruent to $r + kp$ modulo p, the integers $1, 2, \ldots, p - 1$ represent all the units modulo p. Moreover, any integer congruent to 0 modulo p represents the null element. In like manner, the rational integers congruent to 1 modulo p denote the unity element of the set of integral polynomials modulo p. The definition of an identical congruence stated in Chap. 5 is the basis for the statement that if $f(x)g(x) \equiv 0 \pmod{p}$ identically, at least one of the polynomials $f(x)$ and $g(x)$ is identically congruent to 0 modulo p. There are, therefore, no divisors of 0 modulo p in this set of polynomials.

A *monic or primary polynomial modulo* p, a prime, is an integral polynomial whose leading coefficient is congruent to 1 modulo p.

The primary polynomial modulo p in a set of associates of $f(x)$ modulo p is called the *primary associate* of $f(x)$ *modulo* p.

A *prime polynomial modulo* p is an integral polynomial that is not a unit modulo p and which is divisible modulo p by only its associates and the units modulo p.

An integral polynomial that is not congruent modulo p to zero, a unit, or a prime polynomial modulo p is a *composite polynomial modulo* p.

Example. The integers 1, 2, 3, and 4 represent the unit polynomials modulo 5. The primary polynomials modulo 5 of the first and second degree can be reduced modulo 5 to one of the following polynomials:

x	x^2	$x^2 + x$	$x^2 + 2x$	$x^2 + 3x$	$x^2 + 4x$
$x + 1$	$x^2 + 1$	$x^2 + x + 1$	$x^2 + 2x + 1$	$x^2 + 3x + 1$	$x^2 + 4x + 1$
$x + 2$	$x^2 + 2$	$x^2 + x + 2$	$x^2 + 2x + 2$	$x^2 + 3x + 2$	$x^2 + 4x + 2$
$x + 3$	$x^2 + 3$	$x^2 + x + 3$	$x^2 + 2x + 3$	$x^2 + 3x + 3$	$x^2 + 4x + 3$
$x + 4$	$x^2 + 4$	$x^2 + x + 4$	$x^2 + 2x + 4$	$x^2 + 3x + 4$	$x^2 + 4x + 4$

Of these the following are prime polynomials modulo 5:

x	$x + 3$	$x^2 + 3$	$x^2 + 2x + 3$	$x^2 + 4x + 1$
$x + 1$	$x + 4$	$x^2 + x + 1$	$x^2 + 2x + 4$	
$x + 2$	$x^2 + 2$	$x^2 + x + 2$	$x^2 + 3x + 4$	

The associates of this set of primary prime polynomials modulo 5 represent the incongruent prime polynomials modulo 5 of the first and second degree.

A *greatest common divisor modulo* p, a prime, of a set of integral polynomials, not all congruent to zero modulo p, is a common divisor of the set that is divisible modulo p by every common divisor of the set. We refer to the primary associate of a greatest common divisor modulo p as *the greatest common divisor modulo* p.

Theorem 11-15. If $f_1(x)$ and $f_2(x)$ are integral polynomials, not both identically congruent to zero modulo p, a prime, then $D(x)$, the greatest common divisor modulo p of $f_1(x)$ and $f_2(x)$, exists and there are integral polynomials $g_1(x)$ and $g_2(x)$ such that $D(x) \equiv f_1(x)g_1(x) + f_2(x)g_2(x) \pmod{p}$.

If there is any difference in degree, assume that the degree of $f_1(x)$ is higher than that of $f_2(x)$, for the theorem is evident unless both polynomials are nonconstants. Then

$$f_1(x) \equiv f_2(x)q_1(x) + r_1(x) \pmod{p}$$

and either $r_1(x) \equiv 0 (\mod p)$ or $r_1(x)$ is of lower degree than $f_2(x)$. Repeat this process by dividing the remainder into the previous divisor whenever $r_i(x) \not\equiv 0 (\mod p)$, where $i = 1, 2, \ldots, k$. After a finite number of steps we shall arrive at a remainder which is congruent to 0 modulo p, for the degree of the remainder continually decreases. Thus

$$f_2(x) \equiv r_1(x)q_2(x) + r_2(x)(\mod p)$$
$$r_1(x) \equiv r_2(x)q_3(x) + r_3(x)(\mod p)$$
$$\cdots \cdots \cdots \cdots \cdots \cdots \cdots \cdots$$
$$r_{k-2}(x) \equiv r_{k-1}(x)q_k(x) + r_k(x)(\mod p)$$
$$r_{k-1}(x) \equiv r_k(x)q_{k+1}(x)(\mod p)$$

Then every common divisor modulo p of $f_1(x)$ and $f_2(x)$ divides $r_k(x)$, and $r_k(x)$ is a common divisor modulo p of these polynomials. Therefore, $r_k(x)$ is a greatest common divisor modulo p of $f_1(x)$ and $f_2(x)$. By solving successively for the $r_i(x)$ in terms of $f_1(x)$ and $f_2(x)$, we find

$$r_k(x) \equiv f_1(x)h_1(x) + f_2(x)h_2(x)(\mod p)$$

If the leading coefficient c of $r_k(x)$ is not congruent to 1 modulo p, we determine d so that $cd \equiv 1(\mod p)$ and multiply each member of the congruence by d, thereby obtaining

$$D(x) \equiv f_1(x)g_1(x) + f_2(x)g_2(x)(\mod p)$$

Consider the problem of determining when the degree of $g_2(x)$ will be less than the degree of $f_1(x)$ and that of $g_1(x)$ will be less than the degree of $f_2(x)$.

It will now be easy for the reader to prove the following theorems:

Theorem 11-16. If the integral polynomials $f_1(x)$ and $f_2(x)$ are relatively prime modulo p, a prime, and if $f_1(x)$ divides $f_2(x)f_3(x)$ modulo p, then $f_1(x)$ divides $f_3(x)$ modulo p.

Theorem 11-17. If p is a prime, the integral polynomials $f_1(x)$ and $f_2(x)$ are relatively prime modulo p if and only if there exist integral polynomials $g_1(x)$ and $g_2(x)$ such that $f_1(x)g_1(x) + f_2(x)g_2(x) \equiv 1(\mod p)$.

Consider the problem of the unicity of $g_1(x)$ and $g_2(x)$.

Theorem 11-18. A composite integral polynomial modulo p, a prime, can be factored into prime polynomials modulo p, and except for the order of the factors and associated polynomials modulo p the factorization is unique for the modulus p.

11-3. A Method for Solving a Congruence Modulo p, a Prime. If p is a prime, all distinct solutions modulo p of $f(x) \equiv 0(\mod p)$ are among the solutions of $x^p - x \equiv 0(\mod p)$. Therefore, to solve $f(x) \equiv 0(\mod p)$, find $D(x)$, the greatest common divisor modulo p of $f(x)$ and $x^p - x$. Then the solutions of $D(x) \equiv 0(\mod p)$ are the distinct solutions of $f(x) \equiv 0(\mod p)$, and their number is the degree of $D(x)$. Of course,

$f(x) \equiv 0 \pmod{p}$ may have a repeated solution, but the existence of a multiple solution $x \equiv r \pmod{p}$ can be determined by removing the factor $x - r$ modulo p from $f(x)$ and substituting r for x in the quotient.

Example. We can exhibit the usefulness of this device by finding the solutions of $x^5 + x^3 + x^2 - x + 3 \equiv 0 \pmod{5}$. The application of the algorithm to $x^5 - x$ and $x^5 + x^3 + x^2 - x + 3$ shows that $D(x) \equiv x^2 - 3x + 2 \pmod{5}$ and therefore that the only distinct solutions of the given congruence are $x \equiv 1$, $x \equiv 2 \pmod{5}$. But $x^5 + x^3 + x^2 - x + 3 \equiv (x^2 - 3x + 2)(x^3 + 3x^2 + 3x + 4) \pmod{5}$. The congruence $x^3 + 3x^2 + 3x + 4 \equiv 0 \pmod{5}$ has the solution $x \equiv 2 \pmod{5}$, and $x^3 + 3x^2 + 3x + 4 \equiv (x - 2)(x^2 - 2) \pmod{5}$. However, $x^2 - 2 \equiv 0 \pmod{5}$ is satisfied by neither $x \equiv 1$ nor $x \equiv 2 \pmod{5}$. Hence, the solutions of the original congruence are $x \equiv 1$, $x \equiv 2$, $x \equiv 2 \pmod{5}$.

EXERCISES

1. Write the primary prime polynomials modulo 3 of degrees 0, 1, and 2. Then write all the prime polynomials modulo 3 of degree 2 that are incongruent modulo 3.

2. Factor $2x^5 + x^3 + 2x^2 + 2x + 2$ into prime factors modulo 3.

3. Find the solutions of $x^4 - 2x^2 - 3 \equiv 0 \pmod{5}$.

4. Find the solutions of $x^5 - 4x^3 + 3x \equiv 0 \pmod{7}$.

5. Find the solutions of $x^4 - x + 1 \equiv 0 \pmod{7}$.

6. Find the solutions of $2x^4 - 10x - 27 \equiv 0 \pmod{35}$.

7. If $f(x)$ is an integral polynomial and p is a prime, develop a method for solving the congruence $f(x) \equiv 0 \pmod{p}$ by using the derivatives of $f(x)$ with respect to x and certain greatest common divisors modulo p.

CHAPTER 12

PARTITIONS

12-1. The Additive Theory of Numbers. Leibnitz (1646–1716) was among the first mathematicians who paid particular attention to developing the theory concerned with the separation of an integer into all possible summands selected from a given set, for example, the representation of 4 by 4, $3 + 1$, $2 + 2$, $2 + 1 + 1$, $1 + 1 + 1 + 1$, where selections are made from 1, 2, 3, and 4. To Euler, however, is due a large part of the basic theory. This additive theory of numbers is a difficult subject. We shall develop only the fundamental ideas. The student can refer to the work of G. H. Hardy, one of the modern experts in this field, for an extensive treatment of this topic.

If from any set of positive integers a_i, where $i = 1, 2, 3, \ldots$, finite or infinite, we select m numbers so that $n = a_1 + a_2 + \cdots + a_m$, the representation, whether or not it contains repetitions, is a *partition* of the integer n. Thus the representation of n as a sum of primes is a partition of n in which the selection is made from the set of positive primes. In this chapter we shall confine ourselves to selections of addends from the set of positive integers 1, 2, $\ldots$, q or from all the positive integers, considering both the case where repetitions are permitted and where they are prohibited, the order of the summands in each situation being irrelevant.

We shall represent the number of partitions of n containing m selections from the integers 1, 2, $\ldots$, q with repetitions allowed by $P(n, m, \leq q)$. If repetitions are prohibited, we shall use the symbol $Q(n, m, \leq q)$. If the representations are to have at most m parts selected without repetition from 1, 2, $\ldots$, q, their number will be expressed by $Q(n, \leq m, \leq q)$. When the selections are made from the set of all positive integers, we shall employ $P(n, m)$ and $Q(n, m)$ for the number of partitions of n, with repetitions and without repetitions, respectively, that have exactly m parts. If the selections are unrestricted as to the number of parts, we shall write $P(n, U, \leq q)$ to mean the number of partitions of n, with repetitions permitted, into any number of parts all of which are less than or equal to q, and $Q(n, U)$ to mean the number of partitions of n into any number of parts selected without repetition from the positive integers.

190

If the selection of the unrestricted number of parts is to be from among $1, 2, \ldots, q$ and is always to include q, we shall write $P(n, U, q)$ and $Q(n, U, q)$.

12-2. Partitions with Repetitions. To separate n into m parts with repetitions let each of the m parts have one unit, and then distribute the remaining $n - m$ units to one part, to two parts, $\ldots$, to m parts. Thus when $n > m$ and the selections are from the positive integers, we have

$$P(n, m) = P(n - m, 1) + P(n - m, 2) + \cdots + P(n - m, m)$$

But then

$$P(n - 1, m - 1) = P(n - m, 1) + P(n - m, 2) + \cdots + P(n - m, m - 1)$$

Hence,

$$P(n, m) = P(n - 1, m - 1) + P(n - m, m)$$

and we have proved:

Theorem 12-1. When the addends are selected from the positive integers, the number of partitions of n into m parts with repetitions is equal to $P(n - 1, m - 1) + P(n - m, m)$.

Example. To find the number of partitions of 7 into three parts, we find $P(7, 3) = P(6, 2) + P(4, 3)$. Repeating the application of the recursion formula of Theorem 12-1, we obtain

$$P(6, 2) = P(5, 1) + P(4, 2) = 1 + P(4, 2)$$
$$P(4, 2) = P(3, 1) + P(2, 2) = 1 + 1$$
$$P(4, 3) = P(3, 2) + P(1, 3) = P(3, 2)$$
$$P(3, 2) = P(2, 1) + P(1, 2) = 1$$

Hence,

$$P(7, 3) = 4$$

Corollary 1. If $m > n/2$, $P(n, m) = P(n - 1, m - 1)$.
If $m > n / 2$, $n - m < m$ and $P(n - m, m) = 0$.
Corollary 2. $P(2n, 2) = n$, and $P(2n + 1, 2) = n$.
The partitions of an even integer $2n$ into two parts are

$$1 + (2n - 1)$$
$$2 + (2n - 2)$$
$$\cdots \cdots \cdots$$
$$n + (2n - n)$$

The partitions of an odd integer $2n + 1$ greater than 1 into two parts are

$$1 + 2n$$
$$2 + (2n - 1)$$
$$\cdots\cdots\cdots$$
$$n + (n + 1)$$

By making use of the formulas $P(n, n) = 1$, $P(n, n - 1) = 1$, $P(n, 1) = 1$, as well as

$$P(n, 2) = P(n - 1, 1) + P(n - 2, 2) = 1 + P(n - 2, 2)$$
$$P(n, 3) = P(n - 1, 2) + P(n - 3, 3) = P(n - 2, 1) + P(n - 3, 2)$$
$$+ P(n - 3, 3)$$
$$= 1 + P(n - 3, 2) + P(n - 3, 3)$$
$$\cdots\cdots\cdots\cdots\cdots\cdots$$
$$P(n, k) = P(n - 1, k - 1) + P(n - k, k)$$
$$= 1 + P(n - k, 2) + P(n - k, 3) + \cdots + P(n - k, k)$$

we can set up a table of the number of partitions of n into m parts selected from the positive integers with repetitions permitted.

m, the number of parts	Values of n											
	1	2	3	4	5	6	7	8	9	10	11	12
1	1	1	1	1	1	1	1	1	1	1	1	1
2		1	1	2	2	3	3	4	4	5	5	6
3			1	1	2	3	4	5	7	8	10	12
4				1	1	2	3	5	6	9	11	15
5					1	1	2	3	5	7	10	13
6						1	1	2	3	5	7	11
7							1	1	2	3	5	7
8								1	1	2	3	5
9									1	1	2	3

The first row of the table uses $P(n, 1) = 1$. The formulas $P(n, n) = 1$ and $P(n, n - 1) = 1$ account for the two diagonals of 1's. Passing to the second row, to find $P(3, 2)$, we merely add the numbers in the column under $3 - 2 = 1$. To find $P(4, 2)$, add the numbers under $4 - 2 = 2$, etc. To write the third row, sum the numbers under $4 - 3 = 1$ for $P(4, 3)$, the numbers under $5 - 3 = 2$ for $P(5, 3)$, the numbers in the first three rows under $6 - 3 = 3$ for $P(6, 3)$, the numbers in the first three rows under $7 - 3 = 4$ for $P(7, 3)$, etc.

From the way the table has been set up it is evident that we can find $P(n, \leq m)$ by merely looking up $P(n + m, m)$.

12-3. Diagrams of Partitions. If we set up all the partitions of n into exactly m parts selected from $1, 2, \ldots, q$, with repetitions permitted, and always employ at least one q, and then remove one q from each of the partitions, we obviously have the partitions with repetitions permitted of $n - q$ into $m - 1$ parts selected from $1, 2, \ldots, q$; that is, $P(n, m, q) = P(n - q, m - 1, \leq q)$. If repetitions are prohibited, $Q(n, m, q) = Q(n - q, m - 1, \leq q - 1)$.

We can diagram a partition of n into m parts that include q as a greatest integer in the following way and thus graphically exhibit the statement made above:

$$
\begin{array}{llllllll}
1 & 1 & 1 & 1 & \ldots & 1 & \quad (q \text{ units}) \\
1 & 1 & 1 & \ldots & 1 \\
(m \text{ rows}) \quad \cdot & \cdot & \cdot & \cdot & \cdot & \cdot & \cdot & \cdot \\
1 & \ldots & 1
\end{array}
$$

Moreover, if we read the diagram by columns, we have a partition of n into q parts of which the greatest is m. Such partitions are said to be *conjugate*. The diagram shows that the following statement is valid:

Theorem 12-2. There are as many partitions of n into m parts selected from $1, 2, \ldots, q$ and always including q as there are partitions of n into q parts such that one is m and the others are less than or equal to m, repetitions being permitted in each case.

Similarly the diagrams show the following theorem, due to Euler:

Theorem 12-3. The number of partitions with repetitions permitted of n into at most m parts is the same as the number of partitions with repetitions permitted of n into parts which do not exceed m; that is, $P(n, \leq m) = P(n, U, \leq m)$.

Furthermore, by subtracting $P(n, \leq m - 1) = P(n, U, \leq m - 1)$ from $P(n, \leq m) = P(n, U, \leq m)$, we have:

Corollary. $P(n, m) = P(n, U, m)$.

The diagrams also make it clear that:

Theorem 12-4. The number of partitions with repetitions permitted of n into m or more parts is the same as the number of partitions with repetitions permitted of n into parts containing an element that is greater than or equal to m.

12-4. Generating Functions for the Number of Partitions. Consider the addends that are summed to determine the exponents of x in the product $(1 + x)(1 + x^2)(1 + x^3) = 1 + x + x^2 + x^{1+2} + x^3 + x^{1+3} + x^{2+3} + x^{1+2+3}$. It is evident that these exponents are the results arising from all possible selections of one, two, and three distinct summands from the set $1, 2, 3$. Consequently, the coefficient 2 of x^3 gives the number of ways 3 can be produced by adding together distinct integers selected from $1, 2,$ and 3. Similarly the coefficient of x^n in the expansion of $(1 + x)(1 + x^2) \cdots (1 + x^q)$ is the number of partitions of n into distinct integers from the set 1, 2, . . . , q and is, therefore, the value of $Q(n, U, \leq q)$.

Now take the product $(1 + zx)(1 + zx^2) \cdots (1 + zx^q)$. The presence of the z in each factor enables us to count the number of addends used to produce the exponent of x. Thus the coefficient of $z^m x^n$ is the number of ways in which n can be represented by exactly m distinct addends from among 1, 2, 3, . . . , q. It, therefore, enables us to determine $Q(n, m, \leq q)$.

The effect of multiplying $(1 + zx)(1 + zx^2) \cdots (1 + zx^q)$ by $1 + z + z^2 + \cdots + z^{q(q-1)/2}$ is to collect the terms representing the number of ways n can be produced by one, two, . . . , m distinct addends, for zx^n is multiplied by z^{m-1} to produce $z^m x^n$; $z^2 x^n$, by z^{m-2}; etc. Thus the coefficient of $z^m x^n$ is the number of partitions of n that can be obtained by choosing at most m distinct integers from the set 1, 2, . . . , q. It is the value of $Q(n, \leq m, \leq q)$.

The fact that the series $1 + x^m + x^{2m} + \cdots$, developed from the quotient $1/(1 - x^m)$, is absolutely convergent for $0 < x < 1$ enabled Kronecker* to prove that the coefficients of the expansion of the generating function $1/(1 - x)(1 - x^2)(1 - x^3) \cdots$ give the number of partitions of n with repetitions permitted. The discovery of this theorem is due to Euler. We shall merely indicate the truth of the statement by the following argument: To produce any integer n, we need at most n addends, and hence but the first n of the factors $(1 + x + x^2 + \cdots)$, $(1 + x^2 + x^4 + \cdots)$, . . . , $(1 + x^n + x^{2n} + \cdots)$ determined by the generating function. The first term of the $(n + 1)$st factor in the product of the first $n + 1$ factors would merely reproduce the product of the first n factors, and the next term would add $n + 1$ to each of the exponents of x already produced so that the resulting exponents would exceed n. It is evident also that all succeeding exponents so derived would exceed n. Moreover, any term developed from the product of the first n factors is the result of selecting exactly one term from each of these factors. The choice can be represented as the selection of one of each of the factors x^a, x^{2b}, x^{3c}, . . . , x^{nk}, where the values of the integers $a, 2b, 3c, . . . , nk$ are among 0, 1, . . . , n, and a is to be interpreted as the sum of a units, $2b$ as the sum of b 2's, $3c$ as the sum of c 3's, etc. Each time the sum of the exponents, $a, 2b, 3c, . . . , nk$, is n, we have a partition of n. Thus the coefficient of x^n gives the number of partitions of n with repetitions permitted.

Let us illustrate the use of the generating function by finding the partitions of 5. We need but the factors $(1 + x + x^2 + x^3 + x^4 + x^5)$, $(1 + x^2 + x^4)$, $(1 + x^3)$, $(1 + x^4)$, and $(1 + x^5)$. The product is to be

* L. E. Dickson, "History of the Theory of Numbers," Vol. 2, p. 104.

interpreted in the form

$$(1 + x + x^{1+1} + x^{1+1+1} + x^{1+1+1+1} + x^{1+1+1+1+1})(1 + x^2 + x^{2+2})$$
$$(1 + x^3)(1 + x^4)(1 + x^5)$$

Then the expansion is

$$
\begin{aligned}
1 &+ x + x^{1+1} + x^{1+1+1} + x^{1+1+1+1} + x^{1+1+1+1+1} + \cdots \\
&+ x^2 \quad + x^{1+2} \quad + x^{1+1+2} \quad + x^{1+1+1+2} \quad + \cdots \\
&\qquad\qquad\quad + x^{2+2} \quad + x^{1+2+2} \quad + \cdots \\
&+ x^3 \quad + x^{1+3} \quad + x^{1+1+3} \quad + \cdots \\
&\qquad\qquad\qquad\quad + x^{2+3} \quad + \cdots \\
&+ x^4 \quad + x^{1+4} \quad + \cdots \\
&\qquad\qquad\quad + x^5 \quad + \cdots
\end{aligned}
$$

The partitions of 1, 2, 3, 4, as well as 5, are thereby enumerated, and the coefficient 7 of x^5 is the value of $P(5, U)$.

Similarly we can see that $1/(1 - x)(1 - x^3)(1 - x^5) \cdots$ enumerates the partitions of n into odd integers with repetitions permitted and that $1/(1 - x^2)(1 - x^4)(1 - x^6) \cdots$ does the same when the parts are even.

EXERCISES

1. Show that $P(n, \leq m, q) = P(n, q, \leq m)$.

2. Show that $P(n, U, \leq q) = P(n + q, q)$.

3. Find the number of partitions of n into parts selected from 1, 2, 2^2, 2^3, ...

4. Show that the number of partitions of n in terms of odd integers with repetitions is equal to $Q(n, U)$.

5. Write a generating function which will enumerate the partitions of n into parts that are odd and unequal.

6. Show that $x^r/(1 - x^2)(1 - x^4) \cdots (1 - x^{2q})$ enumerates the partitions of $n - r$ into even parts that do not exceed $2q$ with repetitions permitted. Show also that when $n - r$ is even, the same function enumerates the partitions of $(n - r)/2$ into parts not larger than m with repetitions.

7. Find a method for listing all the partitions of n into m parts by starting with $m - 1$ units and the integer $n - m + 1$.

BIBLIOGRAPHY

Bachmann, P., "Die Lehre von der Kreistheilung," B. G. Teubner, Leipzig, 1921.

————, "Grundlehren der neueren Zahlentheorie," Walter De Gruyter & Company, Berlin, 1931.

Cahen, E., "Théorie des nombres," Gauthier-Villars & Cie, Paris, 1900.

Cajori, F., "A History of Mathematics," Macmillan & Co., Ltd., London, 1906.

Carmichael, R. D., "The Theory of Numbers," John Wiley & Sons, Inc., New York, 1914.

Chrystal, G., "Algebra," A. & C. Black, Ltd., London, Vol. I, 1931, Vol. II, 1932.

Dickson, L. E., "History of the Theory of Numbers," Carnegie Institution of Washington, Washington, D.C., 1920.

————, "Introduction to the Theory of Numbers," University of Chicago Press, Chicago, 1929.

————, "Studies in the Theory of Numbers," University of Chicago Press, Chicago, 1930.

————, "Modern Elementary Theory of Numbers," University of Chicago Press, Chicago, 1939.

Hancock, H., "Foundations of the Theory of Algebraic Numbers," The Macmillan Company, New York, Vol. I, 1931, Vol. II, 1932.

Hardy, G. H., "Some Famous Problems of the Theory of Numbers," Oxford University Press, New York, 1920.

———— and E. M. Wright, "The Theory of Numbers," Oxford University Press, New York, 1938.

Hecke, E., "Theorie der algebraischen Zahlen," Akademische Verlagsgesellschaft m.b.H., Leipzig, 1923.

Kraitchik, M., "Théorie des nombres," Gauthier-Villars & Cie, Paris, Vol. I, 1922, Vol. II, 1926.

Landau, E., "Vorlesungen über Zahlentheorie," S. Hirzel, Leipzig, 1927.

Mathews, G. B., "Theory of Numbers," G. E. Stechert & Company, New York, 1927.

Nagell, T., "Introduction to Number Theory," John Wiley & Sons, Inc., New York, 1951.

Ore, Oystein, "Number Theory and Its History," McGraw-Hill Book Company, Inc., New York, 1948.

Reid, L. W., "The Elements of the Theory of Algebraic Numbers," The Macmillan Company, New York, 1910.

Smith, D. E., "History of Mathematics," Ginn & Company, Boston, Vol. I, 1923, Vol. II, 1925.

————, "A Source Book in Mathematics," McGraw-Hill Book Company, Inc., New York, 1929.

Stewart, N. M., "Theory of Numbers," The Macmillan Company, New York, 1952.

Uspensky, J. V., and M. A. Heaslet, "Elementary Number Theory," McGraw-Hill Book Company, Inc., New York, 1939.

Wright, H. N., "First Course in the Theory of Numbers," John Wiley & Sons, Inc., New York, 1939.

INDEX

DATE DUE

WITHDRAWN